Introductory
Symbolic
Logic

Introductory
Symbolic
Logic

———

JOHN K. WILSON
Mott Community College

WADSWORTH PUBLISHING COMPANY

Belmont, California
A Division of Wadsworth, Inc.

Philosophy Editor: Kenneth King
Editorial Assistant: Cynthia Campbell
Production: Greg Hubit Bookworks
Designer: Adriane Bosworth
Print Buyer: Martha Branch
Copy Editor: Tony Hicks
Cover: Adriane Bosworth
Signing Representative: David Leach
Compositor: Monotype Composition Company
Printer: Malloy Lithographing

This book is printed on acid-free paper that meets Environmental Protection Agency standards for recycled paper.

1 2 3 4 5 6 7 8 9 10—96 95 94 93 92

Library of Congress Cataloging-in-Publication Data

Wilson, John K. (John Keith), 1946–
    Introductory symbolic logic / John K. Wilson.
    p. cm.
    Includes bibliographical references and index.
    ISBN 0-534-16818-3
    1. Logic, Symbolic and mathematical. I. Title.
BC134.W455 1992   91-31515
160–dc20   CIP

For the cubs: Elizabeth and Alexander

Preface

There are so many introductory logic texts on the market that anyone who brings forth another one at best owes the world a justification, and at worst an apology.

Virtually every introductory text claims to surpass previous levels of clarity in explaining the subject, and claims to have discovered new ways to generate student interest. After using six different texts over a ten-year period, I became convinced that, although the exercises were often useful, my using the texts often benefited the publishers more than the students. *Introductory Symbolic Logic* was born out of the realization that clear explanations for instructors do not necessarily produce clear understandings for students, and that attempts to generate student interest require considering what students find interesting.

Student Comprehension

Cognitive psychology has shown us that "clear explanation" lacks an absolute meaning. What might be a clear explanation for one person might well be gibberish for someone else. An audience's existing cognitive structures must be taken into account when determining whether an explanation is clear. Rather than dilute course content or bemoan student inadequacies, *Introductory Symbolic Logic* attempts to work with students' abilities. It does so in the following ways:

1. *Introductory Symbolic Logic* is written at a very readable level.
2. All important concepts are boxed off from the body of the text, surrounded with examples, and reiterated in the glossary.
3. *Introductory Symbolic Logic* is written for students who lack a background in mathematics.
4. Concept review questions are provided at the end of each section. The questions require reflection on, rather than regurgitation of, material that has been presented. Answers for all concept review questions are provided in an appendix.

5. I have not attempted to combine either principles of deductive reasoning or semantic interpretations of the connectives with the introduction of symbols. Instead, the entire second chapter is devoted to relating English to the artificial language of logic.

6. A set of exercises follows the introduction of each symbol.

7. The inference rules that make up the system of natural deduction are presented in stages. Each stage is accompanied with a set of exercises that stress the most recently developed inferences.

8. Exercise sets are self-directing in that they contain instructions for completing the problems.

9. Chapters 4 and 5 extensively develop a goals approach for constructing formal proofs. The student acquires a step-by-step method for constructing formal proofs in Chapter 4, and a step-by-step method for developing proof strategies in Chapter 5.

10. The chapters that are devoted to predicate logic, Chapters 7 and 8, present monadic and polyadic predicates separately. Each symbol is developed with a corresponding set of exercises.

11. The deductive system for predicate logic has a minimum number of restrictions and a simplified set of quantifier inferences.

Instructors might try using this text without lecturing through all of the important material. One method I have found effective is to make an assignment requiring students to write down and submit an issue in need of additional explanation in order to participate in class. Class sessions take on a discussion rather than a lecture format, and focus on issues that students find confusing.

Student Interest

When asked to write on a topic that interests them, most students choose to describe the love of their life. They do not choose topical issues. Using topical examples wrongly assumes that student interests peak with the evening newspaper and can be transferred to symbolic logic.

The realistic solution consists in developing enough context so that genuinely interesting issues are seen to be interesting by the students. For example, *Introductory Symbolic Logic* defines "truth-functional" by using examples from the Civil War. Jonathan Swift's modest proposals are used to present formal proofs in predicate logic. Eyewitness accounts of Gandhi's death are used to explain partial truth tables. *Introductory Symbolic Logic* develops examples and exercises based on such topics as the founding of Australia or Machiavelli's outlook on women. It painstakingly presents and references issues that are interesting. In addition to learning principles of symbolic logic, students will be exposed to facts of an interdisciplinary interest.

Content

Introductory Symbolic Logic covers the material that is most frequently taught in first-semester introductory courses in symbolic logic. The first six chapters are devoted to arguments in propositional logic. Chapters 7 and 8 present techniques for appraising arguments in predicate logic. Truth trees, as well as truth tables and partial truth tables, are developed for determining validity in propositional logic. Both truth trees and partial truth tables are developed for specifying interpretations that prove invalidity for arguments in predicate logic. These sections have been written so that either partial truth tables or truth trees, or both, may be developed. Chapter 9 provides a brief introduction to metalogic for propositional logic. A nonmathematical proof of deductive completeness is provided for all truth-functional tautologies and propositional arguments.

Acknowledgments

I first came to appreciate logic and symbolic systems under the guidance of Brad Angell at Wayne State University. My indebtedness to him is enormous.

My logic students at Mott Community College over the last ten years also deserve a special thanks. Not only did they suffer through numerous drafts and make suggestions that I incorporated in the text, but through their test scores and levels of understanding they were its ultimate critics. They helped me to turn a text that *I* thought was understandable into one that students are capable of understanding.

My appreciation to Eli Labiner of Mott Community College and Sherrill Begres of Indiana University of Pennsylvania, who reviewed early drafts of the text and provided support and encouragement. Bethany McCartney and Barbara Allen of Mott's duplication department valiantly struggled with my requests for student copies on a "yesterday basis." Jacqueline Reinertson made reading-level determinations on portions of the text and encouraged me to write for students rather than philosophers. My wife, Nancy, although not always supportive of the project, has always been supportive of me.

My work and the contributions of those listed above would have been for naught had Wadsworth not decided to take the risk of publishing a somewhat unorthodox approach to a subject known for its orthodoxy. I appreciate philosophy editor Ken King's endurance and "therapy" when the project suffered from a multiple personality disorder. I also owe a special thanks to Robert Burch of Texas A&M University and James Garson of the University of Houston, who read draft after draft of this project. I hope that my revisions are as good as their criticisms. I am also indebted to Wadsworth's other reviewers, all of whose suggestions have helped create the final product: David Keyt, University of Washington; Thomas Morrow, Richland

Community College; Richard Parker, California State University, Chico; Thomas E. Pyne, California State University, Sacramento; Caroline Simon, Hope College; Stephen Simon, California State University, Long Beach; Ken Warmbröd, University of Manitoba.

Just as I am certain that there are spies although I do not know where they are, I am certain that this text contains mistakes although I do not know where they are. And the mistakes are mine.

—*John K. Wilson*

Contents

CHAPTER

4 Introduction to Formal Proofs 96

1 Logic: The Subject Matter

KEY TERMS FOR THIS CHAPTER

Use the glossary as necessary, and review the definitions of these terms prior to a second reading of this chapter.

Argument	**Inductively strong (or weak)**
Deductively valid argument	**argument**
Deductively invalid argument	**Statement**

At present, wives, just as much as prostitutes, live by the sale of their sexual charms; and even in temporary free relations the man is usually expected to bear all the joint expenses. The result is that there is a sordid entanglement of money with sex, and that women's motives not infrequently have a mercenary element. Sex, even when blessed by the church, ought not to be a profession.

— Bertrand Russell[1]

You must have diplomatic and correct relations, but there can never be friendship between the British democracy and the Nazi power, that power that spurns Christian ethics, which cheers its onward course by a barbarous paganism, which vaults the spirit of aggression and conquest, which derives strength and perverted pleasure from persecution, and uses, as we have seen, with pitiless brutality the threat of murderous force. That power cannot ever be the trusted friend of British democracy.

— Winston Churchill[2]

---

[1]Bertrand Russell, *Bertrand Russell on Ethics, Sex, and Marriage*, ed. Al Seckel (Buffalo: Prometheus Books, 1987), 224. (This essay was first published in 1936.)

[2]Winston Churchill, "Speech to the House of Commons, October 5, 1938," in *The War Speeches of the Rt Hon Winston S. Churchill*, compiled by Charles Eade (London; Cassell and Co. 1951), 33.

I General Considerations

A. The Subject Matter

Bertrand Russell, one of the founders of logic as it is presented in this text, was concerned about connections that he perceived (in 1936) between money, sex, and marriage. He attempted to persuade others to change their outlook on marriage. In 1938, many people in England wanted to avoid war by befriending Hitler. Winston Churchill attempted to persuade them that such a course was foolish.

People care about a wide variety of things. We care about marriage, sex, war, cars, and many other things. Often, we want to persuade others to see the world as we do. Similarly, others are often intent on persuading us to see the world as they do.

Not all persuasion is either as impersonal, or on as grand a scale, as our opening quotations. One student might attempt to persuade another student to avoid classes that are taught by McWit. We might attempt to persuade a friend that someone is too self-centered to be a suitable spouse.

Our attempts to persuade others, and their attempts to persuade us, should give reasons and provide an argument. Russell gave reasons for accepting an alternative outlook on marriage. Similarly, Churchill gave reasons for not befriending Hitler. If a student attempts to persuade us not to take a class taught by McWit, we expect the student to give reasons. (Perhaps McWit is disorganized, is hard, etc.) If we want to persuade a friend that someone is too self-centered for marriage, we should also give reasons.

But some reasoning is good and some bad. Do Russell's reasons properly support his claim that the institution of marriage should be changed? Do Churchill's reasons properly support his claim that Nazi Germany cannot be a friend of Britain? *Should* we take a class taught by McWit? *Should* our friend be convinced that someone is overly self-centered?

DEFINITION 1.1

Logic is the study of what makes arguments either good or bad. Logicians consider whether an argument's premises correctly support its conclusion.

Logicians seek to discover which arguments are well constructed. They attempt to discover what makes some arguments better than others.

Persuasion can be about almost any subject. Logicians are hardly experts on all of the topics that arguments can be about. Logic is not particularly concerned with what arguments are about. Instead, logic is concerned with *connections* (or lack of them) between the premises and conclusions of arguments.

People can give logically relevant or logically irrelevant reasons for befriending a nation, for getting married, or for taking a particular class. People can give logically relevant or logically irrelevant reasons for buying a particular brand of paper towel. As we will see presently, arguments can have radically different subject matters but still share the same structure. To be able to assess arguments and decide whether they are correct or incorrect, we have to look more closely at how arguments are put together.

DEFINITION 1.2

An *argument* consists of a group of statements, such that one of them is considered to be the conclusion. The conclusion is the statement intended to follow from the other statements that are presented as reasons (or premisses) for it.

The word "argument" has a broader usage in standard English than in logic. Two people screaming abuse at one another in a local bar would normally be said to be having an argument. For our purposes, however, an argument must have premises and a conclusion. A barroom quarrel may not have any point other than the irrational venting of emotions.

Notice as well that, for our purposes, an argument includes the reasons or premisses *and* the conclusion. In standard English, one can be said to "give an argument in favor of a position." In this usage the word "argument" merely refers to the premisses. With our definition, the conclusion is also part of the argument. Later chapters will focus on creating arguments—the process of developing conclusions from premisses. When we examine an argument, we must have the conclusion as well as the premisses before us.

An argument can have any number of premisses, but is always considered to have only one conclusion. Still, the conclusion of one argument may be used as a premiss in another. Consider the following conversation.

A: Getting married is something that, someday, I'd like to do.

B: I hope you enjoy being abused! Whenever you consider marriage, I think that you should go to a crowded shopping center on a Friday night, and notice all of the snarling.

B is obviously making inferences from shopping-center experiences to marriage in general, and then to A's intended involvement. A rather complete (but by no means the only possible) expansion of the reasoning follows.

ARGUMENT I

Premiss: *Married people at the shopping center snarl at one another.*

Premiss: *People that snarl at one another in shopping centers are unhappy.*

Conclusion: *Married people are unhappy.*

ARGUMENT II

Premiss: *Married people are unhappy.*

Conclusion: *If you get married, then you will be unhappy.*

ARGUMENT III

Premiss: *If you get married, then you will be unhappy.*

Premiss: *You do not want to be unhappy.*

Conclusion: *You do not want to get married.*

The conclusion of I becomes a premiss of II, and the conclusion of II becomes a premiss of III. Notice that the conclusions are given as part of the arguments.

Russell's argument (RA) can be paraphrased as follows:

*If we ought to retain our present outlook on marriage, **then** wives should live by the sale of their sexual charms.*

***It is false that** wives should live by the sale of their sexual charms. [He describes the entanglement of money and sex as "sordid" and says marriage ought not to be a profession.]*

*Hence, **it is false that** we ought to retain our present outlook on marriage.*

Churchill's argument (CA) can be paraphrased as follows:

*If Nazi Germany is to be a friend of Britain, **then** Nazi Germany must have acceptable values.*

***It is false that** Nazi Germany has acceptable values. [Nazi power spurns Christian ethics, etc.]*

*Hence, **it is false that** Nazi Germany can be a friend of Britain.*

The two arguments obviously differ in subject matter. As a matter of fact, Russell and Churchill shared few ideas on either topic. Russell was a social reformer, whereas Churchill believed in traditional values. Churchill believed in peace through military strength, whereas Russell was a pacifist.

Still, suppose that we ignore the subjects. The two arguments have the same structure. (Try to ignore the content. Stand back and look for what underlies them.) Several shared aspects become evident:

1. Each argument, RA and CA, has two premisses and one conclusion.
2. The first premiss of each argument is a statement of the form 'if . . . , then . . . .'
3. The second premiss of each argument claims that the statement following 'then' in the first premiss is false.
4. The conclusion of each argument claims that the statement following 'if' in the first premiss is false.

The common structure of the two arguments has the words 'if', 'then', and 'it is false that'. The structure also has what we might call "places" or "positions" for statements about some subject. Let ◯ and ☐ indicate places for statements. Then RA and CA share the following structure or form:

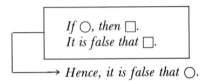

In RA the ◯ is filled with 'we ought to retain our present outlook on marriage'. In CA it is filled with 'Nazi Germany is to be a friend of Britain'.

In RA the ☐ is filled with 'wives should live by the sale of their sexual charms'. In CA it is filled with 'Nazi Germany has acceptable values'.

In addition to identifying a common pattern in *existing* arguments, the above form can also be used to *create* arguments. Suppose we decide to fill the ◯ with 'you ought to take McWit's class', and the ☐ with 'McWit has well-organized class sessions'. The above form or pattern can be used to create the following argument.

*If you ought to take McWit's class, **then** McWit has well-organized class sessions.*

It is false that McWit has well organized class sessions.

Hence, it is false that you ought to take McWit's class.

B. Deductive and Inductive Correctness of Arguments

Logic is typically divided into deductive logic and inductive logic.

i. Deductive Correctness

An argument is considered to be correct (or valid) by the standards of deductive logic, when its conclusion *must* be true if all of its premisses are true.

DEFINITION 1.3

An argument is *deductively valid* if and only if its underlying form or structure guarantees that: if its premisses are all true, then so is its conclusion.

Deductive logic calls incorrectly structured arguments "invalid."

DEFINITION 1.4

An argument is *deductively invalid* if and only if its underlying form or structure does not guarantee that: if its premisses are all true, then so is its conclusion.

CA and RA are both deductively valid arguments. Russell and Churchill may have had false ideas about marriage and the conditions for peace, but the arguments that they presented are put together with a deductively valid form. From the standpoint of deductive logic, the linkage within these arguments is correct. *If* their premisses are all true, *then* their conclusions must be true as well.

Notice that our definitions of 'deductively valid' and 'deductively invalid' are not about whether the premisses of the arguments are true. Rather, these terms relate to a kind of *linkage* or *relationship* that is either present or absent in a particular argument. Since the following argument has the same underlying structure as our previous examples, it is also deductively valid.

> *If Germany lost World War II, then Hitler committed suicide.*
> *It is false that Hitler committed suicide.*
> *Hence, it is false that Germany lost World War II.*

Both the second premiss and the conclusion of this example are false. Hitler committed suicide on April 30, 1945, and Germany surrendered on May 7, 1945. In claiming that this argument is deductively valid, we are claiming that if its premisses *were* all true, then its conclusion *would be* true.

The argument's underlying structure guarantees that, provided its premises are all true, its conclusion will not be false.

This form or pattern—

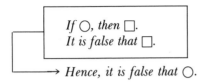

If ◯, then ☐.
It is false that ☐.

——→ *Hence, it is false that ◯.*

—is one of many forms or structures that can be used to put together deductively valid arguments.

Of course, not all arguments are deductively valid. Suppose that someone is indifferent about the amount of waste that they create. Suppose that they are criticized for harming the environment, and that they respond with the following argument.

> *If I used disposable diapers, **then** I would be harming the environment.*
> *It is false that I use disposable diapers.*
> *Hence, it is false that I am harming the environment.*

Using circles and squares as before, this argument can be seen to have the following form.

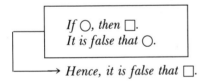

If ◯, then ☐.
It is false that ◯.

——→ *Hence, it is false that ☐.*

Unlike CA and RA, this form of argument is deductively *invalid*. The argument might have all true premises and yet have a false conclusion. One can avoid using disposable diapers and still harm the environment in countless ways. This form does not guarantee that if all the premises of the resulting argument are true, then so is the argument's conclusion.

We have seen that deductively valid arguments can have a false conclusion, provided they do not have all true premises. A deductively invalid argument *can* have a true conclusion and all true premises. For example, the following argument is invalid even though we might claim that all of its premises and its conclusion are true.

> *If used motor oil improves drinking water, **then** it should be added to drinking water.*
> *It is false that used motor oil improves drinking water.*
> *Hence, it is false that used motor oil should be added to drinking water.*

The term 'valid' has a more specialized meaning in deductive logic than it has in ordinary English. As definitions 1.3 and 1.4 note, whether an argument is deductively valid or invalid is determined by its underlying form. We *cannot* determine whether a particular argument is deductively valid or invalid by knowing whether it contains true or false statements (unless the argument has all true premises and a false conclusion, in which case it must be deductively invalid).

The following table summarizes what is possible for deductively valid and deductively invalid arguments. Notice that the only restriction is that deductively valid arguments cannot have all true premises and a false conclusion.

		Deductively Valid	*Deductively Invalid*
All true premises,	true conclusion	possible	possible
All true premises,	false conclusion	*impossible*	possible
One or more false premises,	true conclusion	possible	possible
One or more false premises,	false conclusion	possible	possible

Often we are concerned, particularly in decision making, with connections rather than truth. Decisions are typically based on ideas that we are considering, rather than with establishing truths. In making decisions, the correctness of the reasoning is important.

There are times, however, when we are concerned about whether an argument has true premises. 'Sound' in deductive logic refers to deductively valid arguments that have all true premises.

DEFINITION 1.5

An argument is *sound* if and only if it is both deductively valid and has all true premises.

'Sound' is closer to the standard English meaning of 'valid' than our more specialized usage.

Although this is not strictly a part of the definition, the conclusion of any sound argument must be true. By definition, the premises must be true. If the argument is deductively valid and the premises are true, then the conclusion cannot be false. Hence, the conclusion of any sound argument must be true.

ii. Inductive Correctness

Deductive logic regards argument correctness as all or nothing, either valid or invalid. Inductive logic is concerned with connections from premisses to conclusions that are more or less strong.

DEFINITION 1.6

An argument is *inductively strong* (or weak) in direct proportion to the likelihood of its conclusion being true on the assumption that its premisses are true.

Inductive logic is concerned with kinds of linkages from the premisses to the conclusions of arguments that are different from the linkages of deductive logic. Seeing unhappily married people at a shopping center gives *some* evidence that married people are unhappy. If your logic instructor is late for the first five class sessions, you have *some* evidence that she will be late for the sixth session. Students apply inductive logic when they tend to arrive late for classes that usually begin late! The inductive inference regarding class starting time can be expressed as follows.

> *Logic section 000 began late the first session.*
> *Logic section 000 began late the second session.*
> *Logic section 000 began late the third session.*
> *Logic section 000 began late the fourth session.*
> *Logic section 000 began late the fifth session.*

→ *Hence, Logic section 000 will begin late the sixth session.*

In this argument, the truth of the premisses does not guarantee the truth of the conclusion. It is not deductively valid—but inductive logic has a different *standard* for appraising arguments.

When concerned with inductive logic, logicians ask, "What is the probability or likelihood of the conclusion being true, given that the premisses are all true?" If the conclusion is very likely true given that the premisses are all true, then logicians consider the argument to be inductively *strong*. If the conclusion is only slightly supported by the premisses, then logicians consider the argument to be inductively *weak*.

Arguments that are studied by inductive logic usually proceed from what has been experienced to what has not been experienced. Having seen (experienced) some unhappily married people, we might infer a conclusion about married people generally, including those we have not seen. Having experienced five previous class sessions beginning late, we might infer a conclusion about when the sixth session will begin.

Unless an argument is deductively valid, its inductive strength will be altered by the addition of relevant premises. The more unhappily married people we have encountered, and the more places we have encountered them in, the greater the likelihood that married people in general are unhappy. The more class sessions we know to have started late, the stronger the inference becomes that the next session will start late.

Arguments are neither inductively valid nor inductively invalid. The terms 'valid' and 'invalid' are used only when appraising arguments for deductive correctness. However, some deductively invalid arguments are *very* inductively strong; for example, an argument in support of the conclusion that a particular person will die might be very inductively strong. If the laws of biology continue to hold and they apply to everyone, then the particular person will surely die. It is possible to produce a very inductively strong argument for the conclusion that the laws of biology apply, and will continue to apply, to everyone. The laws of biology are based on countless examples. They have no known exceptions. The conclusion that a particular person will die can be established with *near* certainty.

On the other hand, some deductively invalid arguments are inductively weak. For example, the conclusion that a second class session will begin late, because one previous session began late, is based on a *very* inductively weak argument.

iii. Summary

The major ideas of this subsection can be summarized with the following chart. The center (horizontal) line expresses the probability of an argument's conclusion being true on the condition that all of its premises are true.

```
DEDUCTIVELY VALID
                    |————————Deductively Invalid————————|
  100% probability|————————Argument Strength————————|0% probability
                    |—Inductively Strong   Inductively Weak—|
```

Although we should be aware that logic has both inductive and deductive standards and should have some idea of how these standards differ, *the remaining chapters of this text develop only deductive logic.*[3]

---

[3]For an excellent introduction to inductive logic, see Brian Skyrms, *Choice and Chance: An Introduction to Inductive Logic* (Belmont, Calif.: Wadsworth Publishing Co., 1985).

C. Statements/Propositions

Definition 1.2 says that "arguments consist of statements . . . ." Our outline of deductive logic pointed out that arguments can be created from structures (or forms) by placing statements at the ○ and □ locations. Obviously, statements are important in the study of logic. Throughout the remainder of this text, the words 'statement' and 'proposition' are used interchangeably.

Unfortunately, logicians disagree on what a statement (or proposition) is. They disagree on *what* is being placed in the circles and squares, and what makes up an argument. They also disagree on how extensively this subject should be covered by an introductory text. Appendix A provides a discussion of some of these underlying philosophical issues.

We will be content to say that a statement is a true or false declarative (information-giving) sentence. According to this definition, each of the following is a statement:

Wives should live by the sale of their sexual charms.

Nazi Germany was not a friend of Britain.

Used motor oil improves drinking water.

If you ought to take McWit's class, then McWit has well-organized class sessions.

None of the following are statements, since none of them are either true or false:

Was Bertrand Russell a pacifist?

Stop!

Please give me your problem solutions.

Thus, arguments consist of true or false sentences. True or false sentences are imagined at the ○ and □ locations. Although disagreements about the nature of statements are significant, the above account is sufficient for an initial understanding of logic.

Exercises I

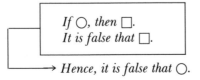

Using the above form, substitute the following statements for the ○ and the □ to create deductively valid arguments.

Example, the following statements—

○ = *The Maginot Line was successful.*
□ = *The Maginot Line stopped Hitler.*

—create the argument:

If the Maginot line was successful then it stopped Hitler.
It is false that the Maginot Line stopped Hitler.
Hence, it is false that the Maginot Line was successful.

Note: Answers for all of the starred problems are in Appendix E.

*1. ○ = You passed all the exams.
     □ = You will pass the course.
 2. ○ = Amelia Earhart flew around the world.
     □ = Amelia Earhart crossed the Pacific.
*3. ○ = The South won at Gettysburg.
     □ = The South won the Civil War.

Exercises II

There are many deductively valid argument forms. Use the following deductively valid form and indicated statements to create arguments.

Either ○ or □.
It is false that ○.
Hence, □.

For example, the following statements—

○ = *Benito Mussolini was the leader of Germany during World War II.*

□ = *Benito Mussolini was the leader of Italy during World War II.*

—create the argument:

Either Benito Mussolini was the leader of Germany during World War II or Benito Mussolini was the leader of Italy during World War II.
It is false that Benito Mussolini was the leader of Germany during World War II.
Hence, Benito Mussolini was the leader of Italy during World War II.

*1. ○ = Booker T. Washington created the NAACP.
   □ = W. E. B. Dubois created the NAACP.
 2. ○ = The Crusades failed in their mission.
   □ = The Crusades conquered the lands where Jesus lived.
*3. ○ = Global temperatures will continue to rise.
   □ = The theory of the greenhouse effect is false.

Concept Reviews

Note: Answers for all of the concept review questions can be found in Appendix D.

1. Suppose two people are screaming abuse at one another in a bar. Are they having an argument as defined in this chapter? Why or why not? What would they have to be screaming at one another in order to be having an argument?

2. Can a deductively valid argument have a false conclusion? Explain.

3. Suppose we accept the premises of two different arguments as being true. One of the arguments is a deductively valid argument; the other is an inductively weak argument. From only this information, how should we view the likelihood that each conclusion is true?

4. Bertrand Russell, who severely disliked Aldous Huxley (the author of *Brave New World*), once provided the following argument for the conclusion that "Huxley found his conversational topics in the Encyclopedia Britannica": "You could always tell by his conversation which volume of the Encyclopedia Britannica he'd been reading. One day it would be Alps, Andes and Apennines, and the next it would be Himalayas and the Hippocratic Oath."

   a. Describe how Russell's argument proceeds from what has been experienced to what has not been experienced.

   b. Indicate additional premisses that would strengthen Russell's inference. Indicate additional premisses that would weaken his inference.

5. Create an argument by providing statements for the following argument form.

   If ○, then □.
   ○.
   Hence, □.

   Using your intuition, do you think that all arguments of this form are deductively valid?

II Arguments in Ordinary Language

Arguments in the real world seldom come with their premisses and conclusions neatly labeled. Two major problems confront us when we consider arguments in ordinary language:

1. The premisses and conclusion are not clearly identified.
2. The argument is incompletely stated.

A. Identifying Premisses and Conclusions

The premisses and the conclusion of an argument must be identified before we can evaluate how well it is put together. The examples that we have considered so far have all stated the premisses first and the conclusion last. The conclusion has been set off from the premisses and identified with 'hence'. In ordinary reasoning, the conclusion might appear at the beginning or middle of an argument, as well as at the end. How, in ordinary reasoning, can we determine which statements are intended to be the premisses and which statement is the conclusion?

English has a number of premiss and conclusion indicators to assist us. Suppose we look at Professor Stephen Hawking's reasoning about our awareness of distant galaxies. He argues that all of our experiences of distant galaxies indicate the way they were in the past, not the way they are now.

> The light that we see from distant galaxies left them millions of years ago, and in the case of the most distant object we have seen, the light left some eight thousand million years ago. *Thus*, when we look at the universe, we are seeing it as it was in the past.[4]

'Thus' tells us that what follows is the conclusion. English has a number of such conclusion indicators. The following is a partial list.

hence	therefore
thus	which shows that
it follows that	we can derive that
so	consequently

Any of the above conclusion indicators can be used to identify the conclusion of Hawking's argument. We could say: "*Hence*, when we look at the universe, we are seeing it as it was in the past"; or: "*It follows that* when we look at the universe, we are seeing it as it was in the past." And so on.

---

[4]Stephen W. Hawking, *A Brief History of Time: From the Big Bang to Black Holes* (New York: Bantam Books, 1988), 28.

In addition to conclusion indicators, English also has a number of premiss indicators. Consider the following:

> Man is the only animal that laughs and weeps; *for* he is the only animal that is struck by the difference between what things are and what they might have been.
>
> – *William Hazlitt*

'For' tells us that the premisses follow. When used in this way, 'for' can be seen as an abbreviation of 'for the reason that'. Why is man the only animal that laughs and weeps? For the reason that he is the only animal that is struck . . . . In addition to 'for', the following words and phrases frequently indicate premisses:

since	follows from
as	because
inasmuch as	may be inferred from
for this reason	is based on

Any of these premiss indicators can also be used to specify Hazlitt's premisses. We could say: "Man is the only animal that laughs and weeps, *since* he is the only animal that is struck by the difference between what things are and what they might have been"; or: "Man is the only animal that laughs and weeps, *because* he is the only animal that is struck. . . ;" and so on.

> **In identifying the premisses and conclusion of an argument, first we should look for our standard English premiss or conclusion indicators.**

An argument's context and intent should always be considered. Viewing arguments as isolated bits of information is a good way to misunderstand them.

Our standard indicators do not always indicate part of an argument. 'Since', in "There have been disagreements *since* the beginning of time," is not being used to indicate a premiss of an argument. In this context, it indicates duration. 'Thus' in "Thus far all of our examples have had standard indicators," does not indicate the conclusion of an argument. In this context, 'thus' is joined with 'far' to indicate 'up to now'.

Conversely, not all arguments come with a standard indicator. Consider the following quotation:

> The only justification for high schools is as therapeutic halfway houses for the deranged. Normal adolescents can find themselves and grow further only by coping with jobs, sex, and chances in the real world.
>
> – *Paul Goodman*

The first sentence expresses Goodman's conclusion, and the second sentence is provided as a premiss. When an argument is stated without premiss or conclusion indicators, we should try adding them to see if they fit. Adding a premiss indicator to our last example results in the same meaning.

> The only justification for high schools is as therapeutic halfway houses for the deranged, *since* normal adolescents can find themselves and grow further only by coping with jobs, sex, and chances in the real world.

Except in logic textbooks, arguments seldom come from nowhere. They are provided by someone with some point in mind. So, context is usually helpful in interpreting arguments. Commercials attempt to have us purchase some product. Candidates try to give us reasons for electing them. We should look for likely motives behind the presentation of an argument. If we read a press release issued by the nuclear power industry, and it seems to argue in favor of coal-fired power plants, we have almost certainly made a mistake!

To summarize:

1. First, look for premiss or conclusion indicators. If present, they will help to identify the parts of an argument.
2. If no premiss or conclusion indicators are present, try adding them. Then ask yourself whether the result has approximately the same meaning as the initial argument.
3. Even though 1 and 2 are helpful, they will not, of course, rule out all mistakes. An argument should always be examined in context. The motives behind its presentation should be considered.

RECOGNIZING PREMISSES AND CONCLUSIONS

Typical Premiss Indicators	*Typical Conclusion Indicators*
because	hence
follows from	thus
as	it follows that
for	so
inasmuch as	therefore
may be inferred from	which shows that
for the reason	consequently
is based on	we can derive that
since	

Exercises III

Each of the following passages contains one argument. Indicate which statement you understand to be the conclusion, and which statements you see as premises. Ask yourself how effectively the premises support the conclusion. (Answers are provided in Appendix E for starred problems.)

*1. "A good painter is to paint two main things, namely, man and the workings of man's mind. The first is easy, the second difficult, for it is to be represented through gestures and movements of the limbs." (Leonardo da Vinci)

 2. "But the Christian God far surpasses the capabilities of any human slavemaster, for He can monitor, not only the actions of men, but their thoughts and feelings as well." (George H. Smith)

 3. "Since most of the propagandists against drug abuse seek to justify certain repressive policies because of the alleged dangerousness of various drugs, they often falsify the facts about the true pharmacological properties of the drugs they seek to prohibit." (Thomas Szasz)

 4. "No, the feminist objection to pornography is based on our belief that pornography represents hatred of women, that pornography's intent is to humiliate, degrade, and dehumanize the female body for the purpose of erotic stimulation and pleasure." (Susan Brownmiller)

*5. "Women, whatever a few male songs and satires may say to the contrary, are more naturally monogamous then men, it is a biological necessity. Where promiscuity prevails, they will therefore always be more often the victims than the culprits." (C. S. Lewis)

 6. "For although it is true that if you want to learn about man, you should study man, it is also true that new light, and more light, may be thrown upon man and the nature of man through knowledge of his near relatives and his ancestors. Consequently, anthropologists study primate and fossil man to unfold his biological background." (E. Adamson Hoebel)

 7. "There is first, the mob, theoretically and in fact the ultimate judge of all ideas and the source of all power. There is, second, the camorra [a secret society known for extortion and violence] of self-seeking minorities, each seeking to inflame, delude and victimize it. The political process thus becomes a mere battle of rival rogues." (H. L. Mencken, "The Disease of Democracy," in *Notes on Democracy*) [Hint: notice the title.]

 8. "The painful fact is that the more crime there is, the less we are able to punish it. This is why the certainty and the severity of punish-

ment must go down when the crime rate goes up." (R. Moran, "More Crime and Less Punishment," *Newsweek*, May 7, 1984)

*9. "Neither a borrower nor lender be, for loan oft loses both itself and friend." (William Shakespeare, *Hamlet*, Act 1, scene 3, lines 75–76)

10. "The cheapness of writing paper is, of course, the reason why women have succeeded as writers before they have succeeded in the other professions." (Virginia Woolf)

11. "The press takes me to task every once in a while, but they have always been very kind, not attributing my hypocrisy to bad motives. They have always attributed it to a lack of mental capacity." (Sam Ervin)

B. Incompletely Stated Arguments

Most arguments in ordinary language are incompletely stated. They are called "enthymemes."

DEFINITION 1.7

An *enthymeme* is an incompletely stated argument.

Both of the examples in section II.A are enthymemes. Suppose that we review Hawking's argument.

The light that we see from distant galaxies left them millions of years ago, and in the case of the most distant object we have seen, the light left some eight thousand million years ago. Thus, when we look at the universe, we are seeing it as it was in the past.

Paraphrasing, we have:

Premiss: *The light that we see from distant galaxies left them millions of years ago.*

Conclusion: *We see distant galaxies as they were in the past.*

Hawking, quite reasonably, expects us to complete his argument by adding the following premiss:

Premiss: *If we see the light from distant galaxies that left them millions of years ago, then we see them as they were in the past.*

It would be ludicrous to criticize Hawking, or claim that his reasoning is invalid, merely because he left out a premiss. If someone stated *every* required premiss, no sane person would want to read what she had written. Even so, although the assumed premiss is perfectly reasonable in the case of Hawking's argument, there are times when assumed premisses are either unclear or questionable. A pamphlet from the Union of Concerned Scientists presents the following argument:

> *Since global warming is caused by human activity, it is a problem we can do something about.*

The argument assumes that humans can do something about the results of any human activity. At the very least, it ignores comparisons between carbon dioxide from natural sources and carbon dioxide from human sources, and it ignores the question of what might be required to make a *significant* difference. Saving the atmosphere from the carbon dioxide produced as a result of inefficient lightbulbs seems inconsequential in relation to what was emitted by the fires that raged through Yellowstone National Park in 1988; perhaps we should concentrate on fighting forest fires. As for human-initiated emissions, the destruction of the rain forests doubtless contributes to global warming through carbon dioxide emissions and the loss of vegetation. Which priority should be higher: better insulated homes or reducing incentives to destroy the forests? In short, merely assuming that we can do something about human activities masks the problem's complexity.

These considerations hardly show that the assumed premiss is false, but they do show that further study is needed before rushing to implement the pamphlet's suggestions. Merely to swallow the implicit premiss in this case would be to ignore a number of important issues.

Incompletely stated arguments, enthymemes, should first be completed and then evaluated.

How we choose to complete an argument depends on our intent. People use reasoning for all sorts of purposes. The goal of a debate may be to win. The goal of a confrontation with an associate may be to get our way. The goal when selling a car may be to get a higher price. Reasoning can be used for lofty and not so lofty purposes. We will adopt the perspective that the point of reasoning is to discover truth. This goal requires arguments to be viewed in the most favorable light possible before we decide to reject them. We will complete enthymemes "with charity."

DEFINITION 1.8

An enthymeme has been *completed with charity* if and only if (1) the completion makes the resulting argument deductively valid and (2) the argument's premises are likely to be accepted.

To apply successfully the principle of charity, we need to be able to structure arguments so that the result is deductively valid. Chapters 2–8 present reasoning structures and discuss them in detail. Certainly not all, but a great many arguments can be reasonably paraphrased and structured in terms of four argument forms. For this reason, we will focus on them at this point. We will use them, at least for the time being, when we are structuring arguments and making charitable completions:[5]

STRUCTURES/FORMS

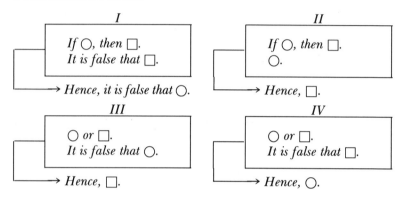

Structures I and II can often be applied when an argument has an 'if–then' premiss. Structure I has one premiss that is an 'if–then' statement, and a second premiss that is the negation of the statement that follows 'then'. It derives a conclusion that is the negation of the statement that follows 'if'.

> ***Structure I can often be used to structure an argument whose conclusion is the denial of a statement.***

Structure II has one premiss that is an 'if–then' statement, and a second premiss that is the same statement that follows 'if'. It derives a conclusion that is the same statement that follows 'then'.

---

[5]Deductively invalid arguments can almost always be expressed as enthymemes, which, when completed, are deductively valid. Suppose we infer that a fifth class session will start late from the fact that the previous four sessions have started late. Since our premisses fail to guarantee our conclusion, we have a deductively invalid argument. Our reasoning can also be expressed with a deductively valid argument by listing the previous four sessions, and adding the premiss, 'If the class started late the last four sessions, then it will start late the fifth session'. Of course, the likelihood of the additional premiss being true is no greater than the inductive strength of the argument prior to our additional premiss. Any *inductive* strength of the original argument has been shifted to the likelihood that a premiss in the deductively valid argument is true.

> **Structure II can often be used to structure an argument whose conclusion is not the denial of a statement.**

Hawking's argument can be structured with form II.

Premiss: The light that we see from distant galaxies left them millions of years ago.
Conclusion: We see distant galaxies as they were in the past.

Hawking's explicit premiss does not contain either the phrase 'it is false that' or some other way to deny a statement. Structure II can be used to link his premiss to his conclusion. In doing so, we can see that it is the first premiss, the 'if–then' statement, that is missing. If we keep the same content for the circles and squares throughout, then we have our earlier completion.

Forms III and IV can often be used to structure arguments that rely on choosing between alternatives. These arguments provide a couple of options, deny one of them, and then have us conclude the other. The following example is an enthymeme—is incompletely stated—since its conclusion has to be added.

Becky's life has either been a daring adventure or it's been nothing; and she's been so preoccupied with safety that she hasn't adventured with anything.

What follows? The first premiss claims that her life has been one or the other of two alternatives. The second premiss denies the first alternative. This argument can be structured with form III. If we keep the same content for the circles and squares throughout, we can derive the conclusion 'Becky's life has been nothing'.

> **Structuring arguments should not be seen as trying to make a literal translation from the English to circles and squares. Rather, the point is to identify the argument's premisses and conclusion, and to give the argument a reasonable structure.**

Our goal in applying structures I–IV is to link an argument's claims together in a way that is reasonable. Applying I–IV might not mirror an argument's presentation; the more important question is whether the result is a charitable way to represent the reasoning. Our next example is based on the French Reign of Terror. It can be viewed in terms of several applications of the above patterns.

The Reign of Terror saw over one thousand people executed without a trial. Maximilien de Robespierre (1758–94) was a particularly vicious leader during this period. After falling into public disfavor, he himself was summarily executed, without a trial. How could someone justify, even to himself, leading a nation through such carnage? The following passage provides several arguments that answer this question.

> He [Robespierre] saw himself as a messianic schoolmaster,
> wielding a very big stick to inculcate virtue. He came to conceive
> of the Revolution itself as a school, but one in which knowledge
> would always be augmented by morality. Both, moreover, de-
> pended on discipline. Terror and virtue, he was fond of saying,
> were part of the same exercise in self-improvement, "virtue with-
> out which terror is harmful and terror without which virtue is im-
> potent".[6]

Robespierre saw himself as a militantly idealistic schoolmaster with all of France as his school. He saw France as being badly in need of education and morality. Both education and morality depend on discipline—the proper exercise of terror. He thought that wielding terror for a moral cause is not only itself moral, but required.

Even though the argument cannot be translated literally into any of the above forms, we can use them to accomplish a charitable completion. Since the argument does not appear to have negated statements, either as parts of conditionals or as alternatives, we should focus on structure II.

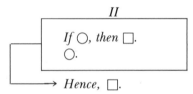

There is no one right way to accomplish charitable completions, even when using our structures. But some ways to express the ideas are more charitable, and hence better, than others.

Suppose we understand the passage to be an argument whose conclusion is 'Robespierre saw himself as being obligated to wield terror'. To structure the reasoning with form II above, we should form a number of 'if–then' statements. Following structure II, the conclusion will be a statement after 'then'. This suggests: 'If Robespierre thought he should convey education and morality to the French people, then he saw himself as being obligated to wield terror.'

Using structure II with uniform content for our circles and squares, we have:

1. *If Robespierre thought he should convey education and morality to the French people, then he saw himself as being obligated to wield terror.*

2. *Robespierre thought he should convey education and morality to the French people.*

Hence,

3. *Robespierre saw himself as being obligated to wield terror.*

---

[6]Simon Schama, *Citizens: A Chronicle of the French Revolution* (New York: Alfred A. Knopf, 1989), 827–28.

We could quit here, but the quotation seeks to make a link between Robespierre's behavior and seeing himself as a messianic schoolmaster. Well, *if* he saw himself as a messianic schoolmaster, *then* he would think he should convey education and morality to the French people. Messianic schoolmasters see themselves as saviors; they want to do that sort of thing. This suggests that the following is a more reasonable way to represent the argument.

1. *If Robespierre saw himself as a messianic schoolmaster, then he thought he should convey education and morality to the French people.*

2. *Robespierre saw himself as a messianic schoolmaster. [A direct quotation.]*

Hence,

3. *Robespierre thought he should convey education and morality to the French people.*

4. *If Robespierre thought he should convey education and morality to the French people, then he saw himself as being obligated to wield terror.*

5. *Robespierre thought he should convey education and morality to the French people.*

Hence,

6. *Robespierre saw himself as being obligated to wield terror.*

Using this interpretation, we can picture two examples of argument pattern II. The first argument derives line 3, which is subsequently used as a premiss for the second argument. The second argument leads to the overall conclusion. As was pointed out earlier, reasoning can frequently be broken down so that the conclusion of one argument is used as a premiss in another.

There are two issues in the above process that deserve particular attention. First, how can we be sure that an answer is correct? Unless we make a glaring mistake, placing arguments into logical structures and completing enthymemes is not the sort of thing that is done correctly or incorrectly. Rather, it is the sort of thing that is done more or less well. There is nothing unique about this. Many, if not most, activities have this quality. We talk of being able to speak English as though doing so was something which a person can or cannot do. In reality, some people speak English well, others speak it less well. Completing enthymemes is also something that is done more or less well.

Second, how should we begin? We should begin by writing down the premisses and conclusion, exactly as we did with Exercises III. Next, we should notice the kinds of statements that we have written down. Do they have negations? If not, we should try paraphrasing the argument with structure II. If they do, we should look at structures I, III, and IV. When we find negations of statements and the argument has us choose between alternatives, we should look at structures III and IV. When we find negations of statements and do not have to choose between alternatives, we should look at structure II.

We will be structuring arguments throughout the remainder of this book. None of the following exercises contain more than one argument, and most of them have suggestions for completing the enthymeme. Not all arguments can be structured in terms of I–IV, but the following arguments have been chosen so that they can be completed by using one of our four structures.

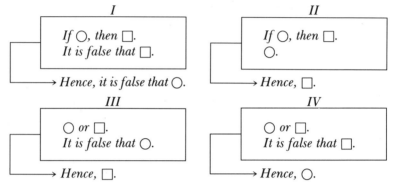

Exercises IV

Use one of our structures I–IV and provide a charitable completion for each of the following enthymemes.

Example: If Leonardo da Vinci painted the workings of the human mind then Leonardo da Vinci painted human beings. Hence, Leonardo da Vinci painted human beings. [Use structure II and supply the second premiss.]

The second premiss of structure II is the same statement that follows 'if' in the first premiss. 'Hence' indicates that the argument's conclusion is 'Leonardo da Vinci painted human beings'. The missing premiss must be 'Leonardo da Vinci painted the workings of the human mind'. The complete argument can be expressed as:

> If Leonardo da Vinci painted the workings of the human mind then Leonardo da Vinci painted human beings.
> Leonardo da Vinci painted the workings of the human mind.
> Hence, Leonardo da Vinci painted human beings.

*1. If promiscuity prevails, then women are more often the victims of promiscuity than the culprits. Hence, women are more often the victims of promiscuity than the culprits. [Use structure II and supply the second premiss.]

2. Many students are lazy. Consequently, teachers attempt to goad students with grades. [Use structure II and supply the first premiss.]

3. Either he put up his sword or he perished with it. It follows that he perished with it. [Use structure III and supply the second premiss.]

4. It is false that drug propagandists admit that many drugs are relatively harmless. Hence, drug propagandists lie about the effects of most drugs. [Use structure III and supply the first premiss.]

*5. If Mencken approves of democracy, then he approves of violence. So, it is false that Mencken approves of democracy. [Use structure I and supply the second premiss.]

6. It is false that the press was cruel to Sam Ervin, since it is false that the press attacked Sam Ervin for hypocrisy. [Use structure I and supply the first premiss.]

7. Either we can afford more prisons or we will have unpunished criminals. Consequently, we will have unpunished criminals. [Use structure III and supply the second premiss.]

8. I am going to be suppressed by "education," since it is false that I'm going to be educated by "education." [Use structure IV and supply the first premiss.]

*9. A girl must, in the course of her development, change the object of her love from a woman (her mother) to a man (her spouse). Hence, a girl's development is more complex than that of a boy. [Use structure II and supply the unstated premiss. This example expresses one of Sigmund Freud's claims regarding childhood development.]

10. It is false that Johnny is ignorant owing to poverty, since it is false that Johnny is ignorant owing to hunger. [Use structure I and supply the unstated premiss.]

11. Either society approves of sex or sexual acts are a sign of rebellion. Thus, sexual acts are a sign of rebellion. [Use structure III and supply the unstated premiss.]

12. Inasmuch as it is false that women are inferior, the physical differences of women have been exploited. [Use structure III and supply the unstated premiss.]

*13. If American professors write obscure articles and dissertations, then they have learned little about learning. Therefore, American professors have learned little about learning. [Use structure II and supply the unstated premiss.]

14. If animals experience pain, then we should refuse to eat them. It is false that we should refuse to eat them. [Use structure I and supply the conclusion.]

15. "In the long run men hit only what they aim at. Therefore, though

they should fail immediately, they had better aim at something high." (Henry David Thoreau, *Walden*)

16. "Work therefore is desirable, first and foremost, as a preventative of boredom, for the boredom that a man feels when he is working is as nothing in comparison with the boredom he feels when he has nothing to do with his days." (Bertrand Russell, *The Conquest of Happiness*)

*17. "The gods had condemned Sisyphus to ceaselessly rolling a rock to the top of a mountain, whence the stone would fall back of its own weight. They had thought with some reason, that there was no more dreadful punishment than futile and hopeless labor." (Albert Camus, "The Myth of Sisyphus")

18. "One may well ask, 'How can you advocate breaking some laws and obeying others?' The answer lies in the fact that there are two types of laws: just and unjust. I agree with St. Augustine that 'an unjust law is no law at all.' " (Martin Luther King, "Letter from Birmingham Jail")

19. " 'When someone is seeking,' said Siddhartha, 'it happens quite easily that he only sees the thing that he is seeking, because he has a goal, because he is obsessed with his goal . . . . In striving towards your goal, you do not see many things that are under your nose.' " (Hermann Hesse, *Siddhartha*)

20. "The greatest secret of vegetarianism is to never eat vegetables." (George Bernard Shaw)

Concept Reviews

1. There is often more than one reasonable completion for an enthymeme. Even so, not all completions will be equally correct. Indicate what makes some completions better than others.

2. If we take the principle of charity seriously, we can find ourselves producing better arguments for a position than those provided by the speaker. When is this desirable? Why? Can you think of an occasion when you would *not* want to improve someone's statement of their position? When?

3. A good deal of humor involves reasoning for an implicit conclusion. People notoriously ruin jokes by getting the parts out of sequence. Also, some jokes take a few minutes to hit. Provide an example of a humorous enthymeme with an unstated conclusion. Next, attempt to relate your enthymeme to one of our structures I–IV.

2 Introduction to the Artificial Language

We know that arguments consist of statements (or propositions). We know that logic is concerned with how statements are connected to form arguments. We know that arguments can be about different subjects and yet have the same structure. The same circle/square structure is common to both Bertrand Russell's argument for changing marriage, and Winston Churchill's argument against befriending Nazi Germany.

The present chapter shifts from considering arguments to considering statements. We have to take a closer look at statements before being able to recognize how they are combined to form arguments. In addition, even though using circles and squares is not incorrect, it is not the typical way of doing things. We should express argument structures as others express them, so that we can discuss formal logic with them.

Hence, one of our goals for this chapter is to develop one of the notations that is standard for the subject. Another goal is to learn how to detect the underlying structure of *statements*. Then, using the ideas that are developed in this chapter, Chapter 3 will reconsider the issue of *argument* structures.

KEY TERMS FOR THIS CHAPTER

Use the glossary as necessary, and review the definitions of these terms prior to a second reading of this chapter.

Statement (or propositional) constant
Simple statement
Compound statement
Statement (or propositional) variable
Antecedent statement
Consequent statement

Conjuncts
Disjuncts
Contradictory statements
Contrary statements
Major connective
Inclusive 'or' statement
Exclusive 'or' statement

I   Background

First, we need a couple of examples that can be used to develop the concepts of this section.

EXAMPLE 1

If Hitler encountered no resistance in attacking the Rhineland, then Hitler could safely attack Czechoslovakia.
Hitler encountered no resistance in attacking the Rhineland.
Hence, Hitler could safely attack Czechoslovakia.

EXAMPLE 2

If The Satanic Verses *mocks Mohammed,*[1] *then it is blasphemous.*
The Satanic Verses *mocks Mohammed.*
Hence, The Satanic Verses *is blasphemous.*

As in Chapter 1, we again have two examples that are about different subjects. The Rhineland was a demilitarized zone created at the end of World War I. Hitler's invasion can reasonably be seen as an act of aggression. *The Satanic Verses* is a novel that mocks Mohammed. Because Mohammed wrote down Allah's words in the Koran, the Muslim religion's holiest writing, *The Satanic Verses* can be seen as mocking the Muslim religion. The statements within each argument are connected to one another, but there is no apparent connection between the foundations of the Muslim faith and the beginning of Hitler's conquests.

The first premiss in Examples I and II claims that *if* one statement is true *then* another statement is true. The second premiss in each example is the same statement as the one that follows the word 'if' in the first premiss. The conclusion of each example is the same statement as the one that follows the word 'then' in the first premiss. Both arguments share the same structure. In terms of the circle/square method of Chapter 1, their common pattern can be expressed as follows:

If ○, *then* □.
○.
Hence, □.

Although it is possible to find argument forms by comparing examples in English, forms can be more easily seen by using 'statement (or propositional) constants'.

---

[1]Salman Rushdie, *The Satanic Verses* (New York: Penguin/Viking, 1988).

DEFINITION 2.1

A *statement* (or *propositional*) *constant* is any capital letter, from *A* to *Z*, that is used to stand for a particular statement (or proposition).

Statement constants provide a way to avoid writing out a lot of English. Rather than writing out an English sentence, we can use a single (capital) letter to abbreviate it. Suppose that we decide to let the capital letter *E* abbreviate the English sentence 'Hitler encountered no resistance in attacking the Rhineland'. Similarly, suppose we let *S* abbreviate the English sentence 'Hitler could safely attack Czechoslovakia'. Example 1 can now be expressed as:

Premiss: *If E, then S.*
Premiss: *E.*
Conclusion: *S.*

We can also use the following abbreviations.

Let *M* abbreviate '*The Satanic Verses* mocks Mohammed'.

Let *B* abbreviate '*The Satanic Verses* is blasphemous'.

Example 2 can now be expressed as follows:

Premiss: *If M, then B.*
Premiss: *M.*
Conclusion: *B.*

We will specify the pattern that underlines both arguments after further clarifying our usage of statement constants.

DEFINITION 2.2

A *compound statement* is any statement that has a statement as a part.

Statements that are not compound are called "simple."

DEFINITION 2.3

A *simple statement* is any statement that does not have a statement as a part.

All of the following are simple statements.

Hitler encountered no resistance in attacking the Rhineland.

Hitler could safely attack Czechoslovakia.

The Satanic Verses mocks Mohammed.

The Satanic Verses is blasphemous.

All of the following are compound statements. Each statement that is a part of the compound statement has been underlined.

If Hitler encountered no resistance in attacking the Rhineland, then Hitler could safely attack Czechoslovakia. Hitler could safely attack Czechoslovakia and Hitler could safely attack Poland.

Either *The Satanic Verses* mocks Mohammed or *The Satanic Verses* is blasphemous. It is false that *The Satanic Verses* is blasphemous.[2]

Statement constants are used to abbreviate *simple* statements. Additional symbols are required by the artificial language to express compound statements.

Any capital letter can be used to stand for any simple statement. We could have used the letter Q to stand for one of the above simple statements. A better habit, however, is to pick a letter that reminds us of the statement. Picking the first letter of a word that stands out usually works well.

In any given argument, a particular letter can be used to abbreviate only *one simple statement.* It is incorrect to use the same letter to stand for two different simple statements. Conversely, every time we have a particular statement, the same letter must be used to abbreviate it. In short, the statement constant and the simple statement should pair off.

Suppose that we wish to write out the structure that underlies our recent examples. As in Chapter 1, we need a way to indicate a 'place' for a statement without actually 'placing' a statement there. We also need a way to indicate that the same statement reappears within the argument.[3] Rather than the circles and squares of Chapter 1, our artificial language uses *statement variables*.

DEFINITION 2.4

A statement variable is any lower-case letter from p to z, that is used as a placeholder for statements.

---

[2]Negated statements, such as this example, are discussed in Section II.D of this chapter.

[3]Some accounts of statements reject this way of speaking. See Appendix A for a discussion of these issues.

We now have enough symbolic machinery to express the form that is present in examples 1 and 2. The two arguments—

If E, then S.   *If M, then B.*
E.   *M.*
Hence, S.   *Hence, B.*

—share the form:

If p, then q.
p.
Hence, q.

Remember that the lower-case letters *p* and *q* do not stand for particular statements. Rather, they indicate *locations* where we can imagine statements. Any number of arguments can have a particular pattern, and there are an infinite number of patterns.

As we saw near the end of Chapter 1, deductive patterns can also be used to *create* arguments. Let *L* abbreviate '22 percent of the *l*osses at ATMs (automatic teller machines) are due to consumer fraud', and let *I* abbreviate 'more positive *i*dentification is needed'. Then the above form can be used to create the following argument:

If L, then I.
L.
Hence, I.

In English we have:

If *22 percent of the losses at ATMs are due to consumer fraud,* then *more positive identification is needed.*
22 percent of the losses at ATMs are due to consumer fraud.
Hence, more positive identification is needed.

Our convention will be to use the lower-case letters as needed, using *p* first, *q* second, *r* third, and so on. Argument structures in this text rarely require more than four variables.

We have started the process of developing an artificial language for expressing logical relationships. The language is called 'artificial' because it is a *planned* language. Natural languages, such as English, French, or Spanish, are not planned; they have evolved. Some students claim that the language in later portions of this text looks like algebra. Although connections to mathematics can be made, none will be developed here. And no mathematical concepts will be required to understand the language as it will be presented. Still, both the logical language and algebra are artificial languages. One difference between algebra and the language of this text is that algebra seeks to reflect mathematical relationships, whereas the one in this text seeks to reflect logical relationships.

II   The Symbols

A. The Conditional

Examples in this chapter and Chapter 1 have included a number of compound statements that are expressed with the English 'if–then' construction. These statements contain two statements as parts: the statement that follows 'if', and the statement that follows 'then'.

1. If Hitler encountered no resistance in attacking the Rhineland, then Hitler realized that he could safely attack Czechoslovakia.
2. If *The Satanic Verses* mocks Mohammed, then it is blasphemous.
3. If we ought to retain the present outlook on marriage then wives should live by the sale of their sexual charms.
4. If Nazi Germany is to be a friend of Britain then Nazi Germany must have acceptable values.

Compound statements that are formed by connecting two statements with 'if' and 'then' are called 'conditionals'. All of examples 1 through 4 are conditionals.

The parts of conditionals have different names.

DEFINITION 2.5

The statement that follows 'if' in a conditional of the form 'if p then q' is called the *antecedent* statement.

DEFINITION 2.6

The statement that follows 'then' in a conditional of the form 'if p then q' is called the *consequent* statement.

The following statement is also a conditional.

If 22 percent of the losses at ATMs are due to consumer fraud, then more positive identification is needed.

In this example the antecedent statement is '22 percent of the losses at ATMs are due to consumer fraud', and the consequent statement is 'more positive identification is needed'.

Our artificial language uses the horseshoe, '⊃', to express conditionals. In our new symbolism the antecedent statement is *always* represented at the left-hand side of the horseshoe. The consequent statement is *always* represented at the right-hand side of the horseshoe. If we let *L* abbreviate '22 percent of the *l*osses at ATMs are due to consumer fraud', and let *I* abbreviate 'more positive *i*dentification is needed', we can express the ATM conditional as:

If L, then I.

Using the horseshoe to express the conditional connection given by the English 'if . . . then . . . ', we have:

L ⊃ *I*

Similarly, 'If *F*, then *P*' should be translated as '*F* ⊃ *P*'. In general:

'If p then q' in English is translated as 'p ⊃ q'.

i. Common English Variations

The 'if–then' construction is not the only means in English of expressing conditionals. The horseshoe is, however, *the only means* of expressing conditionals in the artificial language. Hence, a number of English constructions should be translated with the horseshoe in the artificial language.

In English, often the word 'then' is omitted, but understood. The following sentence has the same meaning as our earlier example.

If 22% of the losses at ATMs are due to consumer fraud, more positive identification is needed.

This sentence should also be represented by '*L* ⊃ *I*'.

Sometimes the word 'if' is used in the middle of a sentence.

More positive identification is needed if 22 percent of the losses at ATMs are due to consumer fraud.

'If' indicates the antecedent, and the antecedent statement is always represented at the left-hand side of the horseshoe. So again we have '*L* ⊃ *I*'.

Sometimes the phrase 'only if' is used to indicate a conditional.

Unlike 'if', 'only if' indicates the consequent.

Hence, the statement indicated by 'only if' is represented at the right-hand side of the horseshoe.

The Satanic Verses mocks Mohammed only if it's blasphemous. Only if it's blasphemous will The Satanic Verses mock Mohammed.

These sentences provide another way of saying that "If *The Satanic Verses* mocks Mohammed, then it's blasphemous." Hence, '*M* only if *B*' and 'only if *B*, *M*' should both be expressed as: '*M* ⊃ *B*'. Notice that using '*B* ⊃ *M*' would be incorrect. 'If it's blasphemous then *The Satanic Verses* mocks Mohammed' is *not* the meaning of either statement. *The Satanic Verses* could be blasphemous without mocking Mohammed. The book could be blasphemous by attacking the Muslim religion, or some other religion, on other grounds.

The words 'entails' and 'implies' can also be used to express conditionals.

That 22 percent of the *l*osses at ATMs are due to consumer fraud implies the need for more positive *i*dentification.

That 22 percent of the *l*osses at ATMs are due to consumer fraud entails the need for more positive *i*dentification.

Both of these sentences approximate our initial conditional in meaning, and should also be translated as '*L* ⊃ *I*'. The words 'implies' and 'entails' also have common passive-voice constructions: 'is implied by' and 'is entailed by'.

The phrase 'provided that' often has the same function in English as the word 'if'.

Provided that 22 percent of the losses at ATMs are due to consumer fraud, more positive identification is needed.

Again, this last sentence should be expressed as '*L* ⊃ *I*'.

When one condition is said to be sufficient for another, the statement indicates a conditional.

The fact that 22 percent of the losses at ATMs are due to consumer fraud is sufficient to show that more positive identification is needed.

Again we have '*L* ⊃ *I*'.

The phrase 'a necessary condition' also expresses a conditional, but notice that *this phrase indicates the consequent*. The claim that the presence of oxygen in a room is a necessary condition for there to be a fire in the room is not an assertion that if we have oxygen in a room, then we have a fire in the room. (What a warm place the world would be if it meant this!) Having oxygen present is a necessary condition, so if we are to have *f*ire in the room (call this statement *F*), then there must be *o*xygen in the room (call this statement *O*). "Oxygen is present in the room" is the consequent statement. Hence, our symbolization is '*F* ⊃ *O*', *not* '*O* ⊃ *F*'.

There are really only three problem cases here: 'if' designates an antecedent, whereas 'only if' designates a consequent; and a necessary condition is expressed as a consequent.

As you may have guessed, the above listing is not complete. In fact, given the flexibility of English, a complete listing is not possible. The following listing does, however, indicate typical ways to express conditionals in English. Another example from Chapter 1:

Whenever you consider getting married, you should go to a crowded shopping center.

Using the abbreviations *M* and *C*, we should express this as '*M* ⊃ *C*'.

CONDITIONAL TRANSLATION SUMMARY

English	Artificial
If p then q	$p \supset q$
If p, q	$p \supset q$
p, if q	$q \supset p$
p only if q	$p \supset q$
Only if p, q	$q \supset p$
p implies q	$p \supset q$
p entails q	$p \supset q$
p is implied by q	$q \supset p$
p is entailed by q	$q \supset p$
p is sufficient for q	$p \supset q$
p is necessary for q	$q \supset p$
Provided that p, q	$p \supset q$

A few rare sentences have the English 'if–then' construction, yet their point is not to convey any conditional.

If I don't get new jeans, then I'll die!

The above sentence is not really about death; it probably expresses the proposition

I want new jeans!

However, in acquiring an awareness of the artificial language, it is best not to dwell on unduly complicated examples at the start. It is preferable to have an awareness of common translations before encountering unusual ones.

Exercises I

Each of the following sentences expresses a conditional. In each case, use the suggested statement constants and produce a translation that employs the horseshoe. All of the patterns in these exercises have been discussed.

   *1. If you *g*o to Daytona, then you'll have an *e*xciting break. *G, E*

    2. If you want to have an *e*xciting break, you ought to *g*o to Daytona. *E, G*

   *3. *E*ating 40 cups of chocolate daily is justified only if it's an *a*phrodisiac [16th century Aztec belief]. *E, A*

    4. Being the most *p*owerful nation on earth implies the responsibility for *r*estraint. *P, R*

   *5. Being a *h*ostile person entails a higher risk of heart *f*ailure [Duke University Medical Report]. *H, F*

    6. That Sean has a high *s*perm count is a necessary condition for him to be *m*arried [Either to ensure fertility or to avoid the unnecessary use of contraceptives]. *S, M*

   *7. Having a sense of *h*umor is a necessary condition for the acquisition of *l*ogic. *H, L*

    8. That 1 in every 8,890 abortions results in a *l*ive birth entails the need to *c*hange our abortion laws [New York Bureau of Statistics]. *L, C*

   *9. Provided that alcohol *i*nhibits the hippocampus, it will *r*etard long-term memory. *I, R*

   10. Whenever a lake *c*ontains toxic chemicals, one should *a*void fishing in it. *C, A*

  *11. That a one-pound fish from Lake Ontario *c*ontains the PCBs of 1.5 million quarts of lake water is sufficient to show that fish can concentrate *t*oxic chemicals. *C, T*

   12. The *n*eed for flame-resistant seats is entailed by a *s*tudy of recent plane crashes. *N, S*

  *13. Only if we *a*ttack Germany, can the world be made *s*afe for democracy [claim made by President Woodrow Wilson in 1917, in support of U.S. involvement in World War I]. *A, S*

Concept Reviews

   1. Describe some of the differences between 'if *P* then *Q*' and 'if *p* then *q*'. What do the capital letters indicate? What do the lower-case letters indicate? What are the names of each?

   2. What are the parts of a conditional called? How are they placed in relation to the horseshoe?

   3. Chapter 1 first introduced circles and squares to express the form involved in the arguments provided by Bertrand Russell and Winston Churchill. Express the following Chapter 1 argument form by using the statement variables *p* and *q*.

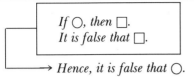

If ○, then □.
It is false that □.

→ *Hence, it is false that ○.*

B. Conjunctions

Although conditionals are of great logical importance, they are not the only type of compound statements that we should consider.

> *The world must be made safe for democracy, and war must be declared on Germany.*
>
> *D. H. Lawrence was a friend of Bertrand Russell, and he was also the author of Lady Chatterley's Lover.*

These compound statements have their parts linked by the word 'and'. Compound statements that are formed by connecting two statements with 'and' are called "conjunctions."

DEFINITION 2.7

The statements that are combined with 'and' to form a conjunction are called *conjuncts*.

Each of the underlined statements in the above examples is a conjunct. The following is also a conjunction statement.

> *22 percent of the losses at ATMs are due to consumer fraud, **and** more positive identification is needed.*

Suppose that we adopt the following abbreviations:

Let S abbreviate 'The world must be made *s*afe for democracy'.

Let D abbreviate 'War must be *d*eclared on Germany'.

Let F abbreviate 'D. H. Lawrence was a *f*riend of Bertrand Russell'.

Let A abbreviate 'D. H. Lawrence was the *a*uthor of *Lady Chatterley's Lover*'.

Let L abbreviate '22 percent of the *l*osses at ATMs are due to consumer fraud'.

Let I abbreviate 'More positive *i*dentification is needed'.

Our three example conjunctions can be expressed as:

S and D.

F and A.

L and I.

Our artificial language uses the dot '·', to express conjunctions. The dot is always placed between the conjuncts. Our three conjunctions can now be expressed as:

$S \cdot D$

$F \cdot A$

$L \cdot I$

Just as English has a number of ways to express conditionals whereas the artificial language has only the horseshoe, English also has a number of ways to express conjunctions whereas the artificial language has only the dot. Hence, there are a number of English constructions that should be expressed by using the dot.

CONJUNCTION TRANSLATION SUMMARY

English	*Artificial*
p, and q	$p \cdot q$
p, but q	$p \cdot q$
p, yet q	$p \cdot q$
p; although q	$p \cdot q$
Although p, q	$p \cdot q$
p; moreover q	$p \cdot q$
p; however q	$p \cdot q$
p; in addition, q	$p \cdot q$
p; still, q	$p \cdot q$

In claiming that each of the above English constructions typically expresses a conjunction, we are *not* claiming that they have identical English usages. For example, contexts where we use 'but' differ from contexts where we use 'and'. 'But' is used when the following conjunct is unexpected. 'The institution of marriage endorses prostitution, but it should not be changed' sounds more natural than 'the institution of marriage endorses prostitution, and it should not be changed'. We expect that someone who compares marriage to prostitution will want to change marriage. The second conjunct, that it should *not* be changed, is unexpected. The above translation summary merely claims that all of the indicated words and phrases typically express conjunctions, not that they all have identical English usages.

We should notice that 'moreover', 'however', and 'still' typically express conjunctions, not conditionals. 'D. H. Lawrence was a friend of Bertrand Russell; moreover he was the author of *Lady Chatterley's Lover*' asserts both that Lawrence was a friend of Bertrand Russell *and* that he was the author of *Lady Chatterley's Lover*. It would be incorrect to interpret this sentence as claiming '*if* D. H. Lawrence was a friend of Bertrand Russell, *then* he was also the author of *Lady Chatterley's Lover*'.

The order in which the conjuncts are placed with the dot does not make any difference.

The above summary lists typical ways to express conjunctions in English. Just as our summary of translations for conditionals was incomplete, however, the above summary of translations for conjunctions is also incomplete.

Note that, although 'and' is commonly used for conjoining statements in English, it also has other English meanings.

i. Alternative Meanings of 'and'

There are three basic English usages of 'and': pure conjunctive, conjunctive with sequence, and nonconjunctive.

a. Pure Conjunction   Most commonly, the English 'and' merely indicates a conjunction of two statements. It functions by connecting two statements that could have been expressed independently. There is no particular significance in the fact that the statements are conjoined rather than expressed one at a time, but the resulting statement often sounds smoother in English. Instead of the conjunction at the beginning of this section, Woodrow Wilson could have used the following separate statements to convey the same meaning.

The world must be made safe for democracy.
War must be declared on Germany.

The conjunction, of course, suggests a reason for wanting to declare war, but Wilson was willing to assert the statements independently. Conjoining them does not change the statements, it merely links them. Pure conjunctions are conjunctions and nothing more.

The dot has the exact meaning of 'and' when 'and' expresses a pure conjunction.

b. Conjunction with Sequence   At times 'and' expresses more than a conjunction. It can be understood to mean 'and then', indicating the order or sequence in which the conjuncts are to be understood. 'And' in the following sentences will likely be understood to express 'and then'.

Japan bombed Pearl Harbor, and the United States declared war on Japan.

The United States declared war on Japan, and Japan bombed Pearl Harbor.

The first sentence gives the correct impression that the United States declared war in self-defense. The second sentence gives the incorrect impression that the attack by Japan was in retaliation. In these examples we have the suggestion that the first conjunct indicates what happened first, and the second conjunct indicates what happened second.

Although the meaning of 'and' changes between purely conjunctive and conjunctive with sequence, *the meaning of the dot is absolutely constant.* The dot *always* expresses a pure conjunction.

We will use the dot to express both the purely conjunctive 'and' and the conjunctive-with-sequence 'and'. When expressing pure conjunctions, the expression with the dot and the original English have the same meaning. When the dot is used to express conjunctions with sequence, the expression with the dot and the original English do *not* both have the same meaning. The idea of sequence that was present in the English will have been lost in going to the expression with the dot.

By using obvious abbreviations, our recent examples on the bombing of Pearl Harbor can be symbolized as follows.

$B \cdot D$

$D \cdot B$

In the artificial language, '$B \cdot D$' and '$D \cdot B$' have the same meaning: pure conjunction. The dot expresses the 'and' part, but it ignores the 'then' part of the 'and then' meaning.

Even though sequence can have logical significance, we will concern ourselves only with pure conjunctions in this text. None of the arguments that we will consider depend on temporal sequence.

c. Nonconjunctive Uses of 'and'   There are times when 'and' fails to express a conjunction at all. Sometimes it is part of a figure of speech. Sometimes it indicates a relationship between two things.

'The land is flowing with milk and honey' is a figure of speech, derived from the Old Testament, indicating that the land has great abundance. It does not express a conjunction.

Don Quixote, a novel written by Miguel de Cervantes in 1615, describes the exploits of Quixote and his faithful squire, Sancho Panza. Someone might claim 'Sancho and Quixote had amusing conversations'. This statement is *not* a conjunction of two statements, one indicating what Sancho did and the other what Quixote did. Rather, it expresses something that happened *between* them.

In contrast, the statement 'Sancho and Quixote were Spaniards' asserts two statements: 'Sancho was a Spaniard' and 'Quixote was a Spaniard'. Hence, this is a conjunction statement.

Using the dot to express 'and' when it has a nonconjunctive meaning is incorrect. Nonconjunctive usages of 'and' should be expressed with an appropriate statement constant. We might let *F* abbreviate 'the land is *f*lowing with milk and honey'. We might let *A* abbreviate 'Sancho Panza and Don Quixote had *a*musing conversations'.

The following exercises are relatively straightforward, since if two statements are being connected then there is a conjunction. The best way to remember the various conjunction indicators and the alternative meanings of 'and' is to think about these issues in relation to particular sentences. Some of the following exercises may have more than one possible interpretation, but you should be able to defend your answer in terms of the concepts of this section.

Exercises II

Each of the following sentences expresses either a pure conjunction, a conjunction with sequence, or a nonconjunctive use of 'and'. Designate your own statement constants, and express each of the following in our artificial language. If the sentence indicates sequence, note the sequence. If the sentence does not conjoin two statements, do not use the dot.

*1. The Lewis and Clark expedition explored the American Northwest.

2. The *Spirit of St. Louis* and the *Voyager* are famous planes. [The *Spirit of St. Louis* was the first plane to fly nonstop across the Atlantic Ocean. The *Voyager* was the first plane to fly around the world without refueling.]

*3. The commission presented only a portion of its data, but said it had identified 'concrete evidence of hunger' in more than 20 states [report on nutrition in Massachusetts by the Citizens' Commission on Hunger in New England].

4. The commission found at least one sign of poor nutrition in 18.1 percent of the low-income preschoolers, and it reported that 9.8 percent of the children had stunted growth [same report cited for number 3 above].

*5. A union must guard its rank and file.

6. The number of alcohol-related deaths has remained constant, whereas fatal accidents [from all causes] have dropped more than 40 percent.

*7. She showed little emotion during the trial, yet she wept as the verdict was read.

8. 'I am Alpha and Omega'. (Statement attributed to God in the New Testament. Alpha is the first letter of the Greek alphabet, Omega the last.)

*9. In addition to being the author of *Lady Chatterley's Lover*, D. H. Lawrence wrote *Women in Love*.

10. Radiation will kill fruit flies; however, studies show that it reduces the vitamin C content of the fruit.

*11. The Austrian archduke was assassinated and World War I began. [Hint: The assassination was interpreted as a hostile act and caused the onset of World War I.]

12. The first pig made a house of straw; still, the wolf blew the house down.

Concept Reviews

1. Create three different sentences that use the word 'and'. One of your sentences should have a purely conjunctive usage of 'and', one of them should have a conjunction-with-sequence usage of 'and', and one of them should have a nonconjunctive usage of 'and'.

C. Disjunctions

Suppose that we are uncertain about which novels were written by D. H. Lawrence. Knowing the titles of two novels possibly written by D. H. Lawrence, we might say:

> D. H. Lawrence wrote *Lady Chatterley's Lover* or D. H. Lawrence wrote *Women in Love*.

This compound statement has its parts linked by the word 'or'. Compound statements that are formed by connecting two statements with 'or' are called "disjunctions."

DEFINITION 2.8

The statements that are combined with 'or' to form a disjunction are called *disjuncts*.

In the above example, the whole statement is a disjunction. Each of the underlined statements is a disjunct. The following statement is also a disjunction.

ATM fraud must drop or *more positive identification is needed.*

Suppose that we let L abbreviate 'D. H. Lawrence wrote *Lady Chatterley's Lover*', let W abbreviate 'D. H. Lawrence wrote *Women in Love*', let D abbreviate 'ATM fraud must drop', and let I abbreviate 'more positive identification is needed'. The statements can be expressed as:

L *or* W.

D *or* I.

Our artificial language uses the wedge 'V' to express disjunctions. Our examples can now be expressed as follows.

$L \lor W$

$D \lor I$

There are only a few common ways to indicate disjunctions in English.

DISJUNCTION TRANSLATION SUMMARY

English	Artificial
p or q	$p \lor q$
p unless q	$p \lor q$
Unless p, q	$p \lor q$
p, otherwise q (rare)	$p \lor q$

Students are often surprised that both 'or' and 'unless' typically express disjunctions. As with the Conjunction Translation Summary, the above Disjunction Translation Summary expresses logical similarities, *not* identical English usages. Statements that are combined by using 'or', 'unless', and 'otherwise' in English typically express disjunctions. The following example points out this logical similarity.

Let us suppose that the final exam for a class has been taken, but that the final semester grade is in the mail. Students often describe the situation as follows.

I'll get an A [or a B, or . . .] unless I flunked the final.

'Unless' adds emphasis; students often feel anxiety after a final exam. But approximately the same meaning is present in the following statement that uses 'or'.

Either I'll get an A [or a B, or . . .] or I flunked the final.

The sentence with 'unless' sounds more natural, since using 'or' makes the student seem almost indifferent about the outcome. Both sentences, however, describe the same situation: either a good grade or a failed exam. This similarity in meaning enables us to express both statements by using the wedge.

Although very few usages of 'or' in English fail to indicate a disjunction, not all usages of 'or' are logically identical. Logically different kinds of 'or' statements are covered in section III.B of this chapter.

The next section presents our last new artificial language symbol until Chapter 5.

D. Negation

i. Standard Indicators

In Chapter 1 we expressed negations by using the phrase 'it is false that'. English, however, usually expresses negation by using the word 'not'. Both of the following have approximately the same meaning:

The game is not worth the candle.[4]

It is false that the game is worth the candle.

If the phrase 'it is not the case that' is used, we can see that the negated statement has the affirmative statement 'the game is worth the candle' as a part. Negations, whether expressed with 'it is false that', 'not', or another negation indicator, are always considered to have an affirmative statement as a part. For this reason, negations are always considered compound.

Suppose we let G abbreviate the simple statement, 'the game is worth the candle'. Our artificial language uses the tilde, '~', to express negation. The statement that is being negated is always represented at the right-hand side of the tilde. 'It is false that the game is worth the candle' and 'the game is not worth the candle', are both expressed as:

$\sim G$

The negation of the statement L is expressed as $\sim L$. If L indicates that D. H. Lawrence wrote *Lady Chatterley's Lover*, then $\sim L$ indicates that D. H. Lawrence did not write *Lady Chatterley's Lover*.

The negation of a statement 'p' is expressed by '~p'.

---

[4]This saying means that the results of an endeavor are not worth the effort required to accomplish it. Its meaning originates from the practice of playing cards by candlelight when the stakes of the game were lower than the cost of the candles that were required to play it.

Just as our artificial language has only one way to express conditionals, only one way to express conjunctions, and only one way to express disjunctions, it has only one way to express negations: the tilde.

English has only a few common methods for expressing negations. In addition to 'it is false that' and 'not', we occasionally encounter the phrase 'it is not the case that'. Someone might say, "It is not the case that D. H. Lawrence wrote *Lady Chatterley's Lover*." Again we have ~L.

NEGATION TRANSLATION SUMMARY

English	Artificial
not p	~p
It is false that p	~p
It is not the case that p	~p

The Exact Significance of the Tilde   'Not' in English *frequently, but not always*, indicates the contradictory of a statement.

DEFINITION 2.9

Two statements are *contradictories* (of one another) when the truth of one statement guarantees the falsity of the other, and the falsity of one statement guarantees the truth of the other.

The obscure word in the above definition is 'guarantee'. Whether two statements are contradictories cannot be determined by merely knowing that one of them is true and knowing that the other is false. For now, we should look at 'guarantee' as being determined by what can be imagined. If two statements are contradictories, then any situation that we might *imagine* that makes one statement true will make the other one false. Any situation that we might *imagine* that makes one statement false will make the other one true.

Each of our artificial language symbols, including the tilde, has a precise meaning.

Applying the tilde expresses the contradictory of the unnegated statement.

The following example relates to slavery in Virginia during the early nineteenth century.

Nat Turner led an effective slave revolt.[5]

The phrase 'it is not the case that' can be used to express the contradictory of this statement.

It is not the case that Nat Turner led an effective slave revolt.

If it is true that Nat Turner led an effective slave revolt, then the negation, 'it is not the case that Nat Turner led an effective slave revolt', *must* be false. It is impossible to imagine *any* situation such that both statements are true. If it is false that Nat Turner led an effective slave revolt, then the negation, 'it is not the case that Nat Turner led an effective slave revolt', *must* be true. It is impossible to imagine *any* situation such that both statements are false.

If we use E to indicate that Nat Turner led an *e*ffective slave revolt, $\sim E$ indicates that it is not the case that Nat Turner led an effective slave revolt. $\sim E$ expresses the contradictory of the statement that is represented by E.

Occasionally, English uses the word 'not' to express what is called a 'contrary', rather than the contradictory, of a statement.

DEFINITION 2.10

Two statements are *contraries* (of one another) when the truth of one statement guarantees the falsity of the other, but the falsity of one statement does not guarantee the truth of the other.

We should also use our imagination to understand contraries. When contraries are present, we will not be able to imagine a situation where both can be true. We should, however, be able to imagine a situation where both are false.

Contraries usually arise when opposing qualities are attributed to a subject, and we can imagine a situation where neither of them apply. 'Alexander's car is red all over' is a contrary of 'Alexander's car is green all over'. Alexander's car cannot be both red and green all over. Both could be false, however; Alexander either might not have a car, or it might be blue.

Occasionally, contraries are expressed by using the English 'not'. Consider the following statements.

Winston Churchill's drinking problem hindered his statesmanship.
Winston Churchill's drinking problem did not hinder his statesmanship.

---

[5]Prior to his hanging in 1831, Nat Turner and his followers killed 51 white Virginians. Slaveholders responded by enacting strict slave-control legislation. The uprising did bring to light some of the dissatisfaction of blacks with slavery.

Provided that we have a clear meaning of 'hinder' in mind, no situation that we can imagine will make both statements true. We can imagine a situation, however, such that both statements are false. At least one historian has claimed that "the legend that [Churchill was] a heavy drinker is quite untrue. Churchill [was] a sensible, if unorthodox, drinker."[6] If we imagine Churchill not having a drinking problem, then it is false that his drinking problem hindered his statesmanship and false that it did not hinder it.

Contraries should not be expressed by using the tilde.

Suppose that we use *H* to abbreviate 'Winston Churchill's drinking problem *h*indered his statesmanship'. Then ~*H* expresses the *contradictory, not a contrary,* of *H*. The expression ~*H* states 'it is false that Winston Churchill had a drinking problem that hindered his statesmanship'.

ii. Prefixes

English sometimes expresses the contradictory of a statement by adding a negating prefix to a key word. The contradictory of 'it is possible to pass this class without using any effort' can be expressed with 'it is *im*possible to pass this class without using any effort'. The contradictory of 'temptation is resistible' can be expressed with 'temptation is *ir*resistible'.

If the *contradictory* of an affirmative statement is expressed by a negating prefix, then it is acceptable to use the tilde to symbolize the negation. Suppose that we let *C* indicate 'it is possible to pass this *c*lass without using any effort'. Then 'it is impossible to pass this class without using any effort' can be expressed as ~*C*.

However, negating prefixes *usually* produce contraries, rather than contradictories. The following statements are contraries.

Nat Turner led an effective slave revolt.
Nat Turner led an ineffective slave revolt.

Provided that we have a clear conception of 'effective' and are referring to a particular revolt, there can be no situation where both are true. We can imagine a situation, however, such that both might be false. Suppose that Nat Turner did not lead a slave revolt, and so did not lead one that was either effective or ineffective.

Contraries should be expressed by using two different statement constants.

---

[6]William Manchester, *The Last Lion: Winston Spencer Churchill—Alone* (Boston: Little, Brown and Co., 1988), 10.

Exercises III

Pick appropriate statement constants, and symbolize each of the following pairs of statements into our artificial language. If the statements are contradictories, then use one statement constant and apply the tilde to symbolize the negation. If the statements are contraries, then use a different statement constant to abbreviate each statement.

*1. a. Michigan is north of Florida.
    b. Michigan is not north of Florida.

 2. a. Pooh went on an 'expotition' to the North Pole.
    b. Pooh did not go on an 'expotition' to the North Pole.

*3. a. Kanga buttoned her pouch.
    b. Kanga unbuttoned her pouch.

 4. a. It is false that Susan B. Anthony was an advocate of women's suffrage.
    b. Susan B. Anthony was an advocate of women's suffrage.

*5. a. Australia is roughly the same size as the contiguous United States.
    b. Australia is not roughly the same size as the contiguous United States.

 6. a. You cannot make a silk purse from a sow's ear. [It is not possible to make good products from poor materials.]
    b. You can make a silk purse from a sow's ear. [It is possible to make good products from poor materials.]

 7. a. The universe is increasing in size.
    b. The universe is not increasing in size.

 8. a. The universe is increasing in size.
    b. The universe is decreasing in size.

*9. a. I am looking for an honest person.
    b. I am looking for a dishonest person.

III More Complex Symbolizations

A. Punctuation in the Artificial Language Structure

The previous section introduced us to four artificial language symbols: the horseshoe, the dot, the wedge, and the tilde. They are called 'connectives'.[7]

---

[7]This list is complete for the moment; in Chapter 5, an additional symbol, the triple bar, is added.

DEFINITION 2.11

The horseshoe, dot, wedge, and tilde are *connectives*.

We are able to represent four different kinds of compound statements with the artificial language: conditionals, conjunctions, disjunctions, and negations. As the following discussion shows, however, we also need to be able to punctuate our artificial language in order to represent more complex statements.

Prior to an automobile accident near Chappaquiddick, Massachusetts, in 1969, Senator Edward Kennedy was a likely Democratic presidential nominee. Kennedy's car went off a bridge and the passenger, a woman on Kennedy's staff, was drowned. The incident caused Kennedy to lose voter confidence. Some people were concerned about whether Kennedy had attempted to save his staff member. How had he been unable to save her, and yet was able to swim to shore himself? Some people were concerned about his delay in reporting the accident. Why did he wait until the next day to report an accident that resulted in a death? Some people were concerned about both of these issues (as well as a few additional ones). Imagine that the following statements were expressed by two different people, A and B, shortly after the accident.

> *A:* Either Senator Edward Kennedy can verify that he *a*ttempted to save his staff member and can verify that he *r*eported the accident as soon as possible, or we have evidence of a *c*over-up.

> *B:* Senator Edward Kennedy can verify that he *a*ttempted to save his staff member; and either he can verify that he *r*eported the accident as soon as possible or we have evidence of a *c*over-up.

Using our previous translation summaries, **both** statements appear to give us the following:

$A \cdot R \vee C$

Still, A and B have asserted two different statements. A is claiming that Kennedy must be able to verify *two* events, or we have evidence of a cover-up. On this account, Kennedy must be able to verify both that he attempted to save his staff member and that he reported the accident as soon as possible. Otherwise, we have evidence of a cover-up.

B is claiming that Kennedy *is* able to verify that he attempted to save his staff member; B is asserting this as a matter of fact. In addition, B is claiming that Kennedy must be able to verify that the accident was reported as soon as possible, or we have evidence of a cover-up.

A's statement suggests that Kennedy has two issues that are still in need of verification. B's statement suggests that Kennedy has one issue that still needs verification. How can the different meanings be expressed in our artificial language?

Here, as in algebra, parentheses, '( )', brackets, '[ ]', and braces, '{ }', are used to punctuate and create groupings.

The first sentence should be expressed as

$(A \cdot R) \vee C$

The second should be expressed as

$A \cdot (R \vee C)$

The horseshoe, dot, wedge, and tilde all generate compound statements in the artificial language. Punctuation in the artificial language determines which statements are being conjoined, negated, and so on.

> **To have a correct expression in our artificial language, the statements that are connected with our connectives must be clearly defined.**

'$A \cdot R \vee C$' is *incorrect*, regardless of any sentence we might be trying to translate. It is not properly constructed within the artificial language, since it is unclear which statements are being connected by the symbols. Without punctuation, we cannot tell whether the dot has R or the group '$R \vee C$' as the second conjunct. Similarly, we cannot tell whether the wedge has the group '$A \cdot R$' or merely 'R' as the first disjunct.

Placing a group in parentheses (or brackets, or braces) causes the group to be considered as a unit for the connective. In our example, placing '$A \cdot R$' in parentheses, '$(A \cdot R) \vee C$', causes the unit '$(A \cdot R)$' to be considered as a disjunct for the wedge. Placing '$R \vee C$' in parentheses, '$A \cdot (R \vee C)$', causes '$(R \vee C)$' to be considered as a conjunct for the dot.

Punctuation works in a similar fashion when we have the horseshoe. '$A \supset R \cdot C$' *must* be incorrect. Either '$(A \supset R) \cdot C$' or '$A \supset (R \cdot C)$' must be used. Although '$(A \supset R) \cdot C$' and '$A \supset (R \cdot C)$' *do not* have the same meaning, they are both properly formed.

'$(A \supset R) \cdot C$' represents a conjunction statement. It can be used to translate the following English:

> *If Senator Edward Kennedy can verify that he attempted to save his staff member, then he can verify that he reported the accident as soon as possible; still, we have evidence of a cover-up.*

'$A \supset (R \cdot C)$' is, as a whole, a conditional. It can be used to translate the following English:

> *If Senator Edward Kennedy can verify that he attempted to save his staff member, then he can verify that he reported the accident as soon as possible and we have evidence of a cover-up.*

DEFINITION 2.12

The *major connective* is the connective that determines whether the statement, considered as a whole, is a negation, a disjunction, a conjunction, or a conditional.[8]

We can usually find the major connective of an expression by ignoring the connectives that are contained within punctuation symbols. Suppose we look at '$(A \cdot R) \lor C$'. If we ignore all connectives that are contained within punctuation symbols, in this case the parentheses, we have '$(A R) \lor C$'. The major connective is the wedge. This overall expression is a disjunction.

If we ignore all of the connectives contained within punctuation symbols in '$A \cdot (R \lor C)$', we have '$A \cdot (R C)$'. The major connective in this expression is the dot. This overall expression is a conjunction.

Brackets and braces function identically to parentheses, but they are used to define larger groupings. Using different punctuation symbols helps to make the groupings stand out.

Suppose that we wish to translate the following sentence into our artificial language.

Either Senator Edward Kennedy can verify that he attempted to save his staff member, that he reported the accident as soon as possible, and that he was sober at the time of the accident, or we have evidence of a cover-up.

This statement, considered as a whole, is a disjunction. It has the conjunction '$A \cdot (R \cdot S)$' as its first disjunct. We can use brackets so that this conjunction functions as a unit (a disjunct): '$[A \cdot (R \cdot S)]$'. Since the statement being translated asserts either this conjunction or that we have evidence of a cover-up, we can complete our translation as follows:

$$[A \cdot (R \cdot S)] \lor C$$

In forming units, we will adopt the convention of using parentheses first, brackets second, and braces third. From a practical standpoint, braces are seldom needed. English sentences with enough complexity to require braces in translation are often incomprehensible in English. It is easier to visualize structures in our artificial language than it is in English!

'$\{[(p \cdot q) \lor r] \supset s\} \cdot t$' considers everything in the braces as a conjunct for t. If we ignore all of the connectives that are contained within punctuation symbols, we have

$$\{[(p\ q)\ r]\ s\} \cdot t$$

The major connective in this example is the remaining dot.

---

[8]The triple bar, introduced in Chapter 5, can also be a major connective.

The statement that is being denied is always represented at the right-hand side of the tilde. The expression '$\sim p \cdot q$' indicates the negation of p in conjunction with q. The expression '$\sim A \cdot R$' translates:

> *Senator Kennedy cannot verify that he attempted to save his staff member, but he can verify that he reported the accident as soon as possible.*

The expression '$p \cdot \sim q$' indicates that some statement p is one conjunct, while the negation of some statement q is the second conjunct. '$A \cdot \sim R$' translates:

> *Senator Kennedy can verify that he attempted to save his staff member, but he cannot verify that he reported the accident as soon as possible.*

'$\sim(p \cdot q)$' is *not* the negation of p, and is *not* the negation of q. Rather, it is the negation of the *conjunction* of p and q.

Negating a conjunction is not the same as negating the conjuncts, either in English or in the artificial language. Suppose that someone called Monogamy claims that:

> *A person should not have both a spouse and a lover.*[9]

Monogamy is denying that a person should have **both**, which is not the same as denying that a person should have a spouse and denying that a person should have a lover. Monogamy did not mean to rule out marriage, she meant to rule out having **both** a spouse and a lover.

The same meanings are available in our artificial language. We can use the following to express Monogamy's claim:

$\sim(S \cdot L)$

'$\sim(S \cdot L)$' *is not the same as* '$\sim S \cdot \sim L$'.

The tilde in

$$\sim\!(p \cdot q)$$

applies to the unit (the conjunction).

'Both' almost always translates as a left-hand punctuation symbol. 'Both' in 'a person should not have **both** a *s*pouse and a *l*over' indicates the left parenthesis in '$\sim(S \cdot L)$'. 'Both' in 'Germany could conquer *E*ngland only if she conquered **both** *P*oland and *F*rance' translates as the left parenthesis:

$E \supset (P \cdot F)$

Similarly, '$\sim(p \lor q)$' is not identical to '$\sim p \lor \sim q$'. The expression '$\sim(p \lor q)$' indicates the negation of the disjunction, since the unit

---

[9]Intended here as different persons.

'$(p \lor q)$', as determined by the parentheses, follows the tilde. Using the above abbreviations, '$\sim(S \lor L)$' claims that a person should not have either a spouse or a lover. '$\sim S \lor \sim L$' claims that either a person should not have a spouse or a person should not have a lover.

The word 'either', when it is significant, also translates as a left-hand punctuation symbol. 'Not either p or q' is normally translated as '$\sim(p \lor q)$'.

B. Disjunctions Revisited

Our English disjunction indicators, 'or' and 'unless', are used to express two different kinds of logical connections. For simplicity, we will call statements that are expressed with our disjunction indicators, 'or' statements.

DEFINITION 2.13

An *inclusive 'or' statement* merely expresses a disjunction of the two component statements. It claims that one or the other statement (disjunct) is true. While not expressly saying so, it leaves open (that is, it includes) the possibility that both disjuncts might be true.

The following cartoon assumes that 'or' is being used inclusively.[10]

Although the cartoon suggests other issues, the student is at least claiming that Ms. Bobbi is *ugly* or Ms. Bobbi is *weird* (or both).

Our translation guidelines produce the following translation.

$U \lor W$

The cartoon claims that one or the other of the disjuncts is true. We have an *inclusive* 'or' statement, since it allows for the possibility that both

---

[10]Berke Breathed, *Bloom County: Babylon—Five Years of Basic Naughtiness* (Boston: Little, Brown, and Co., 1986), 26. © Washington Post Writers Group. Reprinted with permission.

disjuncts might be true. It leaves open the possibility that Ms. Bobbi might be *both* ugly and weird.

For another example, suppose that Myg University has a sports policy such that either students or faculty members can use the racquetball courts. We might symbolize this as

$S \lor F$

The policy clearly allows that someone who is *both* a student and a faculty member can use the courts.

The two 'or' statements discussed so far in this section are inclusive, since they are true when one or the other, or *both*, disjuncts are true. If the statement claims that both disjuncts cannot be true, the 'or' statement is exclusive.

DEFINITION 2.14

An *exclusive 'or' statement* expresses a disjunction of two statements in that it claims that one or the other of them is true. In addition, it denies (excludes the possibility) that both statements are true.

Suppose that someone is trying to clear up her bills. Suppose she discovers that her money is running out faster than her debts. Imagine that she turns to a friend and says:

I can make either the house or the car payment this month.

Exclusive 'or' statements are common when a choice is intended. The fact that the person has to make a choice rules out the possibility of both statements being true.

There are times when it is unclear whether an English 'or' statement should be understood as inclusive or exclusive. Without more context, the following example can be reasonably understood as expressing either type of 'or' statement:

You should pursue a career that is profitable or you should pursue a career that is enjoyable.

Depending on the context, this might indicate that you should pursue either one or the other, and the ideal would be to find a career that is *both* profitable and enjoyable. In a different context, this assertion might indicate that you have to make a choice. You can decide to pursue either money or pleasure, but *not* both.

Given these English variations, how are we to translate English sentences into our artificial language?

i. Translating Inclusive and Exclusive 'or' Statements

The wedge, 'V', always indicates mere disjunction, regardless of the English being translated.

a. Inclusive 'or' Statements   Since the wedge always indicates a disjunction and inclusive 'or' statements are disjunctions, it is perfectly appropriate to use the wedge to translate inclusive 'or' statements.

b. Ambiguous English 'or' Statements   As our artificial language is applied in Chapter 4, there is usually no harm in using the wedge to represent both inclusive and exclusive 'or' statements, even though the wedge always has the inclusive meaning.

If we use the wedge to represent an exclusive 'or' statement, the exclusive meaning of 'not both' is not *caught in the translation.*

As we shall see later, harm will follow from representing an inclusive 'or' statement with the exclusive 'or' translation that is provided below. Hence;

If there is any possibility whatsoever that the 'or' statement is inclusive, it should be translated with the wedge.

c. Statements That Must Be Understood as Exclusive 'or' Statements   Finally, we have those cases where the exclusive meaning is unquestionably intended. Perhaps the English states 'not both'. A disjunctive statement expresses part of an exclusive 'or' statement's meaning. Exclusive 'p or q' has the same meaning as inclusive 'p or q', with the additional meaning of 'not both p and q'.

Exclusive 'or' statements = Disjunction + Not Both

The symbols that we already have can be used to express exclusive 'or' statements. 'I can make either a *h*ouse or a *c*ar payment, but not both' can be translated as:

$$(H \lor C) \quad \cdot \quad \sim (H \cdot C)$$
    or   but not   both

In general, if the exclusive meaning is required, we can use the following translation pattern.

$$(p \lor q) \cdot \sim(p \cdot q)$$

C. Additional Translation Patterns

'Neither p nor q' indicates a *conjunction* of the negations of the two statements. 'Neither nor' sounds like 'either or', but it should *not* be expressed as a standard disjunction. Suppose that you live in neither San Francisco nor Chicago. That means you do not live in San Francisco *and* you do not live in Chicago. Our general pattern for 'neither p nor q' is:

$\sim p \cdot \sim q$

'If p, then if q, then r' contains two conditionals. When the statement is symbolized, the first horseshoe is the major connective. Suppose that we have the following sentence:

If you get married, then if you become pregnant then you will have a child.

Translating, we have:

$M \supset (P \supset C)$

'$(M \supset P) \supset C$' might be a tempting choice, but in English this indicates:

If getting married implies that you will become pregnant, then you will have a child.

Getting married implies a lot of things, but not, regardless of your sex, that you will become pregnant! So, the antecedent of this statement, '$M \supset P$', is not true for anyone. But the English that we are attempting to symbolize can have a true antecedent. Obviously, the original statement is not correctly expressed by having the second horseshoe as the major connective. Our general pattern for 'if p, then if q, then r' is:

$p \supset (q \supset r)$

CHAPTER 2 TRANSLATION SUMMARY

Conditionals	
English	*Artificial*
If p, then q	$p \supset q$
If p, q	$p \supset q$
p, if q	$q \supset p$
p only if q	$p \supset q$
Only if p, q	$q \supset p$
p implies q	$p \supset q$
p entails q	$p \supset q$

(continued)

CHAPTER 2 TRANSLATION SUMMARY (*continued*)

<table>
<tr><td colspan="2" align="center">*Conditionals*</td></tr>
<tr><td>*English*</td><td>*Artificial*</td></tr>
<tr><td>p is implied by q</td><td>$q \supset p$</td></tr>
<tr><td>p is entailed by q</td><td>$q \supset p$</td></tr>
<tr><td>p is sufficient for q</td><td>$p \supset q$</td></tr>
<tr><td>p is necessary for q</td><td>$q \supset p$</td></tr>
<tr><td>Provided that p, q</td><td>$p \supset q$</td></tr>
<tr><td>Whenever p, q</td><td>$p \supset q$</td></tr>
<tr><td>If p, then if q, then r</td><td>$p \supset (q \supset r)$</td></tr>
</table>

<table>
<tr><td colspan="2" align="center">*Conjunctions*</td></tr>
<tr><td>p, and q</td><td>$p \cdot q$</td></tr>
<tr><td>p, but q</td><td>$p \cdot q$</td></tr>
<tr><td>p, yet q</td><td>$p \cdot q$</td></tr>
<tr><td>p; although q</td><td>$p \cdot q$</td></tr>
<tr><td>Although p, q</td><td>$p \cdot q$</td></tr>
<tr><td>p; moreover q</td><td>$p \cdot q$</td></tr>
<tr><td>p; however, q</td><td>$p \cdot q$</td></tr>
<tr><td>p; in addition q</td><td>$p \cdot q$</td></tr>
<tr><td>p; still q</td><td>$p \cdot q$</td></tr>
</table>

<table>
<tr><td colspan="2" align="center">*Disjunctions*</td></tr>
<tr><td colspan="2">**When the 'or' statement is inclusive:**</td></tr>
<tr><td>p or q</td><td>$p \lor q$</td></tr>
<tr><td>p unless q</td><td>$p \lor q$</td></tr>
<tr><td>Unless p, q</td><td>$p \lor q$</td></tr>
<tr><td>p, otherwise q (rare)</td><td>$p \lor q$</td></tr>
<tr><td colspan="2">**When the 'or' statement is clearly exclusive:**</td></tr>
<tr><td>The same English indicators</td><td>$(p \lor q) \cdot \sim(p \cdot q)$</td></tr>
</table>

<table>
<tr><td colspan="2" align="center">*Negations*</td></tr>
<tr><td>Not p</td><td>$\sim p$</td></tr>
<tr><td>It is false that p</td><td>$\sim p$</td></tr>
<tr><td>It is not the case that p</td><td>$\sim p$</td></tr>
<tr><td colspan="2">**When the contradictory is expressed:**</td></tr>
<tr><td>Negating prefix + p</td><td>$\sim p$</td></tr>
<tr><td>Not both p and q</td><td>$\sim(p \cdot q)$</td></tr>
<tr><td>Not either p or q</td><td>$\sim(p \lor q)$</td></tr>
<tr><td>Neither p nor q</td><td>$\sim p \cdot \sim q$</td></tr>
</table>

Exercises IV

Use the suggested statement constants, and symbolize each of the following sentences into our artificial language. All of them can be translated by using the preceding translation summary. Pay close attention to the English punctuation; it will help you to determine the artificial-language punctuation. Once you have completed a given translation, compare your answer to the English. They should both say the same thing. All of the following statements are based on the Battle of Verdun and World War I.

*1. If at least a million soldiers died, then the Battle of Verdun was the bloodiest battle in World War I. D, B

2. Verdun is in northeastern France and was a French fortress facing Germany. N, F

*3. Either at least a million soldiers died or the Battle of Verdun was not the bloodiest battle in World War I. D, B

4. The battle began February 21,1916; yet it was over December 15 of the same year. B, O

*5. Verdun was a French fortress facing Germany; moreover, the French troops had the slogan, 'They shall not pass.' F, S

6. Germany won neither the Battle of Verdun nor World War I. V, W

*7. Unless the British had come to their aid, the French wouldn't have won the Battle of Verdun. A, V

8. Either Petain or Wilhelm, but not both, commanded the French forces.[11] P, W

*9. Haig didn't command either the French or German forces.[12] F, G

10. That Germany used submarines to attack any allied ship implied that the United States needed to enter World War I. A, N

*11. The Battle of Verdun was the bloodiest battle of World War I, if over a million soldiers died. B, D

12. Only if the French counterattacked could Germany be stopped. C, S

*13. If two million soldiers were engaged in battle, then if at least a million soldiers died then at least half of the combatants perished. E, D, P

14. Although Germany wasn't able to conquer Verdun, World War I continued until 1918. A, C

*15. If Germany introduced poison gas and submarine warfare, then Germany changed the nature of war. P, S, C

---

[11]Petain was the French commander; Wilhelm was the German commander.

[12]Haig was the British commander.

16. If war continues to be a human *p*astime, then national *b*oundaries may change; however, grass will always be the *u*ltimate victor.[13]
    P, B, U

Exercises V

Use the suggested statement constants, and symbolize each of the following into our artificial language. The following sentences have been taken from a variety of sources, and they vary in complexity.

*1. In the 1960s the breadwinner won the bread, but today we expect much more. *W, E*

2. Domestic content legislation is not needed. *D*

*3. Nuclear power is neither economically wise nor environmentally safe. *W, S*

4. A person should have either a lover or a spouse, but not both. *L, S*

*5. If a person has marriage without love, they'll find love without marriage [Ben Franklin, *Poor Richard's Almanac*]. *M, L*

6. Waging war on drug abuse hasn't worked, and never will. *A, W*

*7. Shakespeare's plays involve many female roles, but when they were first staged, all the parts were played by male actors. *F, M*

8. If you have an affair with the wrong person at work, then you could end up playing Russian roulette with your career. *A, P*

*9. In addition to the fact that our lives are better in material terms, we expect more pleasure as a matter of course. *M, P*

10. You shouldn't eat either nuts or fruits [You are what you eat—Garfield comic strip]. *N, F*

---

[13]See Carl Sandburg's "Grass":
Pile high the bodies at Austerlitz and Waterloo.
Shovel them under and let me work—
I am grass; I cover all.

And pile them high at Gettysburg
And pile them high at Ypres and Verdun.
Shovel them under and let me work.

Two years, ten years, and passengers ask the conductor:
What place is this?
Where are we now?

I am the grass.
Let me work.

"Grass" from *Cornhuskers* by Carl Sandburg, copyright 1918 by Holt, Rinehart and Winston, Inc. and renewed 1946 by Carl Sandburg. Reprinted by permission of Harcourt Bruce Jovanovich, Inc.

*11. 'Shakespeare's plays' were written by either William Shakespeare or Francis Bacon. S, B

 12. If England had taken a strong stand against Hitler, World War II could have been averted. S, A

*13. A person shouldn't take refuge in a relationship, unless she's willing to accept the price. R, A

 14. When one is in a storm, any port will do. S, P

*15. Lawyers can promote adversary relationships or they can promote healing relationships, but not both. A, H

 16. Having Attila [the Hun] de Sade as your attorney implies that you'll score in court. A, S

*17. The odds of a family having both spouses at work declines only if their household income exceeds $100,000. D, E

 18. We are in danger of becoming a polarized society, if people continue to drop on the economic scale. B, E

*19. Working wives tend to have children at a relatively late age; otherwise they typically remain childless. L, R

 20. "I know what Hitler's up to; he thinks he's outsmarted me, but actually it is I who have outsmarted him." (Josef Stalin) K, T, I

*21. Provided that the woman either quits or cuts down on her smoking, she'll have a healthier infant. Q, C, H

 22. If we have an enormous number of lawyers, then if they charge astronomical fees then the public will lose respect for the legal profession. N, A, L

*23. Having a good home life is necessary in order to produce healthy children. H, P

 24. Brassieres were first invented to prevent sports injuries; yet now even the least athletic women wear them. I, L

*25. The fact that most new jobs are created at the top and the bottom of economic scale entails that America may cease to be a middle-class society. T, B, C

 26. Whenever someone takes a tetracycline medication and lies in the sun, her skin turns red. T, L, R

*27. If the male parent suffers from job stress, then his sons will have less self-esteem and more depression. S, L, D

 28. 'The Soviet Union is willing to start improving relations with the United States if Washington will abide by the principles of equality and equal security.' (Pravda press release) I, E, S

*29. The aggressor in domestic violence is personally rewarded; moreover the battered spouse feels psychological rewards. A, B

 30. Unless the CIA is wrong, homosexuals are automatic security risks in government and defense industry jobs. C, G, D

*31. Although we cannot either intimidate the Soviet Union with our military strength or block their weapons with electronic space shields, we still might be able to reach an arms agreement with them. *I, B, R*

32. If England had taken a strong stand, then if France had signed a nonaggression pact with the Soviet Union then Hitler wouldn't have invaded both Czechoslovakia and Poland. *T, S, C, P*

*33. If neither the United States nor the Soviet Union will adopt a 'no first strike' policy, then the threat of a nuclear war will remain undiminished. *U, S, D*

34. Jones can collect both unemployment and social security benefits only if he either falsifies his work record or falsifies his disability record. *U, S, W, D*

*35. If a person is placed in a padded red cell, then she displays her most aggressive behaviors; however placing a person in a light-blue cell is sufficient to bring out her more passive moods. [A common psychiatric practice.] *R, A, B, P*

The following presents the ultimate challenge! First, note those statements that are asserted unequivocally, and then determine the connectives.

*36. Hitler no doubt wished to dominate the world; yet if either the Treaty of Versailles, which ended World War I, had not treated Germany so badly, or Chamberlain had not adopted a policy of appeasement, then either Hitler would not have been able to rise to power or he would not have been able to begin his mission of world conquest. *W, E, T, A, R, M*

Concept Reviews

1. Try to imagine a situation which shows that the following two statements are contraries rather than contradictories. Describe the situation.

   It's possible to pass Biology 397 without using any effort.
   It's impossible to pass Biology 397 without using any effort.

2. The following sentence, depending on the context, might be an inclusive 'or' statement or an exclusive 'or' statement. Indicate how its meaning will change depending on which type of 'or' statement is expressed. How, given our strategy for creating translations, should we translate it in the artificial language?

   I'll either stay up all night or pass the coming exam.

3. Indicate the major connective in each of the following expressions.

   $(A \supset T) \lor (R \cdot S)$

   $A \supset [T \lor (R \cdot S)]$

   $A \supset [(T \lor R) \cdot S]$

   $[A \supset (T \lor R)] \cdot S$

4. Owing to its lack of punctuation, the following expression is not a proper sentence in our artificial language. Add punctuation in four different ways, to produce four different, but correct, sentences.

   $B \cdot T \lor R \supset L$

5. Does the following sentence express a *simple* or a *compound* statement?

   Australia has ten times more sheep than people.

   Using our definitions of 'simple' and 'compound', indicate the basis for your answer.

6. English, French, and German are all natural languages. Our language of logic and the language of mathematics are both artificial languages. How are artificial languages different from natural languages?

7. What is the name of the statement that is always represented at the left-hand side of the horseshoe? What is the name of the statement that is always represented at the right-hand side of the horseshoe?

8. What are the statements that make up a conjunction called?

9. At times the English 'and' indicates a pure conjunction. At times it abbreviates 'and then' and indicates sequence as well as conjunction. At times it fails to indicate a conjunction at all. Indicate a likely purpose of 'and' when it fails to indicate a conjunction at all.

10. The following expression cannot be correctly used to express any English sentence. Why not?

    $B \supset [T \cdot R \lor L]$

3 Truth-Values and Validity

In Chapter 2, we introduced four artificial-language connectives and used them to represent English sentences. Chapter 3 has four main goals:

1. To determine when statements expressed with our artificial-language symbols are true (or false).
2. To learn how to construct truth tables.
3. To recognize logically true (tautologous) and logically false (self-contradictory) statements.
4. To recognize deductively valid and deductively invalid argument forms.

This chapter will enable us to examine existing arguments. Chapter 4 is concerned with creating deductively valid arguments.

KEY TERMS FOR THIS CHAPTER

Use the glossary as necessary, and review the definitions of these terms prior to a second reading of this chapter.

Truth-value
Truth-functional statement
Truth-functional connective
Truth table
Statement form
Tautology (tautologous statement)
Self-contradiction (self-contradictory statement)

Contingent statement
Argument form
Deductively valid argument form
Deductively invalid argument form

I   Determining the Truth and Falsity of Statements Expressed with Artificial Language Symbols

In Chapter 1 we noted that logic is concerned with statements (or propositions). Every statement (or proposition) is either true or false. Every statement (or proposition) has a "truth-value."

DEFINITION 3.1

The *truth-value* of a true statement is T. The truth-value of a false statement is F.

When discussing the truth-value of a statement, we are merely discussing whether the statement is true or false. Compound statements, as well as simple statements, are either true or false.

A. Conjunction

So that we can become aware of what determines whether a conjunction statement is true, we will consider examples from the American Civil War (1861–65). The Union's fighting performance during the war was uneven. There were battles where the Union infantrymen were aggressive and well led, and there were battles where the Union infantrymen were neither aggressive nor well led. This unevenness will enable us to generate Civil War examples to determine when conjunctions are true. Our first example refers to the battle at Gettysburg.

   The Union infantrymen were aggressive and well led at Gettysburg.

Suppose that each conjunct of this conjunction is true. A conjunction statement merely combines and asserts two statements that could have been expressed independently. If it is true that the Union infantrymen were aggressive at Gettysburg and it is true that the Union infantrymen were well led at Gettysburg, then our conjunction must be true.

   If we assume that

   'The Union infantrymen were aggressive at Gettysburg' **is true,**

and that

   'The Union infantrymen were well led at Gettysburg' **is true,**

then

'The Union infantrymen were aggressive and well led at Gettysburg' is true.

If both of its conjuncts are true, then the conjunction is true.

The success of the Union forces at Gettysburg came after a series of previous failures. The Union infantrymen aggressively charged the waiting Confederate forces at Fredericksburg, and 12,000 Union soldiers were killed before they were able to retreat. The attack was predictably hopeless. Suppose someone asserted the conjunction: "The Union infantrymen were aggressive and well led at Fredericksburg." This conjunction is false, since the second conjunct, 'the Union infantrymen were well led at Fredericksburg', is false.

The Union infantrymen broke and fled in wild retreat at Bull Run. In doing so, they failed to attempt the strategies of their leader, General Irvin McDowell. Suppose that someone asserted the conjunction: "The Union infantrymen were aggressive and well led at Bull Run." This conjunction is false, since the first conjunct, 'the Union infantrymen were aggressive at Bull Run', is false.

At Chancellorsville, 60,000 Confederate infantrymen attacked and defeated 120,000 unsuspecting Union infantrymen. Suppose someone asserted the conjunction: "The Union infantrymen were aggressive and well led at Chancellorsville." This conjunction is false, since both conjuncts are false.

If one or both of its conjuncts are false, then a conjunction is false.

Our examples show that:

A conjunction is true if and only if both of its conjuncts are true.

DEFINITION 3.2

A compound statement is *truth-functional* if and only if its truth-value is determined by the truth-values of statements that it has as parts.

The truth-value of a conjunction is determined by whether its parts (conjuncts) are true. Conjunctions are truth-functional statements.

When we claim that a statement is truth-functional, we are *not* claiming that it is true. The last three of our conjunctions about the Civil War are false, but these conjunctions are truth-functional. When we claim that a statement is truth-functional, we are also not claiming that it is false. Our conjunction example about Gettysburg is true, but this conjunction is truth-functional as well. As our examples in this section show, some compound truth-functional statements are determined to be true by their parts, and some compound truth-functional statements are determined to be false by their parts.

When we claim that a compound statement is truth-functional, we are claiming that its truth-value (either T or F) is determined by the truth-values of its component statements.

Some compound statements are not truth-functional. Pierre de Laplace (1749–1827), a French astronomer and mathematician, developed the theory that the universe originated as a huge cloud of gas. Consider the following statement:

Laplace said that <u>the universe originated as a cloud of gas.</u>

The statement is compound, since it contains the underlined statement as a part, but it is not truth-functionally compound. Sometimes what people say is true, and sometimes what they say is false. Whether or not the universe really originated as a cloud of gas is irrelevant to the truth or falsity of the claim, "Laplace said the universe originated as a cloud of gas." The only thing that is relevant is whether or not Laplace said what is attributed to him.

Although some statements are truth-functional and some not, our present concern is with statements, such as conjunctions, that are truth-functional.

Connectives that are used to express truth-functional statements, such as conjunctions, are called "truth-functional connectives."

DEFINITION 3.3

A *connective* is *truth-functional* if and only if it is used to express truth-functionally compound statements.

Since conjunctions are truth-functional statements and the dot is used to express them, the dot is a truth-functional connective.

Our discussion of the Civil War examples enabled us to summarize the truth-functional nature of conjunction: a conjunction is true if and only if both of its conjuncts are true. Logicians often use what are called "truth tables" to summarize the truth-functional nature of our connectives.

DEFINITION 3.4

A *truth table* provides a complete listing of possible truth-values for statements that can be seen as occupying the "places" (variables) of a statement form, and indicates the truth-value of each possibility.

As noted in Chapter 2, we can use our statement variables (*p*, *q*, etc.) to express the general form of conjunctions:

$$p \cdot q$$

When there are two statement locations, there are four possible truth-value conbinations:

First possibility: both *p* and *q* might be true.

Second possibility: *p* might be true and *q* might be false.

Third possibility: *p* might be false and *q* might be true.

Fourth possibility: both *p* and *q* might be false.

Each of our Civil War examples is an example of one of the above possibilities. Our Gettysburg example has the truth-values listed as the first possibility. Our Fredericksburg example has the truth-values listed as the second possibility. Our Bull Run example has the truth-values listed as the third possibility. And our Chancellorsville example has the truth-values listed as the fourth possibility.

We will indicate possibilities by writing Ts and Fs under a form's variables. The following is another way to express our four possibilities for '*p* · *q*'.

	p ·	*q*
First possibility:	T	T
Second possibility:	T	F
Third possibility:	F	T
Fourth possibility:	F	F

We can now complete our truth table and indicate the truth-functional nature of the dot. We will write the truth-values of the conjunction under the dot:

p ·		*q*
T	T	T
T	F	F
F	F	T
F	F	F

Each horizontal line indicates the truth-value of the dot for the values of *p* and *q* that are on that line. The first horizontal line shows that a conjunction statement, '*p · q*', is true when both conjuncts are true. The remaining lines show that a conjunction statement, '*p · q*', is false when one or both of its conjuncts is false. Our truth table for conjunction provides another way to say that a conjunction is true if and only if both of its conjuncts are true.

B. Disjunction

Chapter 2 noted that a disjunction statement is true when one or the other, or perhaps both, of its disjuncts are true.

Knowing that Confederate troops won the battle, someone might claim:

The Confederate infantrymen were either aggressive or well led at Chickamauga.

Using the non-italicized letters for our statement constants, we can write:

A ∨ L

The above statement will be true if it is true that the Confederate infantrymen were aggressive at Chickamauga, or if it is true that the Confederate infantrymen were well led at Chickamauga. The disjunction will also be true if the Confederate infantrymen were both aggressive and well led at Chickamauga.

A disjunction is false only when both of its disjuncts are false.

We can use '*p ∨ q*' to represent disjunctions. The following truth table expresses the truth-functional nature of disjunctions.

p	∨	*q*
T	T	T
T	T	F
F	T	T
F	F	F

C. Negation

The tilde produces a statement of opposite truth value.

Someone might claim that

The American steel industry has benefited from trade restrictions.

We might decide to symbolize this statement as *B*. If this statement is true, then its contradictory, that the American steel industry has not benefited from trade restrictions, ~*B*, is false.

If it is false that the American steel industry has benefited from trade restrictions, then ~*B* is true—that the American steel industry has not benefited from trade restrictions. We can express the truth-functional nature of the tilde with the following table.[1]

~*p*
F T
T F

As before, the value of the symbol, in this case the tilde, appears under it.

Notice that the truth table for the tilde reflects the fact that the tilde indicates the contradictory, not a contrary, of the original statement. Since contraries might **both** be false, the fact that one is false does not guarantee that the other is true. Since contradictories must have opposite truth-values, the falsity of one statement does guarantee the truth of the other.

D. Conditionals

Our discussion of inclusive and exclusive 'or' statements in Chapter 2 pointed out that an English word or phrase can have logically different meanings. We know that some 'or' statements are inclusive, and some 'or' statements are exclusive. Even so, almost all usages of 'or' in English are one of these two types.

'If–then' in English takes on not merely two, but a variety of logically different meanings. Hence, English expresses a variety of logically different conditionals.

Conditionals differ from one another by intending different kinds of connections between their antecedent and consequent statements. Some conditionals connect their antecedent and consequent statements on the basis of word meanings; for example, 'if Elizabeth is Alexander's sister, then she must be related to him'. Part of what is **meant** by saying that she is his sister is that she is related to him.

Some conditionals connect their antecedent and consequent statements on the basis of cause and effect. Knowing that Aaron Burr and Alexander Hamilton fought a duel in 1804, someone might claim, "If Aaron Burr shot

---

[1]The tilde is normally called a connective, although it does not literally connect two statements. To be more precise, the tilde is classified as a unary truth-functional operator. The horseshoe, the dot, and the wedge are binary truth-functional operators.

Alexander Hamilton, then Alexander Hamilton was wounded."[2] Shooting someone *causes* one to be wounded!

Some conditionals even connect their antecedent and consequent statements on the basis of assumed personality traits. 'If the dictator of Iraq is cornered, then he will fight' connects its antecedent and consequent statements by making assumptions about the dictator's personality.

Conditionals intend additional kinds of connections between their antecedent and consequent statements. Since this is an introductory text, we will not try to specify all of the different kinds of connections that can underlie conditionals. Instead, we will work with an antecedent/consequent connection that is not identical to the connection intended by any of the above conditionals, but that is assumed by all of them. Every conditional denies that its antecedent statement is true when its consequent statement is false. For any conditional:

> *If its antecedent statement is true and its consequent statement is false, then the conditional is false.*

"If Elizabeth is Alexander's sister, then she must be related to him' *at least* denies that Elizabeth is Alexander's sister and she is not related to him. 'If Aaron Burr shot Alexander Hamilton, then Alexander Hamilton was wounded' *at least* denies that Aaron Burr shot Alexander Hamilton and Alexander Hamilton was not wounded. 'If the dictator of Iraq is cornered, then he will fight' *at least* denies that the dictator of Iraq is cornered and will not fight.

Logicians have a special name for the antecedent/consequent relationship that is common to all conditionals. It is called "material implication." A material implication conditional only denies that its antecedent is true and its consequent is false. All conditionals assume that their corresponding material implication conditional is true. Even if the material implication relationship is common to all conditionals, most conditionals in everyday use assume a stronger connection between their antecedent and consequent statements than what is meant by material implication. As we have noted, most conditionals are based on word meanings, causal factors, personality assumptions, and so on. Material implication conditionals are true unless their antecedent statement is true and their consequent statement is false. They are defined solely in terms of this truth-functional relationship.

Although material implication is a weak antecedent/consequent connec-

---

[2]Aaron Burr was vice president of the United States at the time, and Alexander Hamilton was a former secretary of the treasury. Burr shot and killed Hamilton. Burr was later charged with treason for allegedly conspiring to have some of the western states secede from the Union. He was acquitted of this charge.

tion, logicians generally work only with the material implication aspect of conditionals. Material implication is a very important logical relationship.

The horseshoe is defined so that its entire meaning is the material-implication relationship.

Since conditionals expressed in English typically intend a stronger connection than material implication and the horseshoe only expresses the material-implication relationship, a conditional and its artificial language translation typically do not have exactly the same meaning. Translations in our artificial language only express the antecedent/consequent connection, material implication, that is common to all conditionals. Even so, working with material implication will enable us to examine most arguments adequately.

We can use the following truth table to express the truth-functional nature of material implication and the horseshoe.

$p \supset q$
T T T
T F F
F T T
F T F

Since the horseshoe is defined so that it conveys the meaning of material implication, statements expressed with it are true unless their antecedent statement is true and their consequent statement is false.

When attempting to keep the truth tables for our four connectives straight, it is helpful to memorize the exceptions.

Conjunctions are false unless both conjuncts are true. Disjunctions are true unless both disjuncts are false. Negation produces a statement of opposite truth value. Material-implication conditionals are true unless their antecedent is true and their consequent is false.

	Exception	*Value in Other Cases*
$p \cdot q$	T · T = T	F
$p \lor q$	F ∨ F = F	T
$\sim p$	Opposite truth value of p	
$p \supset q$	T ⊃ F = F	T

The following is a summary of symbol truth values:[3]

---

[3]The column for $\sim p$ is a bit redundant. Since p is true in the first two rows, $\sim p$ is false in both of them. Similarly, since p is false in the last two rows, $\sim p$ is true in both of them.

p q	p ⊃ q	p ∨ q	p · q	~p
T T	T	T	T	F
T F	F	T	F	F
F T	T	T	F	T
F F	T	F	F	T

We can determine whether a compound truth-functional statement is true if we know whether its parts are true. Suppose that A represents some true statement and Y represents some false statement. By using these assumptions, we can easily determine whether '$Y \supset A$' and '$\sim A \vee Y$' are true.

Since we have assumed that Y is false and A is true, '$Y \supset A$' is an example of the line of our truth tables where the first statement is false and the second statement is true. '$Y \supset A$' is an example of line three of our truth tables:

$$Y \supset A$$
$$\overline{}$$
$$F \quad T$$

Since the horseshoe is defined as true when its parts have these values, the compound statement '$Y \supset A$' must be true. We can express this by placing a T under its connective.

$$Y \supset A$$
$$\overline{}$$
$$F T T$$

'$\sim A \vee Y$' has two connectives: the tilde and the wedge. Since both of these connectives are truth-functional, we can also determine the truth-value of this compound statement. The tilde applies to the statement that is represented at its right-hand side. In our example, this statement is A, not '$A \vee Y$'. The first disjunct is the negation of the statement A, and the second disjunct is the statement Y. Our compound statement can be unpacked as follows.

$$\sim A \vee Y$$
$$\overline{}$$
$$F T F F$$

'$\sim A \vee Y$' is false.

The best way to learn our values for the symbols is by working with them!

Exercises I

Suppose that A and B represent true statements, and that Y and Z represent false statements. Use the truth-value definitions for the symbols involved, and indicate the truth-value of each of the following.

*1. $Y \supset Z$
2. $A \supset Y$
*3. $A \supset B$
4. $Y \supset A$
*5. $A \cdot Y$
6. $A \cdot B$
*7. $Y \cdot A$
8. $Y \cdot Z$
*9. $B \vee A$
10. $Y \vee A$
*11. $Y \vee Z$
12. $B \vee Y$
*13. $\sim Y$
14. $\sim A$
*15. $Z \supset A$

16. $A \vee Y$
*17. $A \supset Z$
18. $B \cdot A$
19. $Y \vee \sim A$
20. $A \supset \sim B$
*21. $B \vee \sim A$
22. $A \cdot \sim Y$
23. $\sim A \cdot Y$
24. $\sim Y \supset Z$
*25. $A \vee \sim Y$
26. $\sim A \supset \sim B$
27. $\sim A \vee \sim B$
28. $\sim Y \vee \sim Z$
*29. $\sim Y \supset \sim A$
30. $\sim Y \cdot \sim A$

Concept Reviews

1. Contraries are not properly expressed with the truth table for the tilde. Even so, what do you know about one contrary, given that the other one is true? Use the definition of contraries from the previous chapter to justify your answer.

2. A truth table for exclusive 'or' statements is developed in section III. Given the discussion in Chapter 2, indicate the values that you would anticipate for exclusive 'or' statements. Suppose that we had an additional symbol, '$\underline{\vee}$', such that '$p \underline{\vee} q$' indicates exclusive 'p or q'. Create a suitable truth table for '$p \underline{\vee} q$'. Compare your answer to the one given in section III.

3. Suppose that someone suggested the following truth table for the horseshoe.

$p \supset q$

F T T
T T T
T F F
F T F

Does this table meet our definition of a truth table? Why or why not? Could this table be properly used to define the horseshoe? Why or why not?

4. Using the truth-functional definitions from the previous section, indicate a situation, in relation to each of the following statements, that will make the statement false.

a. Benjamin Franklin invented the lightning rod.
b. If only five women have won a Nobel Prize for science, then scientists have discriminated against women.
c. Prominent Republicans attended the Princess Grace Foundation meetings, and were treated to fresh carnation petals in the toilet bowls.
d. Either the state will reduce their tax assessment, or the Schmidt family will turn their land over for use as a prison farm.

II   Truth-Values Combined with Punctuation

To return to a previous example:

Either Senator Edward Kennedy can verify that he attempted to save his staff member and can verify that he reported the accident as soon as possible, or we have evidence of a cover-up.

As before, we can symbolize this sentence with the following:

$(A \cdot R) \lor C$

If we know the truth-values of the simple statements, we can use the definitions of our truth-functional connectives to determine the truth-value of a compound statement. The key to this process consists in finding the truth-value of the smallest unit first, then the truth-value of the next smallest unit, and so on. The major connective is always the last symbol for which a truth-value is determined.

The above example has the wedge as its major connective. If we know the truth-values of its disjuncts, we can use our truth-functional definition of the wedge and determine the truth-value of the whole statement. The first disjunct, '$A \cdot R$', is a conjunction, and its truth-value will be determined by the truth-values of A and R, and our truth-functional definition of the dot.

Suppose, for the purpose of unpacking this statement, that A and R indicate true statements, and that C indicates a false statement. For the purpose of determining truth-values of compound statements, the meanings of the component statements are not important. With our assumptions, we can make the following determinations. First we place the truth-values of the statements under their statement constants:

$(A \cdot R) \lor C$
———————————
  T   T   F

The conjunction is the smallest unit. Conjunctions are true when both conjuncts are true.

$(A \cdot R) \lor C$
_____
T T T   F

Our truth-functional definition of the wedge produces the final answer. Notice that it is written under the major connective.

$(A \cdot R) \lor C$
_____
T T T T F

Hence, should the simple statements in this example have our assumed truth-values, then the compound statement will be true. By solving for the truth-value of '$A \cdot R$' and assuming a truth-value for C, we were able to determine a truth-value for the major connective.

If the example had been more complex, we would have followed the same process, but more steps would have been required.

Suppose that A and B stand for true statements, and that Y and Z stand for false statements. The following applies the above method to '$(A \cdot Y) \lor \sim(B \supset Z)$'.

$(A \cdot Y) \lor \sim(B \supset Z)$
_____
T   F   T   F

$(A \cdot Y) \lor \sim(B \supset Z)$
_____
T F F   T F F

$(A \cdot Y) \lor \sim(B \supset Z)$
_____
T F F   T T F F

$(A \cdot Y) \lor \sim(B \supset Z)$
_____
T F F T T T F F
    ↑_____ The final answer

Exercises II

Assume that A, B, and C are true statements, and that X, Y, and Z are false statements. Indicate the truth-value of each of the following statements.

*1. $A \supset Y$ *3. $\sim(A \cdot Y)$

2. $\sim B \lor C$ 4. $\sim(Y \cdot A)$

*5. ~A ⊃ ~X	16. ~[(X V A) ⊃ (X · A)]
6. ~X ⊃ ~A	*17. [(A · B) V ~C] ⊃ X
*7. A ⊃ (B · Z)	18. [(A · ~C) ⊃ X] ⊃ B
8. ~X ⊃ (Y V Z)	19. ~[(A · ~X) V Y] ⊃ (B · ~Z)
*9. (A · X) V (B · Y)	20. ~(A ⊃ X) ⊃ [B · (X V Z)]
10. (A V X) · (B V Y)	*21. ~(A ⊃ X) ⊃ [B · ~(X V Z)]
*11. ~[(A V X) · (B V Y)]	22. ~(A ⊃ X) ⊃ ~[B · (X V Z)]
12. A ⊃ [X V (B · C)]	23. [(A V B) · X] ⊃ [Y V (A · C)]
*13. (A ⊃ X) V (B · C)	24. [(A ⊃ B) V (X ⊃ Y)] ⊃ [(Z · A) V C]
14. ~(A · X) ⊃ Y	*25. ~{[(A ⊃ X) V (B ⊃ Y)] ⊃ Z}
*15. A ⊃ (~X ⊃ Y)	26. {[(A ⊃ C) · (B ⊃ Z)] V (A · Y)} ⊃ {[(Y ⊃ Z) · A] V C}

III Truth-Table Construction

> **DEFINITION 3.5**
>
> A *statement form* is any properly constructed artificial-language expression that contains statement variables, but no statement constants.

To be a statement form, an expression must have adequate punctuation and properly placed connectives. It must contain statement locations; our lower-case letters p, q, and so on, serve this function. It must not contain any capital letters, since our capital letters identify particular statements rather than locations for statements.

'$p ⊃ q$', '$p · q$', 'p V q', '$~p$', '$p ⊃ (q$ V $r)$', and 'p' are all statement forms. Until now, truth tables have been used only to define our truth-functional connectives. Our present goal is to expand our understanding of truth tables so we are able to construct them for *any* statement form.

We know that each horizontal line of a truth table represents a set of truth-value possibilities.

To review,

$p ⊃ q$

T T T	The possibility that both p and q are placeholders for true statements.
T F F	The possibility that p is a placeholder for a true statement and that q is a placeholder for a false one.

F T T   The possibility that *p* is a placeholder for a false
statement and that *q* is a placeholder for a true one.

F T F   The possibility that both *p* and *q* are placeholders for
false statements.

The first line indicates the possibility of both statements being true. The second line indicates the possibility that the first statement is true and the second statement is false; and so on. Our four lines in the above example express all of the truth-value possibilities for examples of the form, since any statements that might occupy the *p* and *q* locations must exhibit one of the above truth-value combinations.

The number of possible truth-value combinations increases with an increase in the number of different kinds of variables (locations). If we have only two statements, they must exhibit one of the four truth-value combinations listed above. If we have more than two different statements, they can exhibit more truth-value combinations than are listed above.

The number of truth-value possibilities, and hence the number of lines required for a truth table, equals 2 raised to the same power as the number of distinct variables (variable types) in the form.

If a statement form has two variables, *p* and *q*, then the number of possibilities and lines of truth table, equals 2^2, or $2 \times 2 = 4$. Our previous two-variable statement forms have had four-line tables. If a form has three variables, *p*, *q*, and *r*, then the number of possibilities and lines of truth table equals 2^3, or $2 \times 2 \times 2 = 8$. And so on.[4]

Now that we can count the number of distinct variables and determine how many lines are required to express all of a form's truth-value possibilities, we need a pattern for filling in the Ts and Fs to make sure that we hit all of them. The following pattern works (guaranteed!).

Under the first variable, write Ts for the first half of the required lines and Fs for the second half of the required lines. Repeat this column under the same variable if it reoccurs. Write Ts and Fs under the next new variable that is in the form. To do this, use half of the T and F *pattern* that was used for the previous variable. Repeat this column under the same variable if it reoccurs. Be sure to write Ts and Fs under each variable for all of the required lines. Continue this process until each variable in the form has a truth-value for every required possibility.

---

[4]A more precise, if more mathematical way, of putting this is to say that total lines = 2^n, where n = the number of distinct variable types. The base is always 2, since there are two possibilities for each location: true and false. The exponent is determined by the number of different kinds of locations (variables).

Finally, we solve for the values of the compound by working from the smallest units out, in exactly the same way as we solved the last set of exercises. The values for each symbol are placed under the symbol. The values for the possibilities of the form as a whole are placed under its major connective.

The above description makes this process appear to be a lot more complicated than it really is. Some things are a lot easier to see than they are to describe. (Try to describe how to tie a shoelace without using diagrams!)

Step 1   Write the statement form on a line. For example:

$$(p \supset q) \cdot (q \vee p)$$

Step 2   Count the number of different kinds of variables in the form. This example has two different kinds of variables, p and q.

Step 3   Compute the total number of lines. In this example, we have:

$$2^2 = 2 \times 2 = 4 \; lines \; total$$

Step 4   Fill in the values. For this example:

$$(p \supset q) \cdot (q \vee p)$$

T	T	T	T
T	F	F	T
F	T	T	F
F	F	F	F

↑ ⌜ same ⌝ ↑
⌞——— same ———⌟

The pattern under p has pairs of Ts and Fs. (The total number of lines is 4, and $4 \times \frac{1}{2} = 2$.) Notice that the pattern of Ts and Fs under q is half of the pattern of Ts and Fs under p. (q has a column of "ones," since p has a column of "twos.") The column under q alternates Ts and Fs.

Step 5   Compute the truth-values of the compounds by using the truth-functional definitions of the symbols. For this example:

$$(p \supset q) \cdot (q \vee p)$$

T	T	T	T	T	T	T
T	F	F	F	F	T	T
F	T	T	T	T	T	F
F	T	F	F	F	F	F

⌞ 1 ⌟   ⌞ 2 ⌟
↑   3   ↑

The numbers indicate the order of completion. The arrows indicate the columns that have been used to determine the truth-values in columns 1 and 2.

The truth-values for the form, considered as a whole, have been boxed off and are written under its major connective. These values have been determined by using the truth-functional definition of the dot and the truth-values that are in columns 1 and 2.

The following example has been solved by using exactly the same steps that were used in our previous example. Obviously, since it has three variables, it is a bit more complex.

Step 1 $[(p \supset q) \lor (r \supset q)] \supset [(p \cdot r) \supset q]$

Step 2 We have three distinct variables: p, q, and r.

Step 3 *Total lines* $= 2^3 = 2 \times 2 \times 2 = 8$

Step 4 Fill in the values:

$[(p \supset q) \lor (r \supset q)] \supset [(p \cdot r) \supset q]$

T	T	T	T	T	T	T
T	T	F	T	T	F	T
T	F	T	F	T	T	F
T	F	F	F	T	F	F
F	T	T	T	F	T	T
F	T	F	T	F	F	T
F	F	T	F	F	T	F
F	F	F	F	F	F	F

Since we are going to produce an eight-line table, p is assigned four Ts and four Fs. (The total number of lines is 8, and $8 \times \frac{1}{2} = 4$.) q has half of p's pattern, or "twos," and r has half of q's pattern, or "ones."

Step 5 Compute the truth-values of the compounds using the truth-functional definitions of the symbols.

$[(p \supset q) \lor (r \supset q)] \supset [(p \cdot r) \supset q]$

T	T	T	T	T	T	T	T	T	T	T	T	T
T	T	T	T	F	T	T	T	T	F	F	T	T
T	F	F	F	T	F	F	T	T	T	T	F	F
T	F	F	T	F	T	F	T	T	F	F	T	F
F	T	T	T	T	T	T	T	F	F	T	T	T
F	T	T	T	F	T	T	T	F	F	F	T	T
F	T	F	T	T	F	F	T	F	F	T	T	F
F	T	F	T	F	T	F	T	F	F	F	T	F

 1 3 2 6 4 5 Order of completion.

Exclusive 'or' Statements

Earlier, we noted that an exclusive 'or' statement claims that one or the other of its component statements is true, but not both of them. Later, we saw that the following form can be used to express them.

$(p \lor q) \cdot \sim (p \cdot q)$

We have seen truth-value definitions for each of the symbols in this form. By constructing a truth table, we can derive a truth-functional definition for exclusive 'or' statements.

$(p \lor q)$	$\cdot$	$\sim(p \cdot q)$
T T T	F	F T T T
T T F	T	T T F F
F T T	T	T F F T
F F F	F	T F F F

Notice that the form's truth-values show that it is false when both p and q are true, and false when both p and q are false. (Remember that values for the form are under the major connective.) The exclusive meaning of 'or' claims that both statements cannot be true. Hence, an exclusive 'or' statement is false when both statements are true. Exclusive 'or' statements claim that one or the other of their component statements is true, so they are false when both of their component statements are false.

The other two possibilities, lines 2 and 3 of the table, have at least one, and at most one, true component statement. Given our definition of exclusive 'or' statements, they are true in these cases.

Exercises III

Construct a truth table for each of the following statement forms.

*1. $p \supset \sim p$
2. $p \supset \sim(p \cdot q)$
*3. $(p \cdot q) \cdot (p \supset \sim q)$
4. $\sim(p \supset q) \cdot (p \lor q)$
*5. $(p \lor q) \supset (p \lor r)$
6. $(p \supset q) \supset [(p \cdot r) \supset (q \cdot r)]$
*7. $(p \lor q) \supset [(p \lor r) \supset q]$
8. $[(p \supset q) \cdot (r \supset s)] \supset [(p \lor r) \supset (q \cdot s)]$

Concept Reviews

1. Is '$p \supset q \lor r$' a statement form? Why or why not?
2. Is '$A \supset (p \cdot B)$' a statement form? Why or why not?
3. Given our definition of truth tables, why does a truth table for a statement form with three variables have to have at least eight lines?
4. How many lines of truth table would be required for a statement form with six variables?

IV Tautologous, Contradictory, and Contingent Statement Forms and Statements

A. Statement Forms

Truth tables of the sort that we constructed in the last section can be used to determine whether a given statement form is tautologous, contradictory, or contingent. As defined in definition 3.4, a truth table lists all of the possible combinations of truth-values for the form's variables. A truth-functional statement form that is true for *every* possibility is called "tautologous."

DEFINITION 3.6

A truth-functional statement form is *tautologous* if and only if it is true on every line of its truth table.

A truth-functional statement form that is false for every possibility is called "self-contradictory."

DEFINITION 3.7

A truth-functional statement form is *self-contradictory* if and only if it is false on every line of its truth table.

A truth-functional statement form that is neither tautologous nor self-contradictory, because it has both true and false possibilities, is called "contingent."

DEFINITION 3.8

A truth-functional statement form is *contingent* if and only if it is true on at least one line of its truth table, and false on at least one line of its truth table.

When applying definitions 3.6, 3.7, and 3.8, we have to consider the possibilities that are indicated in the column under the form's major connective.

The first example given in section III, '$(p \supset q) \cdot (q \vee p)$', is contingent, since at least one T and at least one F appear under its major connective. The second example in that section, '$[(p \supset q) \vee (r \supset q)] \supset [(p \cdot r) \supset q]$', is tautologous, since it is true on every line under its major connective.

The following example is true on every line. Hence, tautologous.

$$p \vee \sim p$$

| T | T | FT |
| F | T | TF |

The next example is false on every line. Hence, contradictory.

$$p \cdot \sim p$$

| T | F | FT |
| F | F | TF |

In the next example, at least one line is true and at least one line is false. Hence, the statement form is contingent.

$$p$$

| T |
| F |

Notice that it is the net or final truth-values for the form, those which have been boxed off in the examples, that decide whether the form is tautologous, self-contradictory, or contingent.

Exercises IV

Construct a truth table for each of the following statement forms, and determine whether the form is tautologous, self-contradictory, or contingent.

*1. $p \supset p$

2. $(p \lor q) \supset p$

*3. $(p \cdot q) \supset p$

4. $(p \lor q) \cdot (\sim p \cdot \sim q)$

*5. $(p \supset q) \lor (p \supset \sim q)$

6. $p \lor (q \supset r)$

*7. $[p \lor (q \cdot r)] \cdot \sim[(p \lor q) \cdot (p \lor r)]$

8. $[(p \supset q) \cdot (r \supset s)] \supset [(\sim q \lor \sim s) \supset (\sim p \lor \sim r)]$

B. Statements

As was mentioned in Chapter 1, logic is not concerned with particular subject matters. In addition to understanding arguments, however, logic is concerned with understanding what type of evidence is required to show that statements are true (or false).

Tautologous, self-contradictory, and contingent statement forms determine whether statements are tautologous, self-contradictory, or contingent.

DEFINITION 3.9

A truth-functional statement is a *tautology* if and only if its form is tautologous.

We know that '$p \lor \sim p$' is a tautologous statement form, since its truth table shows that its major connective is always assigned the value 'true'. The statement 'Martin Luther King either was, or was not, assassinated in 1968', has this form, and so it is a tautology.[5]

Form: $\quad p \lor \sim p$

Statement: $\quad A \lor \sim A$

---

[5]Connections between statement forms and statements are covered in detail in the next chapter. For now, a statement "has" a form when the statement and the form look alike, except that the form has statement variables and statements are expressed with statement constants.

Since truth tables list all possibilities and tautologous statement forms have only true possibilities, any example of a tautologous statement form must be true.

All tautologies are true.

Tautologies—examples of tautologous statement forms—usually sound trivial in English. Straightforward examples do not seem to give us new information. Although unquestionably true, the above statement about Martin Luther King does not give us any information about his assassination. It is equally true that he either was, or was not, assassinated in 1991. Tautologies are true as determined by forms. They are true no matter what took place, or might take place, in the world.

DEFINITION 3.10

A truth-functional statement is a *self-contradiction* if and only if its form is self-contradictory.

Since its truth table shows that its major connective is always assigned the value 'false', we know that '$p \cdot {\sim}p$' is a self-contradictory statement form. The statement "Martin Luther King was both *a*ssassinated in 1968 and not *a*ssassinated in 1968" corresponds to this form, and so it is a self-contradiction.

Form: $p \cdot {\sim}p$
Statement: $A \cdot {\sim}A$

Since truth tables list all possibilities and self-contradictory statement forms have only false possibilities, any example of a self-contradictory statement form must be false.

All self-contradictions are false.

Self-contradictions in English are often so obviously false that we may try to reinterpret them so that there is no contradiction. We tend to read self-contradictions so that they are not self-contradictory!

We try to make sense out of what we read and hear, and at first it is unclear what a person is claiming if she says that Martin Luther King was both assassinated in 1968 and not assassinated in 1968. We would likely interpret her to be saying that although he was killed in 1968, Martin Luther King's civil rights achievements live on.

Suppose, however, that the sentence is intended to mean exactly what it says: that Martin Luther King was assassinated, shot to death, in 1968; and *also* that Martin Luther King was not assassinated, was not shot to death, in 1968. Understood this way, the sentence, rightfully, strikes us as mad. It is this second meaning that expresses the self-contradiction.

Self-contradictions are always false, no matter what has happened, or might happen, in the world.

DEFINITION 3.11

A truth-functional statement is *contingent* if and only if its form is contingent.

We know that *p* is a contingent statement form, since lines of its truth table indicate both true and false possibilities. The statement 'Martin Luther King was *a*ssassinated in 1968' has this statement form, and so is contingent.

Form: *p*
Statement: A

Truth tables list all possibilities. Truth tables for contingent statement forms indicate that they can have both true and false examples.

Contingent statements owe their truth-value (that is, whether they are true or false) not to their form, but to whether they are making a true or false claim about the world.

The following is also a contingent statement.

The United States has a balanced budget.

It is true that Martin Luther King was assassinated in 1968, and it is false that the United States has a balanced budget. What determines that the statements are contingent is not that one is true and the other false, but rather that their statement form is contingent. What makes one true and the other false is that one makes a factually true claim, and the other makes a factually false claim. The truth-value of a contingent statement cannot be decided by merely looking at its form.

Tautologies are determined to be true by their forms. Self-contradictions are determined to be false by their forms. Contingent statements are *not* determined to be either true or false by their forms. Whether a contingent statement is true is determined by whether it makes a correct factual claim.

Concept Reviews

1. Suppose that you have constructed a truth table and shown that a particular statement form is tautologous. Using the definition of a truth table to justify your answer, indicate why a statement that has this form must be true.

2. Provide an English example of the form '$(p \lor q) \cdot (\sim p \cdot \sim q)$'. This is number 4, Exercises IV, of this chapter. What is the truth-value of your example? Do situations in the world have any effect on the truth-value of your example? Why or why not?

3. The conjunction of two contradictory statements must be both a self-contradiction and false. Will the conjunction of two contrary statements be a self-contradiction, as defined in section IV? Using the definitions of 'contrary' and 'contradiction', explain the basis for your answer.

V   Using Truth Tables to Determine Whether Argument Forms Are Valid

Chapter 1 made the claim that arguments, regardless of their subject matter, can be well constructed or poorly constructed. We noted that arguments can be created from argument forms, and that any number of arguments can share an argument form. Chapter 1 claimed that the following argument form, structure II, is deductively valid.

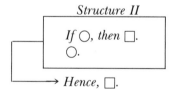

Structure II

If ○, then □.
○.

→ Hence, □.

We can use the horseshoe to express the conditional in the first premiss, and we can use our statement variables to indicate the form's locations.

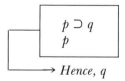

$p \supset q$
p

→ Hence, q

Using arrows and boxes helps to emphasize the idea that forms have locations for statements, but drawing boxes and arrows is inconvenient if we want to consider a number of argument forms. Instead, we will write the premises of an argument or argument form above a line, and write the conclusion of the argument or argument form below the line. The conclusion will be further identified by placing before it three dots, arranged in a triangular pattern: '∴', meaning 'therefore'.

The above argument form will be expressed as:

$$p \supset q$$
$$\underline{p}$$
$$\therefore q$$

DEFINITION 3.12

An *argument form* is a group of statement forms, such that one of them is presented as following from the others.

The statement form that is considered to follow is the form's conclusion. The statement forms that are to provide support for the conclusion are the form's premisses.

We also worked with the following argument form in Chapter 1.

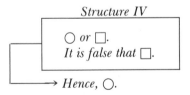

Structure IV

○ *or* □.
It is false that □.

⟶ *Hence,* ○.

Our artificial language expresses this form as:

$$p \lor q$$
$$\underline{\sim q}$$
$$\therefore p$$

Chapter 1 claimed that structures II and IV (and others) are deductively valid forms. Now that we can construct truth tables, we can define 'deductively valid form'. With the understanding that we are working with arguments from the perspective of *deductive logic*, we will merely refer to argument forms and arguments as being "valid" or "invalid."

DEFINITION 3.13

An argument form is *deductively valid* if and only if it is impossible for it to have all true premisses and a false conclusion.

We can also define 'invalid argument form'.

DEFINITION 3.14

An argument form is *deductively invalid* if and only if it is possible for it to have all true premisses and a false conclusion.

We can use truth tables to express all of the possibilities for a truth-functional argument form. By examining an argument form's truth table, we can determine whether it is possible for the form to have all true premisses and a false conclusion. If a form has the possibility of all true premisses and a false conclusion, this possibility will be present on one or more lines of its truth table. Since truth tables express all possibilities, if no line of an argument form's truth table has all true premisses and a false conclusion, then this combination must not be possible. If no line of an argument form's truth table has all true premisses and a false conclusion, then it must be impossible for the form to have all true premisses and a false conclusion.

Hence,

> **A truth-functional argument form is valid if and only if no line of its truth table has all true premisses and a false conclusion.**

And:

> **A truth-functional argument form is invalid if and only if its truth table has one or more lines with all true premisses and a false conclusion.**

Chapter 1 Notation

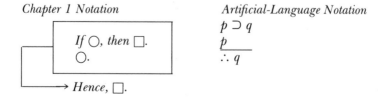

Artificial-Language Notation

$p \supset q$

p

$\therefore q$

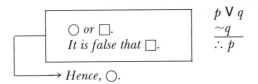

When we claim that the above argument forms are valid, we are claiming that no line of their truth tables expresses the possibility of all true premises and a false conclusion.

We will be able to prove that the above argument forms are valid, as soon as we can apply truth tables to them.

Truth-Table Recipe for Argument-Form Validity

Step 1 Write the argument form on a horizontal line. Leave some space between each of the premises, and also between the premises and the conclusion. The conclusion should be the statement form at the far right. For example,

$p \supset q$
p
$\therefore q$

becomes:

$p \supset q$ $\qquad$ p $\qquad$ q

Step 2 Construct a truth table as before. (See section III.)

$p \supset q$	p	q
T T T	T	T
T F F	T	F
F T T	F	T
F T F	F	F
(premiss 1)	(premiss 2)	(conclusion)

Step 3 Determine whether there is any line that has every premiss true and the conclusion false. If there is no such line, then the form is valid. If there is any such line, then the form is invalid.

   The conclusion is false on lines 2 and 4, but each of these lines has a false premiss as well. The first premiss is false on line 2, and the second premiss is false on line 4. Hence, there is no line where all of the premises are true and the conclusion is false. Since this form does not have the possibility of all true premises and a false conclusion, it is valid.

Notice that when we are determining whether a statement form is tautologous, contradictory, or contingent, the truth table is read by looking at the *column* under the major connective. When we are determining argument-form validity, it is again the values under the major connectives that count, but the values for the premisses are compared to the value for the conclusion by horizontal *lines*.

A truth table shows the following form, also from Chapter 1, to be invalid.

$p \supset q$
$\sim p$
$\therefore \sim q$

Step 1

$p \supset q$ $\sim p$ $\sim q$

Step 2

$p \supset q$	$\sim p$	$\sim q$
T T T	FT	FT
T F F	FT	TF
F T T	TF	FT
F T F	TF	TF
(premiss 1)	(premiss 2)	(conclusion)

Step 3 This form is invalid, since on line 3 all of the premisses are true and the conclusion is false.

Notice that when we examine a truth table to determine whether an argument form is valid, the only combination of truth-values that counts is all true premisses and a false conclusion. If the truth table for an argument form has a line with these values, the argument form is invalid. No line of a truth table ever shows that an argument form is valid.

An argument form is valid when its truth table lacks any line that shows it to be invalid.

In determining whether an argument form is valid, we are not looking at whether particular statements in a particular argument are true. Rather, the truth table indicates possibilities that are allowed by the form. Whether an *argument form* is valid is determined by its truth table. Whether an *argument* is valid is determined by its form.

Chapter 1 listed the following truth-value possibilities for deductively valid and deductively invalid arguments.

		Deductively Valid	Deductively Invalid
All true premises,	true conclusion	possible	possible
All true premises,	false conclusion	*impossible*	possible
One or more false premises,	true conclusion	possible	possible
One or more false premises,	false conclusion	possible	possible

Now we can explain how it is possible for an invalid argument to have all true premises and a true conclusion. An argument can be invalid even though it is not an example of the particular line of truth table that shows its form to be invalid. Our last example proved that the following argument form is invalid.

$$p \supset q$$
$$\frac{\sim p}{\therefore \sim q}$$

Chapter 1 presented the following argument.[6]

> *If used motor oil improves drinking water **then** it should be added to drinking water.*
>
> *It is false that used motor oil improves drinking water.*
>
> *Hence, it is false that used motor oil should be added to drinking water.*

This argument can have all true premises and a true conclusion, even though its form has the possibility of all true premises and a false conclusion. Since its form is invalid, the argument is invalid.

In addition to expressing the possibility of all true premises and a false conclusion (line 3), the truth table for this form also expresses the possibility of all true premises and a true conclusion (line 4). The argument form and the motor oil example are both invalid, owing to the truth-values on line 3. But the motor oil argument is actually an example of line 4 rather than line 3.

Line 4 represents examples where both of the statements that occupy the p and q locations are false. We can see that the motor oil argument is an example of this line, since both of its component statements are false. It

---

[6]The exact connection between arguments and their forms is covered at the outset of the next chapter.

is false that used motor oil improves drinking water, and false that used motor oil should be added to drinking water.

But line 4 is irrelevant in determining whether the argument form and the argument are valid, since *the values on line 3 prove it to be invalid.* To summarize: an invalid argument can have all true premises and a true conclusion, provided its form has the possibility of all true premises and a false conclusion.

We can also explain how a valid argument can have one or more false premises and a false conclusion. A person can begin with nonsense, and validly construct more nonsense. In *Alice's Adventures in Wonderland*, Alice finds herself in a locked room. She had placed the keys on a table when she was of normal size, and then had shrunk until she was no longer able to reach them.

> Soon her eye fell on a little glass box that was lying under the table: she opened it, and found in it a very small cake, on which the words 'EAT ME' were beautifully marked in currants. 'Well, I'll eat it,' said Alice, and if it makes me grow larger, I can reach the key: and if it makes me grow smaller, I can creep under the door: so either way I'll get into the garden, and I don't care which happens!'[7]

Provided we assume, as Alice did, that eating the cake will make her either larger or smaller,[8] Alice provided a perfectly valid argument, even though all of the events occur only in our imaginations. The truth table for the form of Alice's argument, however, does not express the possibility of all true premises and a false conclusion. Hence, Alice's argument is valid.

For arguments of the kind that we are considering:

'Valid' and 'Invalid', when applied to an argument, refer to the way that the argument is put together by its form.

Now we can construct truth tables and determine whether argument forms are valid.

---

[7]Lewis Carroll, *Alice's Adventures in Wonderland* (New York: World Publishing Co., 1946), 25.

[8]This assumption has to be added, since 'the cake will make her larger' expresses a *contrary*, not the contradictory of 'the cake will make her smaller'. Lewis Carroll, of course, recognized this. The cake does not change her size at all, at first. To see how she is ultimately able to leave the room, you will have to read the story!

VI Drawbacks

Truth tables provide a valuable initial understanding of some major issues, but they have two serious drawbacks.

1. They become outrageously long, even when the argument form does not have very many variables. An eight-variable form requires a 256-line truth table!

2. Most importantly, truth tables ignore the active processes in reasoning. When used with enough stamina, they can check arguments that have already been created, but they are of virtually no use in creating arguments. Logic should help us to create argumentation as well as help us to evaluate it.

These issues form the content of Chapter 4.

Exercises V

Construct a truth table for each of the following argument forms, and determine whether the argument form is valid.

*1. $p \lor q$
p
$\therefore \sim q$

2. $p \lor q$
$\sim p$
$\therefore q$

*3. $p \supset q$
$\sim p$
$\therefore q$

4. $p \supset q$
$q \lor \sim p$
$\therefore p$

*5. $\sim(p \cdot q)$
p
$\therefore \sim q$

6. $p \supset q$
$\sim q \lor r$
$\sim r \supset p$
$\therefore \sim p$

*7. $\sim p \supset (p \lor q)$
$\sim q \lor \sim p$
$\therefore r \lor \sim p$

8. $p \supset (q \lor r)$
$\sim q \cdot \sim r$
$\therefore \sim p$

*9. $p \supset q$
$r \supset q$
q
$\therefore p \lor r$

10. $(p \supset q) \cdot (r \supset s)$
$p \lor r$
$\therefore q \lor s$

Exercises VI

Symbolize each of the following with our artificial language. Write out the corresponding argument form. Determine the validity of the argument form by constructing a truth table.
Example:

Not both Booker T. Washington and W. E. B. Du Bois created the NAACP. W. E. B. Du Bois created the NAACP. Hence, Booker T. Washington did not create the NAACP.

$\sim(W \cdot D)$
D

$\therefore \sim W$

$\sim(p \cdot q)$
q

$\therefore \sim p$

$\sim(p$	$\cdot$	$q)$	q	$\sim p$
F T	T	T	T	F T
T T	F	F	F	F T
T F	F	T	T	T F
T F	F	F	F	T F

The argument and the argument form are valid. No line has all true premisses and a false conclusion.

*1. You shouldn't both *s*moke and *t*ake birth control pills. You *t*ake birth control pills. Hence, you shouldn't *s*moke.

2. Animals are capable of experiencing *p*ain. They have *i*nterests if they can experience *p*ain. A necessary condition for animals to have *i*nterests is that they be *a*live. Hence, whenever animals are *a*live, they have *i*nterests.

*3. The Soviet Union is willing to start *i*mproving relations with the United States if Washington will abide by the principles of *e*quality and equal *s*ecurity. The United States is willing to abide by the principle of *e*quality but not the principle of equal *s*ecurity. Hence, the Soviet Union is not willing to start *i*mproving relations with the United States.

4. Sean shouldn't take *r*efuge in a relationship unless he's willing to pay the *p*rice. Sean is willing to pay the *p*rice only if he can be *s*elfless part of the time. Hence, Sean's being *s*elfless part of the time is a necessary condition for Sean to take *r*efuge in a relationship.

*5. Whenever you *t*ake a tetracycline medication and *l*ie in the sun, your skin turns *r*ed. Your skin hasn't turned *r*ed. Hence, you either haven't *l*ain in the sun or you haven't *t*aken a tetracycline medication.

6. Margaret Mead could have been a highly *r*espected anthropologist only if she *c*hanged the way that we see people. Unless she *c*hanged the way that we see people, her theories about stressless adolescence are not *i*mportant. Her theories about stressless adolescence are *i*mportant. Hence, she was a highly *r*espected anthropologist.

*7. Stonehenge either has great *h*istorical importance or people in 1000 B.C. had excessive *l*eisure time. The people in 1000 B.C. had neither excessive *l*eisure time nor sophisticated *m*achinery. Hence, Stonehenge has great *h*istorical importance; moreover, the people in 1000 B.C. did not have sophisticated *m*achinery.

8. If *t*axes aren't increased, then if *m*ilitary spending increases then we can't both retain our *s*ocial security programs and *a*void a large deficit. Although *t*axes haven't increased, *m*ilitary spending has. We have retained our *s*ocial security programs. Hence, we cannot *a*void a large deficit.

Concept Reviews

1. Relate the idea of 'possibility', as expressed in the definition of truth tables, to whether an argument form is valid. How do the truth tables use possibilities in the definition of 'valid'?

2. We know that valid arguments cannot possibly have all true premisses and a false conclusion. What combinations of truth and falsity are possible between the premisses and the conclusions of *invalid* arguments?

4 Introduction to Formal Proofs

Chapter 3 provided a definition of 'valid' for argument forms. Chapter 4 has two main goals:

1. To specify relationships between forms, statements, and arguments. After completing this section, we will be able to clarify some of our previous concepts.

2. To begin the development of a formal deductive system. Most complex arguments can be handled without using truth tables.

In addition, this chapter will cause us to become aware of active reasoning processes.

KEY TERMS FOR THIS CHAPTER

Use the glossary as necessary, and review the definitions of these terms prior to a second reading of this chapter.

Instances of a statement form   **Parallel-instance of an**
Instances of an argument form   **argument form**
Parallel-instance of a statement   **Inferential form**
form   **Formal proof**

I Form-Instance Relationships

Even though previous exercises had us create arguments from forms, it is tempting to see argument forms as resulting from arguments. No small wonder! We have been exposed to reasoning since an early age, but have only recently encountered forms. Then too, at Grauman's and elsewhere,[1] we often do create a form from an example.

Chapter 3 claimed that some statements have particular statement forms, and that some arguments have particular argument forms. The meaning of 'have' needs clarification. Statements and arguments certainly do not have forms as celebrities have forms in concrete!

Statements (or arguments) have statement forms (or argument forms) by being either instances or parallel-instances of statement forms (or argument forms).

A. Instances

The relationship between an argument or statement and its form involves the idea that the variables, but not the connectives (including the tilde), can be seen as blanks or slots that can accept statements. In producing an instance of a form, we can imagine statements replacing the variables, or filling the variable locations of the form. The only restriction in producing an instance, is that the same statement must replace the same variable throughout.

DEFINITION 4.1

A statement is an *instance of a statement form* if and only if the statement can be produced from the form by replacing the variables with statements. The same statement must replace a given variable throughout.

DEFINITION 4.2

An argument is an *instance of an argument form* if and only if the argument can be produced from the form by replacing the variables with statements. The same statement must replace a given variable throughout.

---

[1]Grauman's Chinese Theatre in Hollywood has concrete footprints and other impressions left by celebrities.

We have seen a number of statement forms, including the following:

$p \lor \sim p$

$p \cdot \sim p$

p

We can generate three different statements from these forms by replacing the variable, p, with a statement. The subject matter for this section is taken from Shakespeare's *Hamlet*. Hamlet's mother, Gertrude, says:

The lady doth protest too much.

We can abbreviate this statement with the constant D. Using this statement to replace the variable p, the above forms will generate the following statements.

'$p \lor p$' will produce the tautology '$D \lor D$,' as an instance: Either the lady does protest too much or the lady does not protest too much.

'$p \cdot \sim p$' will produce the contradiction '$D \cdot \sim D$' as an instance: The lady does protest too much and the lady does not protest too much.

'p' will produce the contingent statement D as an instance.

We can add another statement and produce more complex examples that follow the same basic pattern. Let G abbreviate 'the lady is guilty'. Then '$p \supset q$' produces '$D \supset G$': If the lady doth protest too much, the lady is guilty.

We can take any statement form, pick statements to replace its variables, and use the statement form to produce a statement. Even though the examples so far look like the form involved, forms and statements are different kinds of things. Statement constants indicate definite statements; statement variables are placeholders for any statement whatsoever.

Notice that the following three statements will all be instances of the form '$p \lor \sim p$':

$P \lor \sim P$

$D \lor \sim D$

$G \lor \sim G$

Argument-form instances are created in the same fashion as statement-form instances. Suppose that we look at the following argument form.

$p \supset q$

p
_____
$\therefore q$

If we replace the variables with the constants D and G, we can produce the following argument from this form:

$D \supset G$

D
_____
$\therefore G$

It might appear that our earlier usage of 'have' was adequate. Referring back to our definition of an instance, however, and noting that compound statements are also statements, we can see that the definition of 'instance' is much broader than the examples that we have considered thus far. The following statement is also an instance of the statement form '$p \lor \sim p$':

$$(D \supset G) \lor \sim(D \supset G)$$

In this case, the compound statement indicated by '$D \supset G$' has been used to replace the variable p.

Argument forms also generate instances by having their variables replaced with compound statements. First we will consider an expanded version of Gertrude's reasoning, and then we will apply it to the idea of creating instances.

> *Premiss:*   *If the lady swears her unending love and doth protest too much, then her love has ended and she is guilty of deceit.*
>
> *Premiss:*   *The lady swears her unending love and doth protest too much.*
>
> *Conclusion:*   *Her love has ended and she is guilty of deceit.*[2]

We can use the following to symbolize Gertrude's reasoning.

$$(S \cdot D) \supset (E \cdot G)$$
$$\underline{S \cdot D}$$
$$\therefore E \cdot G$$

By using the compound statement indicated by '$S \cdot D$' to replace p throughout, and the compound statement indicated by '$E \cdot G$' to replace q throughout, we can see that the expanded version of Gertrude's reasoning is also an instance of the following argument form.

$$p \supset q$$
$$\underline{p}$$
$$\therefore q$$

It is possible for a given statement or argument to be an instance of more than one form. The expanded argument, symbolized above, is an instance of both of the following argument forms:

---

[2]The quotation, "The lady doth protest too much," is from *Hamlet* by William Shakespeare, act 3, scene 2, line 240. Hamlet's mother, Gertrude, remarried soon after the death of his father. Hamlet arranges for his mother to watch a play in which the queen protests her unending love for her king—love that will remain beyond his death. Hamlet is making the point that his mother's love for his father was quite fickle. Gertrude says of the queen in the play: "The lady doth protest too much, methinks."

$$p$$
$$\underline{q}$$
$$\therefore r$$

and

$$(p \cdot q) \supset (r \cdot s)$$
$$\underline{p \cdot q}$$
$$\therefore r \cdot s$$

To see that the argument is an instance of the first form, visualize the compound statement indicated by '$(S \cdot D) \supset (E \cdot G)$' as a replacement for p, '$S \cdot D$' as a replacement for q, and '$E \cdot G$' as a replacement for r.

> **Any statement can be used to replace a variable when producing an instance, as long as the same statement is used to replace that variable throughout.**

'$D \supset D$' is an instance of '$p \supset q$'. In this case, the same statement, indicated by D, is used to replace the variable p and also the variable q. We have an acceptable instance, since p is replaced with the same statement throughout (p appears only once in the form), and q is replaced with the same statement throughout (q appears only once in the form).

$$D \supset D$$
$$\underline{D}$$
$$\therefore D$$

is an instance of

$$p \supset q$$
$$\underline{p}$$
$$\therefore q$$

This example applies the idea expressed above for statement-form instances to argument-form instances. The statement indicated by D has been used to replace both of the variables p and q. p has been replaced with the same statement throughout, as has q. Hence, we have an acceptable instance.

Even though all of our above examples have been correct instances, not everything is an instance of anything!

$D \supset G$ is *not* an instance of $p \supset p$.

$$D \supset G$$
$$\underline{G}$$
$$\therefore D$$

is *not* an instance of

$$p \supset q$$
$$\underline{p}$$
$$\therefore q$$

> **In producing an instance, each variable must be replaced with the same statement throughout.**

The variable p cannot be replaced with D at one point and G at another. Any statement can be used to replace p, but the *same statement* must continue to replace p.

Instances are not formed by merely pairing off variables and constants. In the first place, since compounds can be used to replace the variables, the notion of "pairing off" is not very clear. In the second place, although the same statement can replace two or more variables, a single variable cannot be replaced with two or more different statements. Finally, the following argument is not an instance of the indicated form.

$$D \supset G$$
$$\underline{D}$$
$$\therefore G$$

is *not* an instance of

$$(p \cdot q) \supset (r \cdot s)$$
$$\underline{p \cdot q}$$
$$\therefore r \cdot s$$

An instance is considered to be created *from the form*. '$(p \cdot q) \supset (r \cdot s)$' has too many variables to produce a statement as simplistic as '$D \supset G$'. To produce an instance from a form, each of the variables must be replaced with a statement. In this case, each of the variables, p, q, r, and s would have to be replaced to produce an instance. It is impossible to fill four locations of a form and have '$D \supset G$' result.

Also remember that the connectives are never replaced in producing an instance.

> **Each connective in a form must appear in all of its instances, and each variable of the form must be replaced with a statement.**

We should begin with the form. If, by designating content for its variables and keeping the same content for a given variable throughout, the statement (or argument) can be created, then we have an instance of the form. If we cannot begin with the form and specify content for the variables, keeping the same content for a given variable throughout and create the statement or argument, then the statement or argument is not an instance of the form.

B. Parallel-Instances

Instances that have the exact structure of a given form are called "parallel-instances" of that form.

DEFINITION 4.3

A statement is a *parallel-instance of a statement form* if and only if (1) the statement is an instance of the statement form, and (2) a unique simple statement is used for each variable.

DEFINITION 4.4

An argument is a *parallel-instance of an argument form* if and only if (1) the argument is an instance of the argument form, and (2) a unique simple statement is used for each variable.

Parallel-instances are those instances that can be easily recognized. Parallel-instances of forms look like the form. As the following examples point out, parallel-instances are related to their forms in the manner that was suggested by 'have' in Chapter 3.

$$D \supset G$$
$$\underline{D}$$
$$\therefore G$$

is a parallel-instance of the form

$$p \supset q$$
$$\underline{p}$$
$$\therefore q$$

In addition to being an instance as defined in the previous section, p pairs off with D, and q pairs off with G. For each statement variable there is a unique simple statement.

$$(S \cdot D) \supset (E \cdot G)$$
$$\underline{S \cdot D}$$
$$\therefore E \cdot G$$

is an instance, but is not a *parallel-instance* of the form

$$p \supset q$$
$$\underline{p}$$
$$\therefore q$$

'$(S \cdot D) \supset (E \cdot G)$' is an instance of '$p \supset q$' because the compound statements '$S \cdot D$' and '$E \cdot G$', can be used to replace the variables p and q as long as a *mere* instance is desired. Our second condition for having a parallel-instance requires, however, that each variable is replaced with a unique simple statement, not a compound statement.

$$D \supset D$$
$$D$$
$$\therefore D$$

is an instance of

$$p \supset q$$
$$p$$
$$\therefore q$$

but it is not a parallel-instance. Our second condition for having a parallel-instance requires that each variable pairs off with a *unique* simple statement. To have a parallel-instance, p and q cannot both be replaced with the same constant, D.

$$D \supset G$$
$$D$$
$$\therefore V$$

is not even an instance of

$$p \supset q$$
$$p$$
$$\therefore q$$

Since it is not an instance of this form, it is not a parallel-instance of it.

Some of the concepts just discussed are more complex than those in earlier chapters. Since this section forms the foundation for the remainder of this chapter and the entire next chapter, go back and carefully review the definitions and examples.

Exercises I

Use the forms listed below, and produce an instance of each by using the indicated statements to replace the variables in the form.

Use T to replace p.
Use U to replace q.
Use $\sim H$ to replace r.
Use '$\sim(V \supset C)$' to replace s.

*1. $p \lor q$
*3. $\sim p$
*5. $(p \cdot q) \supset (p \lor r)$

2. $p \supset q$
4. $p \supset (q \lor r)$
6. $(p \supset q) \cdot (r \supset s)$

*7. $p \supset q$
    p
    $\therefore q$

8. $p \cdot q$
    $\therefore q$

*9. p
    $\therefore \mathrm{p} \vee q$

10. p
    q
    $\therefore p \cdot q$

*11. $p \vee q$
    $\sim q$
    $\therefore p$

12. $p \vee (q \cdot r)$
    $\sim r$
    $\therefore p$

*13. $p \supset q$
    $\therefore (p \vee r) \supset (q \vee r)$

14. $(p \supset q) \cdot (r \supset s)$
    $p \vee r$
    $\therefore q \vee s$

Exercises II

For each statement form listed in the left-hand column, list any and all statements in the right-hand column that are instances. If an instance is a parallel-instance, indicate this as well.

*1. p

2. $p \cdot q$

*3. $p \vee q$

4. $p \supset q$

*5. $p \supset (p \supset q)$

6. $p \supset (q \cdot r)$

*7. $[(p \supset q) \supset r] \supset s$

a. $V \supset D$

b. $R \cdot V$

c. $[(V \supset B) \supset T] \supset H$

d. $[(A \supset B) \supset A] \supset C$

e. $\sim (R \supset S) \vee T$

f. $\sim V$

g. $(C \supset D) \cdot W$

h. $V \vee D$

i. $A \supset (R \supset C)$

j. $U \supset (T \supset S)$

k. A

Exercises III

For each argument form listed in the left-handed column, list any and all arguments in the right-hand column that are instances. If an instance is a parallel-instance, indicate this as well.

*1. $p \supset q$
    p
    $\therefore q$

a. $R \supset S$
    $U \supset C$
    $\therefore (R \supset S) \cdot (U \supset C)$

2. $p \cdot q$
   $\therefore q$

*3. p
   $\therefore p \vee q$

4. p
   q
   $\therefore p \cdot q$

*5. $p \supset q$
   $q \supset r$
   $\therefore p \supset r$

6. $(p \supset q) \cdot (r \supset s)$
   $p \cdot r$
   $\therefore q \cdot s$

b. B
   V
   $\therefore B \cdot V$

c. $H \cdot B$
   $\therefore H$

d. $\sim R \supset W$
   $W \supset T$
   $\therefore \sim R \supset T$

e. $[A \supset (B \cdot W)] \cdot [T \supset (B \cdot C)]$
   $A \cdot T$
   $\therefore (B \cdot W) \cdot (B \cdot C)$

f. $A \supset (U \vee T)$
   A
   $\therefore U \vee T$

g. $A \cdot B$
   $\therefore (A \cdot B) \vee R$

h. $(R \supset T) \cdot (U \supset T)$
   $\therefore U \supset T$

i. $\sim R \supset W$
   $T \supset W$
   $\therefore \sim R \supset T$

j. $(R \supset S) \cdot (V \supset C)$
   $\therefore R \supset S$

k. $(A \supset W) \cdot (U \supset S)$
   $A \cdot U$
   $\therefore W \cdot S$

Concept Reviews

1. Is the statement '$A \supset (B \vee A)$' an instance of the statement form '$p \supset (q \vee r)$'? If so, indicate the statements that replace p, q, and r. If not, indicate why not.

2. Is the argument,

   $B \cdot V$
   $\therefore B$

   an instance of the following argument form?

   $(p \supset q) \cdot (r \supset s)$
   $\therefore p \cdot q$

If so, indicate the statements that replace *p*, *q*, *r*, and *s*. If not, indicate why not.

3. Is the statement '$A \supset (B \lor A)$' a parallel-instance of the statement form '$p \supset (q \lor r)$'? Indicate why or why not.

4. Is the argument,

$$\frac{(D \supset G) \cdot (R \supset E)}{\therefore D \supset G}$$

a parallel-instance of the following argument form?

$$\frac{p \cdot q}{\therefore p}$$

Indicate why or why not.

5. Write out the statement form that has the statement '$(B \supset V) \lor (S \cdot {\sim}T)$' as a parallel-instance.

6. Suppose that a particular argument is not an instance of a particular argument form. Can the argument be a parallel-instance of the form? Why or why not?

II Applying Instance and Parallel-Instance Relationships to Tautologous, Contradictory, and Contingent Statements

A truth table for a tautologous statement form determines that all of its instances are true, regardless of whether the statements that replace its variables are true or false. The examples in Chapter 3 all used simple statements to replace a form's variables; but compound statements are either true or false, just as simple statements are either true or false. Compound statements, considered as units, have the same truth-value possibilities as simple statements. Since our truth tables cover all truth-value possibilities, any instance of a tautologous form that is created by replacing its variables with compound statements will be necessarily true.

Instances of tautologous forms that are created by replacing two or more variables with the same statement will also be necessarily true, since the statement that replaces the variables must be either true or false. Hence, since any instance of a tautologous form must fit one of the above possibilities and each possibility requires that the instance is necessarily true, we have the following result:

Any instance of a tautologous form must be a tautology.

We have already determined that the following statement form is tautologous (Chapter 3, Exercises IV, #3):

$(p \cdot q) \supset p$

Since all of the following statements are instances of the above form, they must all be tautologies.

$(V \cdot D) \supset V$

$(D \cdot D) \supset D$

$[(D \cdot V) \cdot (H \cdot C)] \supset (D \cdot V)$

The same sort of reasoning shows that all instances of self-contradictory forms must be self-contradictory statements. A truth table for a self-contradictory statement form determines that any example of the form will be false, regardless of whether the statements that replace its variables are either true or false.

Any instance of a self-contradictory statement form must be a self-contradictory statement.

We have determined that the following is a self-contradictory statement form (Chapter 3, Exercises IV, #4):

$(p \lor q) \cdot (\sim p \cdot \sim q)$

Since all of the following statements are instances of the above form, they must all be self-contradictory statements.

$(V \lor D) \cdot (\sim V \cdot \sim D)$

$(D \lor D) \cdot (\sim D \cdot \sim D)$

$[(D \cdot V) \lor (H \cdot C)] \cdot [\sim (D \cdot V) \cdot \sim (H \cdot C)]$

Contingent statements fail to follow the pattern that we have noticed for self-contradictory statements and tautologous statements. Self-contradictory statements and tautologies *can* be instances of contingent statement forms. '$D \lor \sim D$' is a tautology, since it is an instance of '$p \lor \sim p$'. The statement form p, is contingent, since it can have both true and false instances. '$D \lor \sim D$' is an instance of p. The problem, of course, is that whereas p has both true and false instances, '$D \lor \sim D$' has another underlying pattern, '$p \lor \sim p$', that makes it tautologous, even though it is an instance of p.

Similarly, '$p \lor q$' is a contingent form, yet it has the tautology '$D \lor \sim D$' as an instance. (Remember that an acceptable instance can be created by having a negated statement replace a variable.) How can we avoid these problems?

When an instance is a parallel-instance, however, there can be no underlying structures that might determine it to be either tautologous or contradictory. Notice that although the above two tautologous statements are instances of the contingent statement form *p*, neither of them is a parallel-instance of *p*.

> *Any parallel-instance of a truth-functionally contingent statement form is a contingent statement.*[3]

'*p* ∨ *q*' is a contingent statement form. '*H* ∨ *C*' and '*V* ∨ *D*' are both parallel-instances, and so both are contingent statements.

> *To determine that a statement is truth-functionally contingent, we must determine that it is a parallel-instance of a contingent statement form.*

The fact that a statement is *merely* an instance of a contingent statement form fails to tell us what kind of statement it is.

III Applying Instance and Parallel-Instance Relationships to Valid and Invalid Arguments

We can apply reasoning similar to that of the last section, to clarify the relationship between valid forms and valid arguments. If an argument form is valid, then regardless of the truth-values of statements that might replace its variables, we know that it is impossible for an example of the form to have all true premises and a false conclusion. Compound statements are either true or false, just as simple statements are either true or false. Hence, it must be impossible for an instance of a valid argument form that is created by replacing its variables with compound statements to have all true premises and a false conclusion.

Similarly, a statement that replaces two or more variables must be either true or false. Again, since truth tables indicate all of the truth-value possibilities for statements that might replace a form's variables, we know as well that it is impossible for this kind of an instance of a valid argument form to have all true premises and a false conclusion. Hence,

> *Any instance of a valid argument form must be a valid argument.*

---

[3]Provided that the statement is a truth-functional statement of the kind that we have been considering. Some predicate-logic statements, covered in Chapters 7 and 8, can be parallel-instances of a contingent form as defined here and yet be either logically true or logically false.

Previous truth tables have proved that the following argument form is valid.

$$p \supset q$$
$$\underline{p}$$
$$\therefore q$$

We know that all arguments that are instances of this form are valid. All of the following arguments are valid.

$D \supset G$	$(S \cdot D) \supset (E \cdot G)$	$D \supset D$
$\underline{D}$	$\underline{S \cdot D}$	$\underline{D}$
$\therefore G$	$\therefore E \cdot G$	$\therefore D$

Earlier we discovered that not every instance of a contingent statement form must be a contingent statement. The same sort of problem arises when we consider instances of *invalid* argument forms. The invalid argument form.

$$p$$
$$\underline{q}$$
$$\therefore r$$

has the three valid arguments, given above, as instances. Valid arguments can be *mere* instances of invalid forms. Even though an argument form is invalid, compound statements may replace its variables so that a particular instance is valid. Using the same statement to replace two or more different variables also can cause a valid argument to be an instance of an invalid form. Resorting to parallel-instances will avoid these problems for truth-functional arguments.

> **Any parallel-instance of an invalid argument form is an invalid argument.**[4]

We have used truth tables to show that the following form is invalid;

$$p \supset q$$
$$\underline{q}$$
$$\therefore p$$

The following parallel-instance must be invalid:

$$D \supset G$$
$$\underline{G}$$
$$\therefore D$$

---

[4]We assume that the argument is of the truth-functional type that we are considering.

> *To know that an argument is invalid, we must know that it is a parallel-instance of an invalid form. The fact that an argument is merely an instance of an invalid form does not tell us that it is invalid.*

Given the complexity of the concepts developed so far in this chapter, a brief summary is in order.

IV Summary

Forms are used to create arguments and statements, not the reverse. Statements and arguments are created by replacing the variables with statements. *Any* statement can be used to replace a variable, so long as the same statement is used for that variable throughout. An argument or statement so created is considered to be an instance of the argument or statement form.

Any instance of a tautologous statement form will be a tautology. Any instance of a self-contradictory statement form will be a self-contradiction. Any instance of a valid argument form will be a valid argument.

To be a parallel-instance of a statement form or an argument form, the replacements that produce the instance must involve only simple statements, and each distinct variable must have a unique simple statement. (A parallel-instance of a form will look like the form.) Any parallel-instance of a contingent statement form will be a contingent statement. Any parallel-instance an invalid argument form will be an invalid argument.

Concept Reviews

1. The reasoning in the previous sections assumes that when an instance of a valid argument form is created by replacing one or more variables with negated statements, the instance must be valid. Carefully review the reasoning for compound statements and indicate why this assumption must be true.

2. Suppose that we know that an argument is a parallel-instance of a valid argument form. Does the argument have to be valid? Why or why not?

3. Suppose we know that an argument is an instance of some valid argument form. Will the form that has it as a parallel-instance be valid? Why or why not?

4. Suppose we know that a particular argument is an instance of a valid argument form and is also an instance of an invalid argument form. It is not a parallel-instance of either form. Is the argument valid or invalid? Why?

V Deduction: Formal Proofs

A. Modus Ponens

Our definitions of 'valid argument form' and 'instance' will enable us to unpack complex valid arguments into simpler valid forms. Our first examples of this process will use a valid argument form that first appeared in Chapter 1 (as structure II) and has also appeared on recent pages:

$$p \supset q$$
$$\underline{p}$$
$$\therefore q$$

Many frequently used valid argument forms have names. The above form is called 'modus ponens.' At first, having names for a variety of forms may seem burdensome. Once we are familiar with them, however, the names provide a convenient method for identifying particular forms. We will be able to indicate a particular form merely by mentioning its name. Having names for argument forms does for them what Frank and Ernie thought ought to be done for penguins![5] In both cases, it makes the differences between apparently similar things stand out.

---

[5]"Frank & Ernest," March 18, 1984. Reprinted by permission of NEA, Inc.

Valid argument forms, such as modus ponens, 'preserve truth.'[6] If all of the premises of a valid argument are true, then the conclusion of the argument must be true as well. Any argument that is an instance of a valid argument form will preserve truth from its premises to its conclusion.

Suppose, however, that the situation is a bit more complex. Suppose that we have an argument with a number of premises (the exact number is not important), and suppose that the argument *as a whole* is not an instance of modus ponens (or some other simple valid form). We will call this complex argument the "initial argument."

Perhaps a couple of the premises in our initial argument are instances of modus ponens premises. We know that if these premises are true, then the conclusion of the modus ponens instance must be true. Suppose we decide to write down the conclusion of the modus ponens instance. It must be true, if the premises of the initial argument are true.

Now suppose that the conclusion we have just written down and another premise of the initial argument are also instances of modus ponens premises. Again, we know that if all the premises of the initial argument are true, the conclusion of this second instance of modus ponens must be true. Suppose we write down this conclusion as well.

Imagine that we continue this process of writing down the conclusions of instances of modus ponens until we end up writing, at some point, the conclusion of the initial argument. Each modus ponens argument that we created was truth preserving. Since each application of modus ponens preserves truth, the series of applications of modus ponens must preserve truth. If the premises of the initial argument are all true, at no point could modus ponens have introduced falsity. Hence, we know that if the premises of the initial argument are all true, then its conclusion must be true. We have shown that the initial argument is valid without using truth tables!

The above process is easier to understand by looking at an example. Keep the idea of preserving truth in mind as we go through it. Also, although our initial examples use only modus ponens, the basic ideas presented here will work for any valid argument form, or any mixture of valid argument forms.

The following example presents reasoning that is related to a rather mysterious aspect of World War II. Why would Hitler, having a nonaggression pact in place, attack the Soviet Union (June 22, 1941), particularly when he was already at war with England? Some accounts consider Hitler's actions to be the effects of drug abuse, primarily the abuse of amphetamines. The following presents an alternative viewpoint.

---

[6]Modus ponens is the name of structure II, first presented with circles and squares in Chapter 1. Structures I, III, and IV from Chapter 1 are discussed in Chapter 5.

Premiss: *Hitler could dominate all of Europe only if he defeated*
                  both England and the Soviet Union.

Premiss: *He could defeat both England and the Soviet Union only if*
                  he attacked the Soviet Union. [He believed that the fall of
                  England would have no effect on the war with the Soviet
                  Union, but that the fall of the Soviet Union would cause
                  England to collapse.]

Premiss: *If he had to attack the Soviet Union, then he had to do so*
                  quickly and before Soviet defences were built up. [Stalin
                  anticipated an attack in 1944, and was rearming accord-
                  ingly.]

Premiss: *Hitler wanted to dominate all of Europe.*

Conclusion: *He had to attack quickly and before Soviet defences were*
                  built up.

His earliest opportunity to attack was June 22, 1941.

Using the non-italicized letters to indicate our statement constants, we can symbolize this argument as follows:

$$D \supset (E \cdot S)$$
$$(E \cdot S) \supset A$$
$$A \supset (Q \cdot B)$$
$$\underline{D}$$
$$\therefore Q \cdot B$$

If we look at the first and fourth premisses of our symbolization, we can see that they are instances of the premisses of modus ponens. (Remember that a compound statement can be used to replace a variable.)

First premiss: $D \supset (E \cdot S)$ *Modus ponens* $p \supset q$
Fourth premiss: $\underline{D}$ $\underline{p}$
                   $\therefore E \cdot S$ $\therefore q$

The conclusion of our modus ponens subargument will be '$E \cdot S$'. Hence, since modus ponens is truth preserving, truth is preserved from the first and fourth premisses to '$E \cdot S$'.

'$E \cdot S$', and the second premiss of our initial argument, form another instance of the premisses of modus ponens.

Second premiss: $(E \cdot S) \supset A$ *Modus ponens* $p \supset q$
Subargument conclusion: $\underline{E \cdot S}$ $\underline{p}$
                             $\therefore A$ $\therefore q$

The conclusion of our second modus ponens subargument will be A. Hence, since modus ponens is truth preserving, truth is preserved from the second premiss of the initial argument and '$E \cdot S$' to A.

A and the third premiss of the initial argument form yet another instance of the premisses of modus ponens.

Third premiss:	$A \supset (Q \cdot B)$	*Modus ponens*	$p \supset q$
Subargument conclusion:	$\underline{A}$		$\underline{p}$
	$\therefore Q \cdot B$		$\therefore q$

The conclusion of our third modus ponens subargument is '$Q \cdot B$'. Truth must be preserved to '$Q \cdot B$'.

'$Q \cdot B$' is the conclusion of our initial argument. Since each of our subarguments preserves truth, and we have proceeded from the premisses of the initial argument to its conclusion, the initial argument must preserve truth. Hence, the initial argument must be valid.

The above may be seen as justifying what we shall call "formal proofs." We need a more efficient way to express the reasoning process, however. Formal proofs (proofs that appeal to form) show that an argument is valid by linking its premisses to its conclusion with valid subarguments. The valid forms that we will use to create subarguments, as in the above process, will be called "inferential forms." They are those argument forms, such as modus ponens, that will allow us to infer, or derive, conclusions from the premisses of an initial argument and previously derived lines.

DEFINITION 4.5

A *valid inferential form* is a valid argument form that may be used to derive statements from previous lines. (A listing of our initial valid inferential forms appears near the end of this chapter.)

At present, modus ponens is our only valid inferential form.

DEFINITION 4.6

A statement is *derivable* from previous statements if and only if there is an argument that is an instance of an inferential form such that the derived statement is the argument's conclusion and the previous statements are the argument's premisses.

DEFINITION 4.7

A *formal proof* for a given argument consists of a list of statements that have been derived either from the argument's premises or from previously derived statements in the list (or both), such that the last derived statement is the argument's conclusion.

Finally, we should have a method for setting up formal proofs. The completed formal proof should indicate both the inferential form and previous lines used in the derivation of the "new" line.

i. Setting Up Formal Proofs

Step 1   Place the premises of the argument in a column, with its conclusion in the upper right corner. Separate the conclusion from the premises with a corner sign, '$\angle$'.

Step 2   Number the premises for easy identification, and underline the last premise to separate it from derived lines.

Step 3   Derive statements from the premises and previously derived lines, numbering them as they are produced. For each produced statement, indicate the inferential form that was used, and the lines that were used as premises in the derivation. Continue this process until the conclusion of the initial argument has been derived. Any line, except the conclusion of the initial argument that is separated from the other lines by the corner sign, can be used as a premiss in deriving later lines.

The following formal proof shows that the invasion-of-the-Soviet-Union example is valid. Notice the similarity between the following formal proof and the previous presentation of subarguments.

Argument: $D \supset (E \cdot S)$
$\qquad\quad (E \cdot S) \supset A$
$\qquad\quad A \supset (Q \cdot B)$
$\qquad\quad \underline{D}$
$\qquad\quad \therefore Q \cdot B$

Step 1:

$\qquad D \supset (E \cdot S) \qquad \angle Q \cdot B$
$\qquad (E \cdot S) \supset A$
$\qquad A \supset (Q \cdot B)$
$\qquad D$

Step 2:

    1. $D \supset (E \cdot S)$ $/Q \cdot B$
    2. $(E \cdot S) \supset A$
    3. $A \supset (Q \cdot B)$
    4. D
    ―――――――――

Step 3:

    1. $D \supset (E \cdot S)$ $/Q \cdot B$
    2. $(E \cdot S) \supset A$
    3. $A \supset (Q \cdot B)$
    4. D
    ―――――――――
    5. $E \cdot S$ *modus ponens 1, 4*
    6. A *modus ponens 2, 5*
    7. $Q \cdot B$ *modus ponens 3, 6*

The proof is completed on line 7, since the argument's conclusion, '$Q \cdot B$', has been derived. The completed formal proof shows that the argument is valid, since it shows that truth is preserved from its premises to its conclusion.

How can we spot an opportunity to apply an inferential form? Trying to label our usable lines with the variables p, q, r, and so on, is not only conceptually incorrect, but also inefficient. Since negated and compound statements can be used to replace the variables in making a derivation, there is no way to be sure just what should be labeled with a p or a q. In addition, the statements that are used to replace the variables of a valid inferential form often change during the completion of a formal proof. When line 5 was derived in our last example, p was replaced with D, and q was replaced with '$E \cdot S$'. When line 6 was derived in the same example, p was replaced with '$E \cdot S$', and q was replaced with A.

Experience is the most valuable asset in making derivations. Still, each of the inferential forms can be described in terms of its effect in a formal proof.

> ***Being able to see the effect of a given inferential form within a formal proof is far more valuable than looking at the inferential form in terms of its variables.***

ii. Using Modus Ponens in Formal Proofs

Modus ponens produces the consequent of a conditional. In order for modus ponens to be used, previous lines must include the conditional and an additional line that is the conditional's antecedent.

Conditional: $p \supset q$
The conditional's antecedent: p
The conditional's consequent: $\therefore q$

We can see this pattern in our previous formal proof example:

1. $D \supset (E \cdot S)$ $\quad \angle Q \cdot B$
2. $(E \cdot S) \supset A$
3. $A \supset (Q \cdot B)$
4. D
5. $E \cdot S$ modus ponens 1, 4

Modus ponens has *produced the consequent* of line 1's conditional. Line 4, the additional premiss, is the antecedent of the conditional.

6. A modus ponens 2, 5

Modus ponens has *produced the consequent* of line 2's conditional. Line 5, the additional premiss, is the antecedent of the conditional.

7. $Q \cdot B$ modus ponens 3, 6

Modus ponens has *produced the consequent* of line 3's conditional. Line 6, the additional premiss, is the antecedent of the conditional.

B. Simplification, Conjunction, and Addition

Our initial valid inferential forms will also include simplification, conjunction, and addition.

When each of our valid inferential forms is used to derive a line in a formal proof, the derived line is always seen as an instance of the form's conclusion, and previous lines are seen as instances of the form's premisses. Since each of our valid inferential forms is a valid argument form, applications of any of them must preserve truth. A formal proof that is completed with any mixture of our inferential forms shows that the initial argument is valid.

i. Simplification

Notice that simplification includes two inferential forms:

$p \cdot q$ $\qquad and \qquad$ $p \cdot q$
$\therefore p$ $\qquad\qquad\qquad$ $\therefore q$

Using Simplification in Formal Proofs
Simplification produces a (previous) conjunct as a derived line. To be used, the conjunction (having a dot as the major connective) must be a usable line.

Conjunction: $p \cdot q$ $p \cdot q$

A previous conjunct: $\therefore p$ *or:* $\therefore q$

When constructing formal proofs, simplification enables us to break up conjunctions. To be used, the dot must be the major connective. (Otherwise we would not have a proper instance.) Suppose that we look at the following conjunction.

Hitler attacked the Soviet Union and was defeated by "General Winter."

Using the non-italicized letters to indicate our statement constants, we can represent this example with the following:

$A \cdot W$

For a conjunction to be true, each conjunct must be true. Hence, truth must be preserved when either conjunct is derived from a true conjunction. Simplification acknowledges this.

$$\frac{A \cdot W}{\therefore A} \quad and \quad \frac{A \cdot W}{\therefore W}$$

ii. Conjunction

$$\frac{\begin{array}{l} p \\ q \end{array}}{p \cdot q}$$

Using Conjunction in Formal Proofs

Conjunction produces a conjunction as a derived line. To be used, each conjunct must be a usable line.

A usable line: p

A usable line: q

The derived conjunction: $p \cdot q$

In formal proofs, conjunction has an effect that is the opposite of simplification. Conjunction combines lines to form conjunctions. If each conjunct is true, then the conjunction of them must be true.

$$\frac{\begin{array}{l} A \\ W \end{array}}{\therefore A \cdot W}$$

iii. Addition

$$\frac{p}{\therefore p \lor q}$$

Using Addition in Formal Proofs

Addition produces a disjunction as a derived line. The first disjunct must be a usable line; the second disjunct can be any statement whatsoever.

A usable line: p
The derived disjunction: $p \lor q$

The conclusion is a disjunction such that the first disjunct was a previous line. q can be replaced with any statement whatsoever.

A disjunction is true when one or the other, or both, disjuncts are true. Hence, if a statement is true, then the disjunction of it and any other statement must be true. The following argument is an instance of addition.

Premiss: *Hitler decided to attack the Soviet Union.*
Conclusion: *Either Hitler decided to attack the Soviet Union or he decided to continue fighting England.*

A
$\therefore A \lor F$

Although some instances of addition sound reasonable, others do not. The following argument is also an instance of addition.

Premiss: *Hitler decided to attack the Soviet Union.*
Conclusion: *Either Hitler decided to attack the Soviet Union or the devil can quote Scripture.*

A
$\therefore A \lor Q$

A valid argument is defined as an argument that cannot possibly have all true premisses and a false conclusion. If we ignore all subject matter considerations, some instances of addition sound a bit peculiar!

For an argument to sound reasonable, we often require more than mere validity. Our inferential forms prove that an argument is valid, but we also expect all of the statements in an argument to be about the same subject, at least indirectly. Addition is an acceptable *inferential form*, but an argument can be an instance of addition and not be reasonable when judged by other standards. Other constraints than validity rule out adding the reference to the devil in the above example.

As addition is used in formal proofs, we *can* add any statement whatsoever. But realistically, it is beneficial to add only statements that are related to other statements in the argument.

C. Complex Formal Proofs

We can view the following argument in terms of the effects of our inferential forms.

1. $(K \lor R) \supset S$
2. $(S \cdot T) \supset F$
3. $K \cdot T$
$\therefore F$

Since the conclusion of the argument, F, is the consequent of our second premiss, we should expect to end the formal proof by using modus ponens to derive it. Modus ponens requires that we have an additional premiss, the antecedent of the conditional, as a line. In this case we need '$S \cdot T$'. '$S \cdot T$' is obviously a conjunction, and we can reasonably expect an application of our conjunction inferential form to produce it. To use conjunction, we will need a line S and a line T.

S is the consequent of line 1; we should expect to use modus ponens to produce it, provided that we can create a line which is '$K \lor R$', line 1's antecedent.

T is a conjunct on line 3, and so we can derive it with simplification. Our only real problem consists in finding a way to derive '$K \lor R$'.

'$K \lor R$' is a disjunction. Disjunctions can be produced with addition, provided that we have a line that is the same as the first disjunct. K is a conjunct on line three, and so we can get it by itself with simplification. Done!

The formal proof:

1. $(K \lor R) \supset S$ $/F$
2. $(S \cdot T) \supset F$
3. $K \cdot T$
4. K simplification 3
5. $K \lor R$ addition 4
6. S modus ponens 1, 5
7. T simplification 3
8. $S \cdot T$ conjunction 6, 7
9. F modus ponens 2, 8

Formal proofs can become quite complex. Being able to construct them is a skill. As with any skill, practice is essential. A person's ability to do formal proofs can be improved by seeing examples and noticing how each inferential form is applied, but there is no substitute for practice.

Formal Proof Strategies

Find the conclusion of the argument within its premisses. Decide which inferential form will likely be required to produce it. Seeing further into the proof is fine, but not essential. If there is an opportunity to apply one of our inferences, then do so. At worst, there will be another line to look at in relation to the conclusion.

The "goals approach" outlined below will not solve all problems, but it will prove helpful for most.

D. The Goals Approach to Formal Proofs

Most formal proofs can be constructed by looking at the problem as a series of goals as defined by our inferential forms. Modus ponens and simplification produce *parts* of a line, whereas addition and conjunction build compound statements. Moreover, each of our inferential forms can be applied only in relation to a statement's major connectives.

List the conclusion of the argument as a goal (*G*), and begin looking for it and subgoals in available lines as follows.

If *G* is within a compound statement, look at the major connective of the line that has *G*, and

1. If the major connective is a horseshoe and *G* is somewhere in the consequent, list the antecedent as a new goal. Once we have the antecedent, we will be able to apply modus ponens and get the consequent.
2. If the major connective is a dot, take a simplification step. Write down the conjunct that contains *G*.

If *G* is a compound statement, note its major connective. So far, we can only create conjunctions and disjunctions.

3. If *G*'s major connective is a dot, list each conjunct as a new goal. Once we have each conjunct, we will be able to get the conjunction by using conjunction.
4. If *G*'s major connective is a wedge, list the first disjunct as a new goal. We will be able to use addition to create the wedge once we have the first disjunct.

Write goals, and apply steps 1–4 above to each of them. Keep a current list of goals, and continue applying steps 1–4. Cross off obtained goals. Cross off any goals that can be derived when the listed goals are obtained. We have a solution for a given problem when all of our goals have been crossed off.

Take steps to construct the formal proof whenever possible.
Our previous example can be solved by using the goals approach.

1. $(K \lor R) \supset S$ $/F$
2. $(S \cdot T) \supset F$
3. $K \cdot T$

Goals: F

Our goal is the consequent of line 2. Step 1 has us list the antecedent as a new goal.

Goals: F̶; S · T

Since F can be derived when '$S \cdot T$' is obtained, F has been crossed off. '$S \cdot T$' has the dot as its major connective. Step 3 has us list each conjunct as a new goal.

Goals: F̶; S̶ ̶·̶ ̶T̶; S; T

Since '$S \cdot T$' can be derived when S and T are obtained, '$S \cdot T$', has been crossed off. T is within line 3 of the problem. Since it is a conjunct, we can use simplification to obtain it in the formal proof. So T can be crossed off. S is the consequent of line 1 of the problem; Step 1 has us list its antecedent, '$K \lor R$', as a goal.

Goals: F̶; S̶ ̶·̶ ̶T̶; S̶; T̶; K \lor R

Since S can be derived when '$K \lor R$' is obtained, S has been crossed off. '$K \lor R$' has the wedge as its major connective. Step 4 has us list its first disjunct as a goal.

Goals: F̶; S̶ ̶·̶ ̶T̶; S̶; T̶; K̶ ̶\lor̶ ̶R̶; K̶

Since '$K \lor R$' can be derived when K is obtained, '$K \lor R$' has been crossed off. K is a conjunct on line 3 of the problem, so we can use simplification to obtain it. K can therefore be crossed off our goals list. All of our goals have been crossed off. We have discovered a solution!

Our inferential forms will enable us to construct a formal proof for a problem that has been solved by using the goals approach. When we read our crossed-off goals *from right to left*, each crossed-off goal becomes a line in the completed formal proof.

Our completed goals approach for the example indicates that we derive '$K \lor R$' from K by using addition. We can derive T from line 3 by using simplification. We can derive S from '$K \lor R$' and line 1 of the problem by using modus ponens. We can derive '$S \cdot T$' from S and T by using conjunction. We can derive the argument's conclusion, F, from '$S \cdot T$' and line 2 of the problem by using modus ponens. Completed!

E. Summary of Valid Inferential Forms

Each of our valid inferential forms can be referred to by its abbreviation within a formal proof. Instead of writing out "modus ponens," for example, we will merely write "M.P."

MODUS PONENS (M.P.)	SIMPLIFICATION (SIMP.)

$$p \supset q$$
$$p$$
$$\therefore q$$

$$\underline{p \cdot q} \qquad \underline{p \cdot q}$$
$$\therefore p \qquad \therefore q$$

CONJUNCTION (CONJ.)	ADDITION (ADD.)

$$p$$
$$\underline{q}$$
$$\therefore p \cdot q$$

$$\underline{p}$$
$$\therefore p \vee q$$

i. Using Valid Inferential Forms in Formal Proofs

a. Modus Ponens ·Used to produce the consequent of a conditional. Both the conditional and its antecedent must be separate lines to use modus ponens.

b. Simplification Used to produce a conjunct. The conjunction must be a line (with the dot as the major connective) to use simplification.

c. Conjunction Used to produce a conjunction. Each conjunct must be a line to use conjunction.

d. Addition Used to produce a disjunction. The first disjunct must be a line to use addition. Any disjunct can be added.

Exercises IV

Each of the following is a completed formal proof for the indicated argument. Indicate the inferential form, and the lines used, for each derived line. In each case, try to view the inferential form in terms of its formal proof effects. Look at this set of exercises as a means to help you with the next set. Your goal should be to construct formal proofs yourself!

*1. 1. $(B \vee V) \supset C$ $\diagup C$
    2. B
    3. $B \vee V$
    4. C

2. 1. A $\diagup C$
    2. B
    3. $(A \cdot B) \supset C$
    4. $A \cdot B$
    5. C

*3.   *1.* $\sim V \cdot D$ $\diagup \sim V \lor D$ 4. *1.* $(B \lor V) \supset (D \cdot C)$ $\diagup C$
     2. $\sim V$ *2.* B
     3. $\sim V \lor D$ *3.* $B \lor V$
                                          4. $D \cdot C$
                                          5. C

*5.   *1.* $A \supset B$ $\diagup D$ 6. *1.* $B \cdot V$ $\diagup W$
     2. $(B \lor C) \supset D$ *2.* $[(V \lor C) \cdot D] \supset (T \supset W)$
     3. A *3.* $T \cdot D$
     4. B *4.* V
     5. $B \lor C$ *5.* $V \lor C$
     6. D *6.* D
                                          7. $(V \lor C) \cdot D$
                                          8. $T \supset W$
                                          9. T
                                         10. W

*7.   *1.* $B \supset V$ $\diagup T$
     2. $B \supset (D \cdot C)$
     3. $[V \cdot (D \cdot C)] \supset (R \cdot T)$
     4. B
     5. V
     6. $D \cdot C$
     7. $V \cdot (D \cdot C)$
     8. $R \cdot T$
     9. T

Progress in constructing formal proofs can be broken down into two steps. First, a person has to see that she is the one who is deriving the lines in a formal proof. The second step is to develop skill in solving them. This is accomplished with practice.

Understanding formal proofs that someone else has constructed is not the same as being able to construct them. It is possible to acknowledge correct answers without being able to produce them! Try diligently to avoid looking at an answer in the appendix. Compare the problem to previous problems and use the goals approach first. Look at the solution only if you are absolutely stuck.

Exercises V

Construct a formal proof for each of the following arguments. All of them can be completed by adding only two lines.

*1. T
     $(T \lor W) \supset A$
     $\therefore A$

2. U
    P
    $\therefore (U \lor D) \cdot P$

*3. H
     S
     $\therefore (H \cdot S) \lor I$

4. $I \cdot F$
    $I \supset H$
    $\therefore H$

*5. $D \cdot P$
     $\therefore D \lor T$

6. $(A \cdot D) \supset F$
    $A \cdot D$
    N
    $\therefore F \cdot N$

*7. $R \supset V$
     R
     $\therefore V \lor L$

8. O
    S
    $(O \cdot S) \supset D$
    $\therefore D$

*9. $A \cdot U$
     P
     $\therefore A \cdot P$

10. $C \supset (O \cdot L)$
     C
     $\therefore O$

*11. $M \cdot T$
      $\therefore M \lor E$

12. $A \cdot N$
     $M \cdot S$
     $[(A \cdot N) \cdot (M \cdot S)] \supset C$
     $\therefore C$

*13. $B \supset E$
      $[(B \supset E) \lor (P \cdot H)] \supset M$
      $\therefore M$

14. J
     $\sim P$
     $\therefore (\sim P \lor \sim S) \cdot J$

*15. $F \lor T$
      $(F \lor T) \supset [(L \supset I) \cdot (R \lor E)]$
      $\therefore R \lor E$

Exercises VI

Construct a formal proof for each of the following arguments. If you become stuck, compare the problem to other problems and try the goals approach. Following these exercises, there is a set of recipes for the first eight problems. If you find yourself unable to begin a problem, try to apply the recipe given for it. Carry out the indicated steps. Using a recipe is not the same as doing all of the problem yourself, but it will help you see the effects of the inferential forms far more than looking at the completed answers.

You should check the answers in the appendix only as a last resort.

*1. $(S \cdot T) \supset C$
   S
   $\underline{T }$
   $\therefore C$

3. $S \cdot T$
   $\underline{(T \vee W) \supset C}$
   $\therefore C$

*5. U
   $U \supset (A \cdot E)$
   $(A \cdot R) \supset T$
   $\underline{R }$
   $\therefore T$

7. $(E \cdot U) \cdot \sim D$
   $\underline{(E \cdot \sim D) \supset R}$
   $\therefore R$

*9. $(A \vee F) \supset [(B \vee T) \supset R]$
   A
   $\underline{B }$
   $\therefore R$

11. T
    W
    $(T \cdot W) \supset R$
    B
    V
    $\underline{(B \cdot V) \supset D}$
    $\therefore D \cdot R$

*13. A
    $A \supset (V \supset R)$
    $(R \vee T) \supset (C \cdot D)$
    $\underline{V }$
    $\therefore C$

15. $(B \supset V) \cdot (D \supset C)$
    $(B \supset V) \supset \sim(R \vee S)$
    $\underline{[\sim(R \vee S) \vee (\sim R \cdot \sim S)] \supset U}$
    $\therefore U$

16. $\sim(A \cdot V)$
    $\sim(A \cdot V) \supset [T \supset (U \cdot \sim R)]$
    $[U \vee (\sim V \supset W)] \supset (\sim W \cdot \sim R)$
    $\underline{T }$
    $\therefore \sim W$

2. $(S \vee T) \supset (C \cdot D)$
   $\underline{S }$
   $\therefore C$

4. $A \supset B$
   $(B \vee C) \supset \sim T$
   $\underline{A }$
   $\therefore \sim T$

6. $J \cdot D$
   $\underline{(D \vee C) \supset T}$
   $\therefore T \vee S$

8. $F \supset (A \supset \sim E)$
   $\underline{F \cdot A }$
   $\therefore \sim E$

10. $I \cdot W$
    $I \supset (T \cdot V)$
    $\underline{(W \cdot T) \supset R}$
    $\therefore R$

12. $\sim O \supset \sim B$
    $\sim I \supset \sim C$
    $\underline{\sim O \cdot \sim I}$
    $\therefore \sim B \cdot \sim C$

14. $\sim I \cdot (R \supset G)$
    $(R \cdot G) \supset D$
    $\underline{R }$
    $\therefore G \cdot D$

*17. $\sim(M \supset T)$
      $[(\sim M \supset T) \cdot (S \vee F)] \supset (E \supset N)$
      $U \supset (S \cdot E)$
      $\underline{U}$
      $\therefore N$

18. $\sim(E \cdot H) \supset (D \cdot F)$
     $(A \cdot \sim O) \supset (W \cdot B)$
     $[(D \cdot F) \vee U] \supset A$
     $\sim(E \cdot H)$
     $\underline{[(D \cdot F) \vee U] \supset \sim O}$
     $\therefore B$

19. $(U \cdot A) \supset (H \cdot C)$
     $(Q \vee S) \supset U$
     $(Q \vee T) \supset A$
     $\underline{Q}$
     $\therefore H \vee C$

20. $[(A \cdot B) \supset (R \cdot N)] \cdot [(D \vee C) \supset T]$
     $\underline{(A \cdot B) \cdot D}$
     $\therefore R \cdot T$

Recipes for the first eight problems of Exercises VI:

1. Conjoin lines 2 and 3 to produce line 4. Use modus ponens with lines 1 and 4 to produce line 5.

2. Add T to line 2 to produce line 3. Use modus ponens on lines 1 and 3 to produce line 4.

3. Use simplification on line 1 to produce line 3. Add W to line 3 to produce line 4. Use modus ponens on lines 2 and 4 to produce line 5.

4. Use modus ponens on lines 1 and 3 to produce line 4. Add C to line 4 to produce line 5. Use modus ponens on lines 2 and 5 to produce line 6.

5. Use modus ponens on lines 1 and 2 to produce line 5. Use simplification on line 5 to produce line 6. Conjoin lines 6 and 4 to produce line 7. Use modus ponens on lines 3 and 7 to produce line 8.

6. Use simplification on line 1 to produce line 3. Add C to line 3 to produce line 4. Use modus ponens on lines 2 and 4 to produce line 5. Add S to line 5 to produce line 6.

7. Use simplification on line 1 to produce line 3. Use simplification on line 1 to produce line 4. Conjoin lines 3 and 5 to produce line 6. Use modus ponens on lines 2 and 6 to produce line 7.

8. Use simplification on line 2 to produce line 3. Use modus ponens on lines 1 and 3 to produce line 4. Use simplification on line 2 to produce line 5. Use modus ponens on lines 4 and 5 to produce line 6.

Concept Reviews

1. Briefly explain what it means to claim that an inferential form preserves truth.

2. Does a formal proof for a given argument show that it is sound? Why or why not?

3. You may have thought it strange that the last set of exercises lacks problems that require a symbolization from the English. When an argument is symbolized, there is the danger that it might be incorrectly symbolized, which could result in writing down an invalid argument. Given that our formal proofs show that an argument is valid, what would happen if you were to try a formal proof on an invalid argument? Explain the basis for your answer.

4. Explain why some formal proofs cannot be done by labeling an argument's premises with statement variables from our inferential forms.

5. Suppose that you are applying the goals approach on a given problem. Suppose as well that you have '$(A \cdot B) \supset C$' as a usable line and you have C as one of your goals. Under these conditions, what new goals should you list?

6. Suppose that one of your goals when using the goals approach is '$(A \lor B) \cdot C$'. Under these conditions, what new goals should you list?

7. The goals approach has us look at the major connective of a line that contains a goal statement. Why, given how our valid inferential forms derive lines, should we be more concerned with the major connective of a line that contains a goal statement than with other connectives that might appear in the same line?

8. Our goals approach also has us look closely at the major connective of a goal when the goal is a compound statement. Why, given how our valid inferential forms derive lines, is the major connective of a line to be derived more important than other connectives that might appear in the same line?

VI Conditional-Proof Procedure

A. Intuitive Support

Our valid inferential forms will account for much, but certainly not all, of our standard valid reasoning. Often, they are combined with conditional proof.

We tend to use conditional proofs when we ask someone to agree with us "for the sake of argument," or when we are attempting to make a decision about something in the future.

Suppose that someone is considering taking a trip to Jamaica over the winter break. Not being sure what they are going to do, they might find themselves daydreaming about warm beaches and scenery. The conclusion of their thoughts will be a conditional. *If* they go to Jamaica, *then* they will experience warm beaches and see scenery. Having this conditional in mind might provide a good reason for them to go. Forming a conditional about the expenses and the time involved may give good reasons for them not to go.

Suppose that we outline the pro-Jamaica reasoning as follows:

Premiss: *If I go to Jamaica, then I'll experience warm beaches.*
Premiss: *If I go to Jamaica, then I'll see scenery.*
Hence: *If I go to Jamaica, then I'll experience warm beaches and see scenery.*

We can symbolize this argument, and prepare for a formal proof, as follows:

1. $G \supset B$ $/G \supset (B \cdot S)$
2. $G \supset S$

Although the above argument is valid, we cannot at present construct a formal proof. The argument's conclusion is a conditional, and we do not have a way to derive conditionals. Conditional-proof procedure will enable us to derive conditionals.

We can informally outline the reasoning behind the pro-Jamaica argument as follows.

1. The person made an assumption and treated it as true, in their imagination. [They imagined that they were in Jamaica.]
2. They drew conclusions that were based on their assumption. [They saw themselves experiencing warm beaches. They saw themselves looking at scenery.]
3. They ended their reasoning with a conditional. The statement that was assumed became the antecedent, and the conclusion that was

derived on the basis of it became the consequent. [*If* I go to Jamaica, *then* I'll experience warm beaches and see scenery.]

B. Use in Formal Proofs

Step 1   Any statement, simple or compound, may be written on any line in a formal proof. The line should be indented, and justified as a 'conditional-proof assumption' (C.P.A.). To indicate that a conditional proof is in progress, additional lines of the conditional proof should be equally indented.

Step 2   The formal proof is now continued. The conditional-proof assumption may be used as any other line.

Step 3   When the proof has been completed to the desired subconclusion, the conditional proof is ended. To do this, form a box containing the conditional proof assumption and the desired subconclusion; that is, box off the conditional proof.

Step 4   The next line must be a conditional, such that the conditional-proof assumption is its antecedent and the subconclusion that ended the conditional proof is its consequent. This line is justified by "conditional proof" (C.P.). Indicate the lines that are contained within the box.

We can now provide the following formal proof for the Jamaica argument.

1. $G \supset B$ $\diagup G \supset (B \cdot S)$
2. $G \supset S$

3. G C.P.A.
4. B M.P. 1, 3
5. S M.P. 2, 3
6. $B \cdot S$ Conj. 4, 5

7. $G \supset (B \cdot S)$ C.P. 3–6

C. Restrictions

First, every conditional proof must be ended as in step 4 of our "Use in Conditional Proofs." In the Jamaica example, it would have been incorrect for the person to conclude that they are presently experiencing warm beaches and seeing scenery. "Experiencing warm beaches and seeing scenery" was based on the assumption that the person was in Jamaica. Conclusions within a conditional proof are justified *only* on the basis of the assumption.

The assumption must be specified as the antecedent of the conditional that ends the conditional proof.

Second, once a conditional proof has been ended, no following lines can be derived from those within the conditional proof. All of the lines within the box are ruled out from any use in additional derivations. The conditional derived by conditional proof can be used in additional derivations, however. Again, the lines within the box were validly derived only on the basis of the assumption. Lines 3–6 in the formal proof of the Jamaica argument cannot be used to derive later lines.

Third, it is possible for a formal proof to contain multiple conditional proofs. Conditional proofs can follow one another and can be entirely contained within one another. Conditional proofs cannot partially overlap, however. Using the box procedure, one conditional-proof box can follow another conditional-proof box. One conditional-proof box may be entirely contained within another conditional-proof box. But the boxes cannot partially overlap one another.

D. Conditional-Proof Strategies

We should use conditional proof whenever we desire to derive a conditional. Begin the conditional proof by making a conditional-proof assumption that is the antecedent of the desired conditional. Use our inferential forms to derive a line that is the same as its consequent. Ending the conditional proof will derive the desired conditional.

Our goals approach to formal proof can be amended to include conditional proof.

i. The Goals Approach

List the conclusion of the argument as a goal (G), and begin looking for it and subgoals in available lines as follows.

If G is within a compound statement, look at the major connective of the line that has G, and

1. If the major connective is a horseshoe and G is somewhere in the consequent, list the antecedent as a new goal. Once we have the antecedent, we will be able to apply modus ponens and get the consequent.
2. If the major connective is a dot, take a simplification step. Write down the conjunct that contains G.

If G is a compound statement, note its major connective. We can create conjunctions, disjunctions, and conditionals.

3. If *G*'s major connective is a dot, list each conjunct as a new goal. Once we have each conjunct, we will be able to get the conjunction by using conjunction.

4. If *G*'s major connective is a wedge, list the first disjunct as a new goal. We will be able to use addition to create the wedge once we have the first disjunct.

5. If *G*'s major connective is the horseshoe, begin a conditional proof. The conditional-proof assumption should be the antecedent of the desired conditional. List the consequent of the desired conditional as a new goal. Since the conditional can be derived when its consequent is derived, the conditional can be crossed off the goals list.

Write goals, and apply steps 1–5 above to each of them. Keep a current list of goals, and continue applying steps 1–5. Cross off obtained goals. Cross off any goals that can be derived when the listed goals are obtained. We have a solution for a given problem when all of our goals have been crossed off.

Take steps to construct the formal proof whenever possible.

We will use an example from John Steinbeck's *Grapes of Wrath* to point out how the goals approach is applied when a conditional is to be derived.

Steinbeck's novel portrays a wretched journey from Oklahoma to California. The main characters are the Joad family. Their journey moves from poverty to abject poverty, from misery to terror. Before they decide to leave, however, they think of California with the following images:

> But I like to think how nice it's gonna be, maybe, in California. Never cold. An' fruit ever'place, an' people just bein' in the nicest places, little white houses in among the orange trees. I wonder— that is, if we all get jobs an' all work—maybe we can get one of them little white houses. An' the little folks go out an' pick oranges right off the tree. They ain't gonna be able to stand it, they'll get to yellin' so.[7]

For a version that is easier to symbolize, though less eloquent:

If we go to California, then we'll never be cold. If we go to California, there will be fruit everywhere and jobs for all. If there are jobs for all, then we can get one of the white houses. If we're never cold and there's fruit everywhere and we can get one of the white houses, then it's going to be nice. Hence, if we go to California, then it's going to be nice.

---

[7]John Steinbeck, *The Grapes of Wrath* (New York: Viking Press, 1958; first published 1939), 124.

Symbolically we have:

1. $G \supset C$ $\diagup G \supset N$
2. $G \supset (F \cdot J)$
3. $J \supset H$
4. $[C \cdot (F \cdot H)] \supset N$

As in the previous section, we will begin by listing the conclusion of the argument as a goal.

Goals: $G \supset N$

Since our goal is a conditional, we will apply step 5 of the goals approach. We will indent and begin a conditional proof that has G, our desired antecedent, as its conditional-proof assumption. We will list the desired consequent, N, as a new goal.

1. $G \supset C$ $\diagup G \supset N$
2. $G \supset (F \cdot J)$
3. $J \supset H$
4. $[C \cdot (F \cdot H)] \supset N$
    5. G C.P.A.

Goals: $\cancel{G \supset N}$; N

Our present goal, N, is the consequent of line 4. Step 1 has us list the antecedent of line 4 as a new goal.

Goals: $\cancel{G \supset N}$; $\cancel{N}$; $C \cdot (F \cdot H)$

The dot is our new goal's major connective. Step 3 has us list each of its conjuncts as a goal.

Goals: $\cancel{G \supset N}$; $\cancel{N}$; $\cancel{C \cdot (F \cdot H)}$; C; $F \cdot H$

C is line 1's consequent. Since we have line 1's antecedent as a usable line (line 5), we know that we can derive C by using modus ponens. C can be crossed off our goals list. '$F \cdot H$' is a conjunction, and step 3 of our goals approach has us list each conjunct as a new goal.

Goals: $\cancel{G \supset N}$; $\cancel{N}$; $\cancel{C \cdot (F \cdot H)}$; $\cancel{C}$; $\cancel{F \cdot H}$; F; H

H is line 3's consequent, and so we should list line 3's antecedent, J, as a new goal.

Goals: $\cancel{G \supset N}$; $\cancel{N}$; $\cancel{C \cdot (F \cdot H)}$; $\cancel{C}$; $\cancel{F \cdot H}$; $\cancel{F}$; $\cancel{H}$; J

F is contained in line 2's consequent. We can derive '$F \cdot J$' by using modus ponens on lines 2 and 5. Step 2 of the goals approach has us derive F and

J from '*F · J*' by using two simplification steps. Since all of our goals have been crossed off, we have a solution.

1. G ⊃ C   ∕*G ⊃ N*
2. G ⊃ (F · J)
3. J ⊃ H
4. [C · (F · H)] ⊃ N

> *5. G C.P.A.*
> *6. F · J M.P. 2, 5*
> *7. J Simp. 6*
> *8. H M.P. 3, 7*
> *9. F Simp. 6*
> *10. F · H Conj. 9, 8*
> *11. C M.P. 1, 5*
> *12. C · (F · H) Conj. 11, 10*
> *13. N M.P. 4, 12*

14. G ⊃ N C.P. 5–13

The following examples point out some basic patterns for using conditional proof. They also point out a few of our conditional-proof restrictions.

Example 1 follows the same basic pattern as the two formal proofs that we have already seen. Notice that in example 1, both the antecedent and consequent statements of the desired conditional are compound statements. This does not present a problem, however, since a conditional-proof assumption can be any statement whatsoever. We can make our assumption the conditional's antecedent, derive its consequent, and let conditional proof derive the horseshoe.

EXAMPLE 1
1. (U ∨ W) ⊃ S   ∕*(U · R) ⊃ (S · T)*
2. T

> *3. U · R C.P.A.*
> *4. U Simp. 3*
> *5. U ∨ W Add. 4*
> *6. S M.P. 1, 5*
> *7. S · T Conj. 6, 2*

8. (U · R) ⊃ (S · T) C.P. 3–7

Example 2 has two conditional proofs, one entirely following the other. Notice that the boxes in this example do not overlap. This pattern is usually used when a formal proof requires us to establish two separate conditionals.

EXAMPLE 2

1. $O \supset A$ $\angle (O \supset \sim H) \cdot (I \supset \sim H)$
2. $A \supset \sim H$
3. $I \supset U$
4. $U \supset \sim H$

> 5. O C.P.A.
> 6. A M.P. 1, 5
> 7. $\sim H$ M.P. 2, 6

8. $O \supset \sim H$ C.P. 5–7

> 9. I C.P.A.
> 10. U M.P. 3,9
> 11. $\sim H$ M.P. 4,10

12. $I \supset \sim H$ C.P. 9–11
13. $(O \supset \sim H) \cdot (I \supset \sim H)$ *Conj.* 12, 8

Notice that lines 5–7 are boxed off. Since they are boxed off, they cannot be used to derive additional lines. Line 8, which is outside the box, *can* be used to derive additional lines.

Example 3 has one conditional proof entirely contained within another. Notice that the boxes do not overlap. This pattern is typically used when the conclusion of an argument contains two conditionals such that the horseshoe is the major connective, and its consequent is another conditional.

EXAMPLE 3

1. $(O \lor W) \supset [(U \lor A) \supset \sim H]$ $\angle O \supset [(U \cdot A) \supset \sim H]$

> 2. O C.P.A.
> 3. $O \lor W$ Add. 2
> 4. $(U \lor A) \supset \sim H$ M.P. 1, 3
>
> > 5. $U \cdot A$ C.P.A.
> > 6. U Simp 5
> > 7. $U \lor A$ Add. 6
> > 8. $\sim H$ M.P. 4,7
>
> 9. $(U \cdot A) \supset \sim H$ C.P. 5–8

10. $O \supset [(U \cdot A) \supset \sim H]$ C.P. 2–9

A conditional proof for a statement of the form '$p \supset (q \supset r)$' is started by making a conditional proof assumption that is an instance of p. Next, we should make a conditional-proof assumption that is an instance of q. The conditional proofs should be ended when an instance of r has been derived. To prove '$p \supset (q \supset r)$':

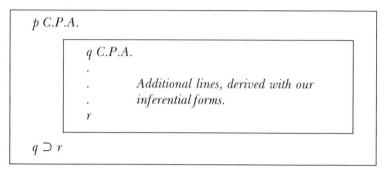

$p \supset (q \supset r)$

Example 4 indicates an *incorrect* use of conditional proofs. Our third restriction requires that conditional proofs do not overlap one another. Notice how the boxes incorrectly overlap, and how the conditional proofs are partially contained in one another.

EXAMPLE 4: *An incorrect application of conditional proof*

1. $O \supset A$ / $I \supset [(O \supset \sim H) \cdot A]$
2. $A \supset \sim H$

3. O C.P.A.	*This line is acceptable.*
4. I C.P.A	*This line is acceptable too.*
5. A M.P. 1, 3	
6. $\sim H$ M.P. 2, 5	
7. $O \supset \sim H$ C.P. 3–6	
8. $(O \supset \sim H) \cdot A$ Conj. 5, 7	*Incorrect c.p. ending*

9. $I \supset [(O \supset \sim H) \cdot A]$ C.P. 4–8   *Incorrect line*

All of the lines prior to line 8 are acceptable. Even so, taking line 7 prevents us from properly ending both conditional proofs. The only way to avoid overlapping boxes with simultaneous conditional proofs is to end them in the opposite order from that in which they were started. Conditional proofs that are started later must be ended earlier.

Whenever a conditional proof is used, a conditional *must* be derived. Hence, there is no point in using a conditional proof unless we desire to derive a conditional. At present, conditional proofs are the only way that we have to derive conditionals.

E. Justification of Conditional Proof

Our opening examples in section VI. A show that conditional proof is a frequently used reasoning process. To formally justify conditional proof, however, we must justify a procedure, rather than a single valid argument form. A formal justification of conditional proof is provided in Appendix B.

VII Summary

A. Valid Inferential Forms

MODUS PONENS (M.P.)

$p \supset q$
p
$\therefore q$

SIMPLIFICATION (SIMP.)

$\dfrac{p \cdot q}{\therefore p}$ $\dfrac{p \cdot q}{\therefore q}$

CONJUNCTION (CONJ.)

p
q
$\therefore p \cdot q$

ADDITION (ADD.)

$\dfrac{p}{\therefore p \vee q}$

i. Using Valid Inferential Forms in Formal Proofs

a. Modus Ponens   Used to produce the consequent of a conditional. Both the conditional and its antecedent must be separate lines to use modus ponens.

b. Simplification   Used to produce a conjunct. The conjunction must be a line (with the dot as the major connective) to use simplification.

c. Conjunction   Used to produce a conjunction. Each conjunct must be a line to use conjunction.

d. Addition   Used to produce a disjunction. The first disjunct must be a line to use addition. Any disjunct can be added.

B. Conditional-Proof Procedure

$k.$ p C.P.A.

.

.

$m.$ q

$m + 1.$ $p \supset q$ C.P. k–m

k and m indicate lines appearing within a formal proof. p may be any statement whatsoever. q indicates a statement derived on the basis of previous lines.

Once a conditional proof has been ended, no following lines can be derived from those within the conditional proof. In the case of multiple conditional proofs, one conditional proof cannot partially overlap another. (See earlier pages for a more complete explanation.)

C. The Goals Approach to Formal Proofs

List the conclusion of the argument as a goal (G), and begin looking for it and subgoals in available lines as follows:

If G is within a compound statement, look at the major connective of the line that has G, and

1. If the major connective is a horseshoe and G is somewhere in the consequent, list the antecedent as a 'new' goal (G). Once we have the antecedent, we will be able to apply modus ponens and get the consequent.

2. If the major connective is a dot, take a simplification step. Write down the conjunct that contains G.

If G is a compound statement, note its major connective. We can create conjunctions, disjunctions, and conditionals.

3. If G's major connective is a dot, list each conjunct as a new goal. Once we have each conjunct, we will be able to get the conjunction by using conjunction.

4. If G's major connective is a wedge, list the first disjunct as a new goal. We will be able to use addition to create the wedge once we have the first disjunct.

5. If G's major connective is the horseshoe, begin a conditional proof. The conditional-proof assumption should be the antecedent of the

desired conditional. List the consequent of the desired conditional as a new goal. Since the conditional can be derived when its consequent is derived, the conditional can be crossed off the goals list.

Write goals, and apply steps 1–5 above to each of them. Keep a current list of goals, and continue applying steps 1–5. Cross off obtained goals. Cross off any goals that can be derived when the listed goals are obtained. We have a solution for a given problem when all of our goals have been crossed off.

Take steps to construct the formal proof whenever possible.

Exercises VII

Construct a formal proof for each of the following arguments. In each case, use our conditional proof procedure to establish the required conditionals.

*1. $B \supset V$
$V \supset R$
∴ $B \supset R$

2. $A \supset G$
∴ $(A \cdot W) \supset G$

3. $W \supset P$
$(P \lor R) \supset T$
∴ $W \supset T$

4. $A \supset (V \supset S)$
$A \supset V$
∴ $A \supset S$

*5. $(B \cdot D) \supset (C \cdot R)$
D
∴ $B \supset R$

6. $(B \supset V) \cdot (D \supset C)$
$V \supset R$
∴ $(B \cdot D) \supset (R \cdot C)$

7. $A \supset (V \cdot R)$
$B \supset (D \cdot S)$
∴ $(A \supset R) \cdot (B \supset S)$

8. $(K \cdot V) \supset (B \cdot C)$
$V \cdot (B \supset {\sim}O)$
∴ $K \supset {\sim}O$

*9. $(K \supset P) \supset T$
$K \supset (P \cdot D)$
∴ T

10. ${\sim}B \supset (V \supset {\sim}R)$
$V \cdot K$
$(S \lor N) \supset T$
∴ $({\sim}B \supset {\sim}R) \cdot [S \supset (K \cdot T)]$

11. $T \supset W$
$B \supset (V \cdot S)$
∴ $T \supset [B \supset (W \cdot V)]$

12. $[({\sim}M \supset T) \cdot F] \supset (E \supset N)$
$S \supset F$
S
∴ $[{\sim}(M \supset T) \cdot E] \supset N$

*13. $(B \lor K) \supset [(V \lor R) \supset C]$
$(C \lor A) \supset S$
∴ $B \supset (V \supset S)$

14. ${\sim}E \supset (Q \cdot S)$
$[(Q \cdot S) \cdot U] \supset {\sim}O$
$({\sim}E \cdot R) \supset (U \cdot V)$
∴ $({\sim}E \cdot R) \supset {\sim}O$

15. $[(M \supset T) \cdot (C \supset {\sim}U)] \supset B$
    $(M \lor R) \supset (A \cdot O)$
    $A \supset T$
    $(C \cdot V) \supset {\sim}U$
    $\underline{V}$
    $\therefore B$

Exercises VIII

Construct a formal proof for each of the following arguments. Any of our inferential forms may be required. The conditional-proof procedure should be used as needed.

*1. $C \supset (S \cdot M)$
   $\underline{C}$
   $\therefore M$

2. $\underline{C \supset (S \cdot M)}$
  $\therefore C \supset M$

3. $O \supset T$
   $T \supset F$
   $\underline{(O \supset F) \supset R}$
   $\therefore R$

4. $E \supset (T \supset M)$
   $\underline{T \supset (M \supset S)}$
   $\therefore E \supset (T \supset S)$

*5. $(H \cdot I) \cdot (A \cdot P)$
   $(I \supset W) \cdot (H \supset R)$
   $\underline{(A \supset E) \cdot (P \supset M)}$
   $\therefore (W \cdot R) \cdot (E \cdot M)$

6. $R \supset I$
   $\underline{N \supset Y}$
   $\therefore (R \cdot N) \supset (I \cdot Y)$

7. $O \cdot (F \cdot R)$
   $[(R \lor P) \supset D] \cdot [(F \lor P) \supset N]$
   $\underline{(D \cdot N) \supset T}$
   $\therefore T$

8. $(D \lor M) \supset (R \cdot T)$
   $\underline{(T \lor B) \supset F}$
   $\therefore D \supset F$

*9. $J \cdot D$
   $(D \lor C) \supset T$
   $\underline{(R \cdot T) \supset M}$
   $\therefore R \supset M$

10. $B \supset (V \cdot H)$
   $\underline{(H \cdot S) \supset W}$
   $\therefore (E \cdot B) \supset [S \supset (W \lor T)]$

11. $(R \lor W) \supset (S \cdot T)$
   $\underline{(R \lor V) \supset (E \cdot L)}$
   $\therefore R \supset (S \cdot E)$

12. $M \supset B$
   $W \supset (C \cdot H)$
   $B \supset T$
   $H \supset {\sim}O$
   $\underline{(R \cdot W) \supset M}$
   $\therefore R \supset [W \supset ({\sim}O \cdot T)]$

*13. $S \supset (R \supset V)$
   $\underline{V \supset (T \cdot W)}$
   $\therefore (S \cdot R) \supset (T \lor W)$

14. $M \supset (O \cdot C)$
   $T \cdot {\sim}E$
   $\underline{(H \cdot {\sim}E) \supset B}$
   $\therefore (M \supset O) \cdot (H \supset B)$

15. $S \supset (N \cdot P)$
$(N \lor B) \supset A$
$(A \supset T) \cdot F$
$\underline{[(S \supset A) \cdot F] \supset O}$
$\therefore S \supset O$

Concept Reviews

1. Suppose that you begin a formal proof by making a conditional-proof assumption. After making the C.P.A., but without ending the conditional proof, you find that you have derived the conclusion of the initial argument. Why would it be wrong to think that you have demonstrated the validity of the initial argument?

2. Why, when using multiple conditional proofs to derive a statement with two conditionals, should the conditional proof for the major (horseshoe) connective be started first?

3. Suppose that you wish to derive '$A \supset [B \supset (C \supset D)]$'. What conditional-proof assumptions will be required? What statement should you derive before you begin to close off the boxes and derive the conditionals?

5 Formal Proofs: Equivalence Inferential Forms

This chapter adds equivalence inferential forms to the valid inferential forms that were developed in Chapter 4. First, an additional connective is presented, the triple bar.

KEY TERMS FOR THIS CHAPTER

Use the glossary as necessary, and review the definitions of these terms prior to a second reading of this section.

Material equivalence   **Logical equivalence**

I   The Biconditional

A. Symbolization

You should stay in the kitchen if and only if you can stand the heat.[1]
An early diagnosis is a necessary and sufficient condition for Ayurveda to be able to cure cancer.[2]

Chapter 2 provided an adequate basis for translating the above sentences. First, we can use the non-italicized letters for our statement constants.

---

[1]The original slogan, "If you can't stand the heat, get out of the kitchen," was made popular by President Harry Truman. Truman had little patience with people who accepted jobs but were unwilling also to accept the pressure involved.

[2]'Ayurveda' refers to the medicinal treatments concocted by the ayurvedic physicians of India. Ayurvedic physicians believe that body "humors" cause all of our bodily ills. Their arsenal of cures includes about 700 herbs and vegetables. Sometimes they prescribe metals. Other times they prescribe animal bile.

S if and only if H.

D is a necessary and sufficient condition for C.

'If' indicates an antecedent. Hence, '*S if H*' can be expressed as:

$H \supset S$

'Only if' indicates a consequent. Hence, '*S only if H*' can be expressed as:

$S \supset H$

'And' can be expressed with the dot. Putting all of this together, we have the following translation:

$$(H \supset S) \quad \cdot \quad (S \quad \supset \quad H)$$
$$\quad if \quad\quad and \quad\quad only\ if$$

The statement about Ayurvedic physicians can be similarly unpacked. A necessary condition is expressed as the consequent statement. A sufficient condition is expressed as the antecedent statement. 'And' in 'necessary and sufficient' can be rendered with the dot. Hence, the statement about Ayurvedic physicians can be expressed as:

$$(C \quad \supset \quad D) \quad \cdot \quad (D \quad \supset \quad C)$$
$$\quad necessary \quad\quad and \quad\quad sufficient$$

The two statements that we have looked at in this section are called "biconditionals." 'Bi-' is a prefix that means "two." Each of the examples for this section, as reflected in the translations, expresses two conditionals. Each of the simple statements is an antecedent of one conditional, and the consequent of the other conditional.

Biconditionals are common in English. In addition, they enable us to expand our deductive system. Since they are so significant and the above double-horseshoe pattern is clumsy, we will add a new symbol, '≡', called the "triple bar," to express them. The triple bar is a connective, just as the horseshoe, dot, and wedge are connectives. It is placed between the statement constants to express biconditionals.

'$p \equiv q$' abbreviates '$(q \supset p) \cdot (p \supset q)$'.

Our interpretation of Truman's slogan about heat in the kitchen can now be expressed as:

$S \equiv H$

Similarly, the example about Ayurveda can be expressed as:

$D \equiv C$

We can now add the triple bar to our previous translation summaries.

English	Artificial
p if and only if *q*	$p \equiv q$
p is a necessary and sufficient condition for *q*	$p \equiv q$

Exercises I

Symbolize each of the following with the artificial language. In each case, use the italicized letters to indicate the required statement constants. If necessary, review the translation summaries near the end of Chapter 2.

*1. Food is *f*attening if and only if it *t*astes good.

2. Most whites will *a*ccept integration if and only if it means that blacks adopt the white people's *c*ulture.

3. Blaming one's *t*ools is a necessary and sufficient condition for being a bad *w*orkman.

4. Water will *b*oil at room temperature if and only if the air *p*ressure is reduced.

*5. A necessary and sufficient condition for Alexander the Great to *r*ule all of Asia was *c*utting the Gordian knot.[3]

6. Waterskiing is *f*un if and only if the water is *c*alm and the air *t*emperature is over 70°.

7. If some rock groups *c*ontinue to endorse drug abuse, then we'll have a future *s*urge in addiction if and only if people don't develop *a*lternative values.

8. If Rover is not on a heartworm *p*reventative, then being *b*itten by an infected mosquito is a necessary and sufficient condition for Rover to get heartworm *d*isease.

*9. Necessary and sufficient conditions for realistically *s*pecifying the interest rate require taking *t*ax benefits and *i*nflation rates into account.

10. The United States is a country supposedly based on *l*aw; still, we can *f*lout United Nations positions and use *i*llegal bookeeping methods to exceed congressional limits, if and only if we ignore both the *W*orld Court and *C*ongress.

---

[3]Legend had it that whoever could untie the Gordian knot would rule all of Asia. Alexander the Great cut the knot with his sword, and went on to rule Asia. Doing a difficult task quickly is therefore referred to as "cutting the Gordian knot."

B. Truth-Values

Since '$p \equiv q$' is an abbreviation of '$(q \supset p) \cdot (p \supset q)$' and the horseshoe and the dot are truth-functional connectives, the triple bar must be a truth-functional connective. The horseshoe and dot have clearly defined truth-values as determined by their truth tables. '$p \equiv q$', being an abbreviation, must have the same truth-values as '$(q \supset p) \cdot (p \supset q)$'.

$(q \supset p)$	$\cdot$	$(p \supset q)$		p	$\equiv$	q
T T T	T	T T T		T	T	T
F T T	F	T F F		T	F	F
T F F	F	F T T		F	F	T
F T F	T	F T F		F	T	F

———————— same ————————

Written under the triple bar by definition.

The triple bar is true when both of the statements that it connects have the same truth-value. It is false when the statements that it connects have different truth-values.

DEFINITION 5.1

Two statements are *materially equivalent* if and only if they both have the same truth-value.

Notice that material equivalence does not refer to equivalence of content or to equivalence of meaning. Given that the following statements are both true, they are materially equivalent:

The assassination of Archduke Francis Ferdinand started World War I.
Alice Walker wrote The Color Purple.

There is no obvious subject-matter connection between the onset of World War I and the author of a novel that testifies to the stamina of oppressed black women. ***The mere fact that both statements are true, and hence have the same truth-value, makes them materially equivalent.*** Any two false statements will, of course, also be materially equivalent.

Exercises II

For each of the following expressions, assume that A, B, and C all indicate true statements, while X, Y, and Z all indicate false statements. Indicate the truth-value of each of the following.

*1. $X \equiv Y$ *5. $(A \cdot X) \equiv (C \cdot Z)$

 2. $A \equiv X$ 6. $(A \cdot B) \supset (\sim A \equiv \sim Z)$

 3. $A \equiv \sim Z$ 7. $(A \lor X) \equiv (Z \supset \sim C)$

 4. $\sim A \equiv X$ 8. $(C \cdot B) \equiv \sim (C \cdot B)$

II Logical Equivalence

Although any two true statements are equal in truth-value and any two false statements are equal in truth-value, not all statements are equal in truth-value for the same reasons. The statement about the onset of World War I and the statement about Alice Walker being the author of *The Color Purple* are both true owing to unrelated events in the world. Using our terminology from Chapter 3, the fact that they have the same truth-value is a **contingent truth.**

Material equivalence, by itself, is not very important from the standpoint of logic. A relationship that holds between **any** two true statements and **any** two false statements cannot give much information. Material equivalence, however, enables us to define logical equivalence. Logical equivalence *is* important.

DEFINITION 5.2

Two statements are *logically equivalent* if and only if they must have the same truth-value, owing to their respective forms.

Logical equivalence is based on the forms of the statements involved, just as being tautologous and contradictory depended on the forms involved. When we ask whether two statements are logically equivalent, we are not asking whether they are true. Instead, we are asking whether the two statements **must** have the same truth-value.

Two statements are logically equivalent if the assertion that they are materially equivalent is a tautology.

A biconditional is true when both sides have the same truth-value. When a biconditional is tautologous, both sides have the same truth-value *for each line of the truth table.* Since the truth table covers all of the possibilities for statements that might replace the variables, when a material equivalence is tautologous there is no possibility that the statements might have opposite truth-values.

Notice that it is the biconditional, the triple bar, that is necessarily true when two statements are logically equivalent, *not* the individual statements that are combined with the triple bar. '$p \supset q$' is a contingent statement form. '$\sim q \supset \sim p$' is a contingent statement form. They are logically equivalent, however, since the **biconditional** between them is tautologous.

$(p \supset q)$	$\equiv$	$(\sim q \supset \sim p)$
T T T	T	F T F
T F F	T	T F F
F T T	T	F T T
F T F	T	T T T

└──── same ────┘

It is necessarily true that an instance of '$p \supset q$' has the same truth-value as the corresponding instance of '$\sim q \supset \sim p$'.

Although some people would like to believe that an early diagnosis is sufficient for Ayurveda to be able to cure cancer, many cancer specialists deny it. '$D \supset C$' might be true or might be false. '$\sim C \supset \sim D$' has the *same* truth-value as '$D \supset C$'. If an early diagnosis is sufficient for Ayurveda to be able to cure cancer, then the statement that Ayurveda is unable to cure a cancer implies that the cancer was not diagnosed early enough.

A. Summary: Material and Logical Equivalence

Suppose that we use S to abbreviate 'the assassination of Archduke Francis Ferdinand *s*tarted World War I', and W to abbreviate 'Alice Walker *w*rote *The Color Purple*'. Given that both of these statements are true, '$S \equiv W$' indicates a true **material** equivalence.

S is not **logically** equivalent to W, however, since '$S \equiv W$' is not a tautology. In contrast, '$D \supset C$' is logically equivalent to '$\sim C \supset \sim D$', since '$(C \supset D) \equiv (\sim D \supset \sim C)$' is a tautology.

Two statements can be materially equivalent without being logically equivalent. If two statements are logically equivalent, however, they **must** be materially equivalent, since their forms guarantee that they have the same truth-value.

Of the two ideas in this section, logical equivalence is far more important than material equivalence. The triple bar indicates **material** equivalence. We need a way to indicate that two statements are not merely materially equivalent, but are logically equivalent.

We will use four dots, '::', to indicate logical equivalence.

Since '$p \supset q$' is logically equivalent to '$\sim q \supset \sim p$', we are justified in writing:

$(p \supset q) :: (\sim q \supset \sim p)$

Since '$p \equiv q$' is not a tautology and p is not logically equivalent to q, we are **not** justified in writing:

$p :: q$

When there is no danger of ambiguity, we will drop the outer parentheses (or brackets or braces) from logically equivalent forms when using our four-dot symbol to express them. Instead of writing '$(p \supset q) :: (\sim q \supset \sim p)$', we will merely write '$p \supset q :: \sim q \supset \sim p$'.

Exercises III

It has been some time since you have worked with truth tables. For the sake of review and to reinforce the truth-functional nature of the triple bar, construct truth tables and determine which, if any, of the following statement forms are tautologous. Place four dots between those forms that are logically equivalent.

*1. $\sim(p \cdot q) \equiv (\sim p \cdot \sim q)$

 2. $(p \supset q) \equiv (\sim p \lor q)$

 3. $\sim(p \lor q) \equiv (\sim p \lor \sim q)$

 4. $\sim(p \lor q) \equiv (\sim p \cdot \sim q)$

*5. $[p \lor (q \cdot r)] \equiv [(p \lor q) \cdot (p \lor r)]$

 6. $[p \lor (q \cdot r)] \equiv [(p \lor q) \cdot r]$

Concept Reviews

1. The pattern for biconditionals, developed from the English, was '$(q \supset p) \cdot (p \supset q)$'. Since our earlier convention was to use p first, q second, and so on, we might have expected '$(p \supset q) \cdot (q \supset p)$'.

Indicate why, given the initial definition of the dot, these two forms are equivalent.

2. Indicate why, using the definitions involved, two statements that are logically equivalent must be materially equivalent. How do these ideas relate to statements that are tautologous and true, as compared to those that are contingent and true?

3. Suppose that we have any two tautologous forms, such as '$p \lor \sim p$' and '$p \supset (q \supset p)$'. Are they logically equivalent to one another? Why or why not?

III Equivalence Inferential Forms

A. Initial Survey

Our formal proof system as developed in Chapter 4 is incomplete. There are valid arguments for which no formal proof is possible, using only the procedures of Chapter 4. At present, we are unable to provide a formal proof for the following valid argument.

Premiss: *Either D. H. Lawrence wrote L*ady Chatterley's Lover
                   or D. H. Lawrence wrote Women in Love.

Conclusion: *Either D. H. Lawrence wrote* Women in Love *or*
                   *D. H. Lawrence wrote L*ady Chatterley's Lover.

$\underline{L \lor W}$
$\therefore W \lor L$

None of our valid inferential forms will enable us to switch the order of the above disjuncts.

DEFINITION 5.3

A system of propositional logic is *deductively complete* for arguments if and only if it is capable of providing a formal proof for every valid propositional argument.

By making use of ideas that we have developed in this chapter, we will add inferences to our formal proof system so that the resulting system is deductively complete.[4] First, however, we should note some aspects of logically equivalent forms.

---

[4]The system of propositional logic is proved deductively complete in Chapter 9.

> **Any instances of logically equivalent forms must be logically equivalent statements.**

Logically equivalent forms must have the same truth-values on every line of their truth tables. Hence, they must have the same truth-values regardless of whether the variables stand for true or for false statements. Compound (including negated) statements are either true or false, just as simple statements are either true or false. Hence, instances of logically equivalent forms must have the same truth-value, regardless of whether the variables are replaced with simple or compound statements.

Suppose that we are trying to construct a formal proof for a given argument. Imagine that we can visualize one of our usable lines as an instance of a particular statement form, and that we are aware of a logically equivalent statement form. We can derive a statement that is logically equivalent to our usable statement, by writing the corresponding instance of the equivalent form. Since the usable statement and the one that we have just derived are logically equivalent, they both must have the same truth-value. We cannot proceed from truth to falsity, if the starting and ending truth-value is the same. Hence, deriving a logically equivalent statement must preserve truth.

> **Deriving a line that is logically equivalent to a previous line is an acceptable formal proof technique.**

Since logically equivalent statements are equivalent to each other, either statement can replace the other in a formal proof. The left side of a logical equivalence can replace the right, and the right side can replace the left.

The following statement form is tautologous.

$$\sim(p \cdot q) \equiv (\sim p \lor \sim q)$$

Hence, '$\sim(p \cdot q)$' is logically equivalent to '$\sim p \lor \sim q$'.

We will write '$\sim(p \cdot q) :: \sim p \lor \sim q$' to express the logical equivalence. The following formal proof uses this equivalence to derive line 4.

1. $\sim(R \cdot S) \supset V$ /V
2. $\sim R$
------
3. $\sim R \lor \sim S$ Add. 2
4. $\sim(R \cdot S)$ Logically equivalent to line 3
5. V M.P. 1, 4

We can see that line 4 is logically equivalent to line 3, since '$\sim R \lor \sim S$' is an instance of '$\sim p \lor \sim q$', and '$\sim(R \cdot S)$' is an instance of '$\sim(p \cdot q)$'.

$\sim(p \cdot q) :: \sim p \lor \sim q$
$\sim(R \cdot S) \quad (\sim R \lor \sim S)$
$\quad \textit{line 4} \qquad \textit{line 3}$

The inference from line 3 to line 4 should be acceptable within any formal proof.

Suppose, however, that the situation is a bit more complex. Instead of recognizing that a whole line is logically equivalent to a particular statement, suppose we know that ***part*** of a usable line is logically equivalent to another statement. The logically equivalent statement must have the same truth-value as the portion of our usable line. The truth-value of a compound statement is determined by the truth-values of its parts. If we do not change the truth-values of the parts, then we cannot change the truth-value of the compound. Hence, a statement that is derived by replacing part of a line with a statement that is logically equivalent to the part, must have the same truth-value as the initial statement.

> ***Replacing a portion of a line with a statement that is logically equivalent to that portion is an acceptable formal proof technique.***

The following example applies the above logical equivalence to a portion of a line. It also provides an alternative solution for the last problem.

1. $\sim(R \cdot S) \supset V \qquad \underline{/V}$
2. $\sim R$ _____
3. $(\sim R \lor \sim S) \supset V$ Logically equivalent to line 1
4. $\sim R \lor \sim S$ *Add.* 2
5. V *M.P.* 3, 4

We have already shown that '$\sim(R \cdot S)$' is logically equivalent to '$\sim R \lor \sim S$'. In the above example, the antecedent of line 1 has been replaced with a logically equivalent statement. Line 3 must have the same truth-value as line 1. Notice that the remainder of line 1 has been brought down unchanged to form the remainder of line 3. '$\sim R \lor \sim S$' is equivalent to the antecedent of line 1, ***not*** to line 1 as a whole.

To complete our formal proof system, we only need to stipulate usable logical equivalences, called "equivalence inferential forms," and to add rules that enable us to use them.

Rules for Using Equivalence Inferential Forms

1. A line may be derived within a formal proof when a previous line is an instance of one side of an equivalence inferential form and the derived line is an instance of the other side of the equivalence inferential form.

2. A line may be derived within a formal proof when a portion of a previous line is an instance of one side of an equivalence inferential form and the derived line is identical to the previous line, except that the portion has been replaced with the instance of the other side of the equivalence inferential form.

DEFINITION 5.4

A logical equivalence is an *equivalence inferential form* if and only if it is one of the following:

De Morgan's laws (D.M.)

$$\sim(p \cdot q) :: \sim p \lor \sim q$$
$$\sim(p \lor q) :: \sim p \cdot \sim q$$

Double negation (D.N.)

$$p :: \sim\sim p$$

Wedge equivalence (W.E.)

$$p \supset q :: \sim p \lor q$$

Commutation (Comm.)

$$p \cdot q :: q \cdot p$$
$$p \lor q :: q \lor p$$

Association (Assoc.)

$$p \cdot (q \cdot r) :: (p \cdot q) \cdot r$$
$$p \lor (q \lor r) :: (p \lor q) \lor r$$

Duplication (Du.)

$$p :: p \lor p$$
$$p :: p \cdot p$$

Material equivalence (M.E.)

$$p \equiv q :: (p \supset q) \cdot (q \supset p)$$

Distribution (Dist.)

$$p \lor (q \cdot r) :: (p \lor q) \cdot (p \lor r)$$
$$p \cdot (q \lor r) :: (p \cdot q) \lor (p \cdot r)$$

The above equivalence inferential forms might seem to be quite a chunk. But most people find that learning them is no more difficult than learning how to use our four valid inferential forms. The following pages provide a description of each equivalence inferential form, and the exercises at the end of this section provide a gradual introduction to them.

B. Specific Descriptions

i. De Morgan's Laws (D.M.)

$\sim(p \cdot q) :: \sim p \lor \sim q$

$\sim(p \lor q) :: \sim p \cdot \sim q$

a. English Usage This equivalence inference is named after Augustus De Morgan (1806–71), a renowned mathematician and logician who taught at the University of London. De Morgan, however, was not the first person to notice these equivalences. They were recognized by Peter of Spain (and perhaps others) at least as early as 1250. Both forms of De Morgan's Laws are common in everyday reasoning.

Suppose that someone (incorrectly) claimed:

Bonnie Parker and Clyde Barrow were not both 1930s bank robbers.[5]
$\sim(P \cdot B)$

By forming an instance of the first of De Morgan's laws, we can realize that this claim is logically equivalent to:

Either Bonnie Parker was not a 1930s bank robber or Clyde Barrow was not a 1930s bank robber. $\sim P \lor \sim B$

Suppose that someone (incorrectly) claimed:

Not either Bonnie Parker or Clyde Barrow was a 1930s bank robber.
$\sim(P \lor B)$

By forming an instance of the second of De Morgan's laws, we can realize that this claim is logically equivalent to:

Neither Bonnie Parker nor Clyde Barrow was a 1930s bank robber.
$\sim P \cdot \sim B$

b. Using De Morgan's Laws in Formal Proofs In Chapter 2 we noted that '$\sim(p \cdot q)$' is **not** equivalent to '$\sim p \cdot \sim q$', and that '$\sim(p \lor q)$' is not equivalent to '$\sim p \lor \sim q$'. The negation of a whole (a conjunction or a disjunction) is not equivalent to the negation of its parts, unless the connective is switched from the dot to the wedge or from the wedge to the dot. De Morgan's laws cannot be applied to horseshoes.

---

[5]Bonnie Parker and Clyde Barrow formed the team known as Bonnie and Clyde. Finally shot to death in an ambush, they had robbed and murdered their way across the American Southwest during the 1930s.

Both of De Morgan's laws can be used in either direction when constructing a formal proof. Since none of our remaining inferential forms work on either negated conjunctions or negated disjunctions, both laws are most commonly used by deriving an instance of the right side from the corresponding instance of the left side. The following examples use the second of De Morgan's laws. They point out typical whole-line and part-line derivations.

1. $A \supset \sim(R \lor T)$	$\diagup \sim R$	1. $A \supset \sim(R \lor T)$	$\diagup \sim R$
2. A		2. A	
3. $\sim(R \lor T)$ M.P. 1, 2		3. $A \supset (\sim R \cdot \sim T)$ D.M. 1	
4. $\sim R \cdot \sim T$ D.M. 3		4. $\sim R \cdot \sim T$ M.P. 3, 2	
5. $\sim R$ Simp. 4		5. $\sim R$ Simp. 4	

ii. Double Negation (D.N.)

$p :: \sim\sim p$

a. English Usage   Examples in English typically use different methods to express successive negations. We might let R abbreviate 'Doritos are resistable'. Given that the contradictory, not a contrary, is understood, 'Doritos are irresistable' is expressed as $\sim R$. '$\sim\sim R$' indicates 'Doritos are not irresistable'. 'Doritos are not irresistable' has the same meaning as 'Doritos are resistable'.

b. Using Double Negation in Formal Proofs   Double negation is typically used to add tildes so that an inferential form can be applied, or to eliminate a pair of tildes that has resulted from using an inferential form.

Tildes must be applied, or removed, as a pair.

Suppose that we wish to derive a conditional from '$B \lor C$'. Wedge equivalence, '$p \supset q :: \sim p \lor q$', will enable us to derive a conditional from a disjunction, ***provided that the first disjunct is negated.*** The first disjunct must be negated, because '$B \lor C$' is ***not*** an instance of '$\sim p \lor q$'. (Only the variables, p and q, are replaced in forming an instance, so $\sim p$ cannot be replaced with B.) Double negation enables us to add a pair of tildes and derive '$\sim\sim B \lor C$'. We can now form an instance of the right side of wedge equivalence, and derive the logically equivalent conditional, '$\sim B \supset C$'. In forming the instance, $\sim B$ replaces p throughout, and C replaces q throughout.

$$p \supset q :: \sim p \lor q$$
$$\sim B \supset C \quad \sim\sim B \lor C$$

The following formal proof illustrates how double negation can be used to remove an excess pair of tildes.

1. $U \supset \sim(\sim B \vee \sim C)$ $\angle B$
2. U
3. $\sim(\sim B \vee \sim C)$ M.P. 1, 2
4. $\sim\sim(B \cdot C)$ D.M. 3. *Notice the pair of tildes that resulted*
5. $B \cdot C$ D.N. 4   *from applying De Morgan's laws.*
6. B Simp. 5

The De Morgan's–law step is a bit complex. Line 4 results from an application of the first of De Morgan's laws from right to left. Double negation merely removes the resulting pair of tildes.

When using double negation, the pair must be applied to, or removed from, ***the same statement.*** Double negation can be used to derive '$A \cdot R$' from '$\sim\sim A \cdot R$'. It cannot be used to derive '$A \cdot R$' from '$\sim(\sim A \cdot R)$'.

iii. Wedge Equivalence (W.E.)

$p \supset q :: \sim p \vee q$

a. English Usage   This statement:

Either we will not balance the budget or we'll increase taxes. $\sim B \vee I$

is logically equivalent to:

If we balance the budget then we'll increase taxes. $B \supset I$

b. Using Wedge Equivalence in Formal Proofs   Wedge equivalence enables us to derive a conditional from a disjunction, or to derive a disjunction from a conditional. In deriving a conditional from a disjunction, we must remove a tilde from the first disjunct. (If the first disjunct has no tildes, two tildes can be added with double negation.) In deriving a disjunction from a conditional, we must add a tilde to the new disjunct.

Wedge equivalence is often used to derive a premiss for modus ponens, or to derive a disjunction after completing a conditional proof.

APPLICATION WITH M.P.

1. $\sim(\sim R \cdot C)$ $\angle \sim C$
2. $\sim R$
3. $\sim\sim R \vee \sim C$ D.M. 1
4. $\sim R \supset \sim C$ W.E. 3
5. $\sim C$ M.P. 4, 2

APPLICATION WITH CONDITIONAL PROOF

1. $A \supset B$ $\angle \sim A \vee C$
2. $B \supset C$

> 3. A C.P.A.
> 4. B M.P. 1, 3
> 5. C M.P. 2, 4

6. $A \supset C$ C.P. 3–5
7. $\sim A \vee C$ W.E. 6

iv. Commutation (Comm.)

$p \cdot q :: q \cdot p$

$p \vee q :: q \vee p$

a. English Usage   Remember that the dot indicates pure conjunction and not 'and then' (see Chapter 2). Both forms of commutation are used in everyday reasoning.

The following conjunctions are logically equivalent to one another:

Bonnie Parker and Clyde Barrow were 1930s bank robbers. P · B

Clyde Barrow and Bonnie Parker were 1930s bank robbers. B · P

The following two disjunctions are logically equivalent to one another:

Clyde Barrow murdered either to escape the authorities or for pure sport.

Clyde Barrow murdered either for pure sport, or to escape the authorities.

b. Using Commutation in Formal Proofs   Commutation can be applied to any conjunction or to any disjunction. It merely switches the order of the conjuncts or disjuncts. Example 1 shows a straightforward application of commutation with the dot. In this example, switching the order of the conjuncts allows us to apply modus ponens. Example 2 points out that only one application of commutation separates the premiss of our D. H. Lawrence example from its conclusion.

EXAMPLE 1

1. $S \cdot M$ $\diagup A$
2. $(M \cdot S) \supset A$
3. $M \cdot S$ Comm. 1
4. A M.P. 2, 3

EXAMPLE 2

Either D. H. Lawrence wrote Lady Chatterley's Lover *or D. H. Lawrence wrote* Women in Love.

Hence, either D. H. Lawrence wrote Women in Love *or D. H. Lawrence wrote* Lady Chatterley's Lover.

1. $L \vee W$ $\diagup W \vee L$
2. $W \vee L$ Comm. 1

v. Association (Assoc.)

$p \cdot (q \cdot r) :: (p \cdot q) \cdot r$

$p \vee (q \vee r) :: (p \vee q) \vee r$

a. English Usage   English does not usually discriminate subgroupings in a collection of conjuncts or a collection of disjuncts.

Consider the following statement:

Bonnie Parker, Clyde Barrow, and Al Capone were all 1930s criminals.

In our artificial language, '$P \cdot B \cdot C$' must be incorrect, since the major connective is not specified. '$(P \cdot B) \cdot C$' and '$P \cdot (B \cdot C)$' are both correct expressions in the artificial language. Association is usually not present in standard English, since it is less demanding in specifying connections between statements. In the artificial language, association merely indicates that both ways of connecting them have the same meaning.

  b. Using Association in Formal Proofs Parentheses (or brackets or braces) can be shifted when the statements are connected with either dots or wedges. Parentheses (or brackets or braces) cannot be shifted when the statements are connected with either the horseshoe, or a mixture of dots and wedges. From '$(A \cdot B) \lor C$' to '$A \cdot (B \lor C)$' is not association, or anything else for that matter.

  Both of the following examples can be done without using association. Association, however, enables us to provide shorter solutions.

EXAMPLE 1

1. $\sim D \supset R$ $\angle \sim D \supset (R \lor S)$
2. $\sim\sim D \lor R$ W.E. 1
3. $(\sim\sim D \lor R) \lor S$ Add. 2
4. $\sim\sim D \lor (R \lor S)$ Assoc. 3
5. $\sim D \supset (R \lor S)$ W.E. 4

EXAMPLE 2

1. $\sim D \cdot (R \cdot S)$ $\angle S$
2. $(\sim D \cdot R) \cdot S$ Assoc. 1
3. S Simp. 2

vi. Duplication (Du.)

$p :: p \lor p$

$p :: p \cdot p$

  a. English Usage Expressing the same statement twice in a conjunction or a disjunction does not make it more (or less) true. At times, doing so adds emphasis. Suppose that we listened to a National Weather Service forecast, and discovered that there was a zero percent chance of precipitation for the day. Later on, in the midst of a cloudburst, we might exclaim:

  Either it's going to rain or it's going to rain!

or:

  It's going to rain and it's going to rain!

In both cases we have claimed that it is going to rain.

  b. Using Duplication in Formal Proofs Duplication is normally used to eliminate repetitions of the same statement. Hence, both forms are typically applied from right to left. To apply duplication, both disjuncts, or both conjuncts, must be the same. The following proof illustrates a typical usage of duplication.

1. $A \supset (A \supset R)$ $\angle A \supset R$
2. $\sim A \lor (A \supset R)$ W.E. 1

3. *~A* V (*~A* V *R*)   *W.E. 2. Note: separate lines for each application.*
4. (*~A* V *~A*) V *R*   *Assoc. 3*
5. *~A* V *R*   *Du. 4. '~A* V *~A' is logically equivalent to ~A.*
6. *A* ⊃ *R*   *W.E. 5*

vii. Material Equivalence (M.E.)

p ≡ *q* ∷ (*p* ⊃ *q*) · (*q* ⊃ *p*)

a. English Usage   As indicated at the outset of this chapter, material equivalence merely provides a way to express biconditionals with one symbol, the triple bar.

b. Using Material Equivalence in Formal Proofs   None of our other inferential forms work on the triple bar. Hence, when a premiss of an argument contains a triple bar, the first step of the formal proof is usually an application of material equivalence.

None of our other inferential forms derive statements that are expressed with the triple bar. Hence, when the conclusion of an argument has a triple bar, the last step of the formal proof is usually material equivalence.

The following formal proof begins and ends with applications of material equivalence.

1. *E* ≡ *G*   ∕*E* ≡ *L*
2. *G* ≡ *L*
3. (*E* ⊃ *G*) · (*G* ⊃ *E*)   *M.E. 1*
4. (*G* ⊃ *L*) · (*L* ⊃ *G*)   *M.E. 2*

   5. *E*   *C.P.A.*
   6. *E* ⊃ *G*   *Simp. 3*
   7. *G*   *M.P. 6, 5*
   8. *G* ⊃ *L*   *Simp. 4*
   9. *L*   *M.P. 8, 7*

10. *E* ⊃ *L*   *C.P. 5–9*

   11. *L*   *C.P.A.*
   12. *L* ⊃ *G*   *Simp. 4*
   13. *G*   *M.P. 12, 11*
   14. *G* ⊃ *E*   *Simp. 3*
   15. *E*   *M.P. 14, 13*

16. *L ⊃ E   C.P. 11–15*
17. *(E ⊃ L) · (L ⊃ E)   Conj. 10, 16*
18. *E ≡ L   M.E. 17*

viii. Distribution (Dist.)

p ∨ (*q* · *r*) ∷ (*p* ∨ *q*) · (*p* ∨ *r*)
p · (*q* ∨ *r*) ∷ (*p* · *q*) ∨ (*p* · *r*)

a. English Usage   Although distribution is not often used in normal conversation, examples sound valid. Consider an example from Chapter 2:

> *Senator Edward Kennedy can verify that he attempted to save his staff member; and either he can verify that he reported the accident as soon as possible or we have evidence of a cover up. A · (R ∨ C)*

The example sounds, and is, logically equivalent to:

> *Either Senator Edward Kennedy can verify that he attempted to save his staff member and that he reported the accident as soon as possible, or he can verify that he attempted to save his staff member and we have evidence of a cover up. (A · R) ∨ (A · C)*

b. Using Distribution in Formal Proofs   Distribution is frequently used to split conjunctions or disjunctions in a formal proof. For example:

1. *A ⊃ (B · C)*   ∕*A ⊃ B*
2. *~A ∨ (B · C)   W.E. 1*
3. *(~A ∨ B) · (~A ∨ C)   Dist. 2. Notice how 'B · C' has been split.*
4. *~A ∨ B   Simp. 3*
5. *A ⊃ B   W.E. 4*

Try to visualize distribution from left to right.

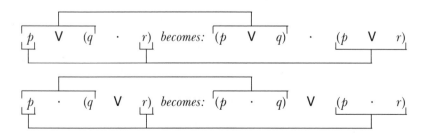

Although it is helpful to attempt to visualize distribution, there is no real substitute for practice when attempting to use this inferential form.

IV Formal-Proof Strategies and Suggestions

Most students do not find that constructing formal proofs is a major problem. Most students do, however, find that a fair amount of practice is required in order to become proficient.

It is not possible to provide a list of steps that will work for every conceivable problem.

Sometimes insight, more than a mechanical procedure, is required. The following suggestions are intended to assist your insight, not replace it.

Students who have been stuck on a problem often claim that they were able to finish it by looking at one line of a solution. Once they took the previously unseen step, they were able to continue the proof by themselves and derive the argument's conclusion. Being stuck on a problem usually results from not having an overall conception of how it is put together. A person who is stuck on a problem is usually not looking at it in a way that will cause her to see some necessary step. Suppose we look at how our formal proof system works to generate conclusions, and ask how we can develop global strategies for completing formal proofs.

Using an equivalence inferential form does not change a statement's content. An application of an equivalence inferential form must derive a line that is logically equivalent to the line that was used as a premiss. Unlike our equivalence inferential forms, our valid inferential forms do produce lines that differ in content from the statements that were used as premisses.

The reason for working with our Chapter 4 inferences first is obvious; global strategies should be conceived in terms of them, not the equivalence inferential forms of this chapter. In order to form overall strategies for the problems in this chapter, we should look for potential applications of our Chapter 4 inferential forms.

A. The Goals Approach

The goals approach that we presented in Chapter 4 can be applied to the problems of this chapter when we are looking for problem solving *strategies,* but we should not see it as providing a recipe for finding problem *solutions.* Listing goal statements should be seen as scratch-paper work that might help us find a solution.

i. Problematic Applications

When we apply the goals approach to find problem-solving strategies, four equivalence inferential forms are problematic: Distribution, Material equivalence, De Morgan's laws, and Wedge equivalence.

a. Distribution   Any problem that can be done by using distribution can also be done without using it.[6] Even so, some problems require lengthy solutions if we ignore it. Exercises V provide practice in using the various forms of distribution.

b. Material Equivalence   As previously mentioned, if one or more triple bars are in the premisses of an argument, we should use material equivalence to eliminate them before either beginning the problem or attempting to apply the goals approach. If a goal statement contains a triple bar, cross it off and list the equivalent biconditional as a new goal.

c. De Morgan's Laws   When stuck on a problem, apply De Morgan's laws to all negated conjunctions and disjunctions that are in the premisses. If a goal statement is the negation of either a conjunction or a disjunction, do not cross it off, but add the result of applying De Morgan's laws as an additional goal. Negated compound statements tend to be locked away from applications of our inferential forms.

d. Wedge Equivalence   When stuck on a problem, use double negation as necessary and apply wedge equivalence to all disjunctions and conditionals that are in the premisses. If a goal statement is a disjunction, do not cross it off, but add the result of applying wedge equivalence (and double negation if needed) as an additional goal.

ii. Restatement of the Goals Approach

List the conclusion of the argument as a goal (*G*), and begin looking for it and subgoals in available lines as follows.

If *G* is within a compound statement, look at the major connective of the line that has *G*, and

1. If the major connective is a horseshoe and *G* is somewhere in the consequent, list the antecedent as a new goal. Once we have the antecedent, we will be able to apply modus ponens and get the consequent.
2. If the major connective is a dot, take a simplification step. Write down the conjunct that contains *G*.

If *G* is a compound statement, note its major connective. We can create conjunctions, disjunctions, and conditionals.

3. If *G*'s major connective is a dot, list each conjunct as a new goal. Once we have each conjunct, we will be able to get the conjunction by using conjunction.

---

[6]See section VI of this chapter. Distribution can be established as a derived rule of inference.

4. If *G*'s major connective is a wedge, list the first disjunct as a new goal. We will be able to use addition to create the wedge once we have the first disjunct.

5. If *G*'s major connective is the horseshoe, begin a conditional proof. The conditional proof assumption should be the antecedent of the desired conditional. List the consequent of the desired conditional as a new goal. Since the conditional can be derived when its consequent is derived, the conditional can be crossed off the goals list.

We can apply the above suggestions to the following problem:

1. $(A \lor D) \supset C$ $\underline{/\sim B \lor C}$ **Goal:** *~B*
2. $\sim(B \cdot \sim A)$

The conclusion is a disjunction statement. Step 4 of the goals approach has us set *~B* as a goal. There is no obvious way to apply our valid inferential forms. Line 2 is a negated conjunction, and the conclusion is a disjunction. Our strategies tell us to take the De Morgan step with line 2, and to apply wedge equivalence to the conclusion to create an additional goal. We now have the following:

1. $(A \lor D) \supset C$ $\underline{/\sim B \lor C}$ **Goals:** *~B*; *B* $\supset$ *C*
2. $\sim(B \cdot \sim A)$
3. $\sim B \lor \sim\sim A$ *D.M. 2*

Step 5 of the goals approach has us cross off '*B* $\supset$ *C*' as a goal, and make *B* a conditional-proof assumption. If, however, we see the problem in terms of deriving *~B* and then using addition, the conditional-proof assumption should not be taken. We now have two approaches for this problem.

APPROACH 1
1. $(A \lor D) \supset C$ $\underline{/\sim B \lor C}$ **Goal:** *~B*
2. $\sim(B \cdot \sim A)$
3. $\sim B \lor \sim\sim A$ *D.M. 2*

APPROACH 2
1. $(A \lor D) \supset C$ $\underline{/\sim B \lor C}$ **Goals:** $\cancel{B} \cancel{\supset} \cancel{C}$; *C*
2. $\sim(B \cdot \sim A)$
3. $\sim B \lor \sim\sim A$ *D.M. 2*
    4. B   *C.P.A.*

Approach 2 has us notice that *C* is the consequent of line 1. We should add '*A* $\lor$ *D*' as a goal and cross off *C*.

APPROACH 2

1. $(A \lor D) \supset C$ $\angle\sim\!B \lor C$ ***Goals:*** $\not{B}$ $\not\supset$ $\not{C}$; $\not{C}$; $A \lor D$
2. $\sim\!(B \cdot \sim\!A)$
3. $\sim\!B \lor \sim\!\sim\!A$ *D.M. 2*
   4. B *C.P.A.*

We are stuck, and likely because of an equivalence inferential form! We have converted all the negated conjunctions and disjunctions, and there are no triple bars in the problem. Our strategies have us use wedge equivalence on line 3. This gives us:

APPROACH 2

1. $(A \lor D) \supset C$ $\angle\sim\!B \lor C$ ***Goals:*** $\not{B}$ $\not\supset$ $\not{C}$; $\not{C}$; $A \lor D$; A
2. $\sim\!(B \cdot \sim\!A)$
3. $\sim\!B \lor \sim\!\sim\!A$ *D.M. 2*
   4. B *C.P.A.*
   5. $B \supset \sim\!\sim\!A$ *W.E. 3*

Lines 4 and 5 can now be seen as premises for modus ponens! Provided we remember that $\sim\!\sim\!A$ is equivalent to A, the remainder of the proof falls into place.

   1. $(A \lor D) \supset C$ $\angle\sim\!B \lor C$ ***Goals:*** $\not{B}$ $\not\supset$ $\not{C}$; $\not{C}$; $\not{A} \not\lor \not{D}$; $\not{A}$
   2. $\sim\!(B \cdot \sim\!A)$
   3. $\sim\!B \lor \sim\!\sim\!A$ *D.M. 2*

> 4. B *C.P.A.*
> 5. $B \supset \sim\!\sim\!A$ *W.E. 3*
> 6. $\sim\!\sim\!A$ *M.P. 5, 4*
> 7. A *D.N. 6*
> 8. $A \lor D$ *Add. 7*
> 9. C *M.P. 1, 8*

10. $B \supset C$ *C.P. 4–9*
11. $\sim\!B \lor C$ *W.E. 10*

B. Recapitulation of Valid Inferential Forms

MODUS PONENS (M.P.)

$p \supset q$

p

$\therefore q$

SIMPLIFICATION (SIMP.)

$p \cdot q$ $p \cdot q$

$\therefore p$ $\therefore q$

CONJUNCTION (CONJ.)	ADDITION (ADD.)

$$p$$
$$\underline{q}$$
$$\therefore p \cdot q$$

$$p$$
$$\overline{\therefore p \lor q}$$

i. Using Our Valid Inferential Forms

a. Modus Ponens   Used to produce the consequent of a conditional. Both the conditional and its antecedent must be separate lines to use modus ponens.

b. Simplification   Used to produce a conjunct. The conjunction must be a line (with the dot as the major connective) to use simplification.

c. Conjunction   Used to produce a conjunction. Each conjunct must be a line to use conjunction.

d. Addition   Used to produce a disjunction. The first disjunct must be a line to use addition. Any disjunct can be added.

C. Recapitulation of the Conditional-Proof Procedure

$$k. \quad p \quad C.P.A.$$
$$\vdots$$
$$m. \quad q$$

$$m + 1. \quad p \supset q \quad C.P. \quad k\text{–}m$$

k and m indicate lines appearing within a formal proof. p may be any statement whatsoever. q indicates a statement derived on the basis of previous lines.

Once a conditional proof has been ended, no following lines can be derived from those within the conditional proof. In the case of multiple conditional proofs, one conditional proof cannot partially overlap another. (See Chapter 4 for a more complete explanation.)

D. Summary of Equivalence Inferential Forms

i. De Morgan's Laws (D.M.)

$$\sim(p \cdot q) :: \sim p \lor \sim q$$
$$\sim(p \lor q) :: \sim p \cdot \sim q$$

The negation of a conjunction is logically equivalent to a disjunction in which the previous conjuncts become negated. The negation of a disjunction is logically equivalent to a conjunction in which the previous disjuncts become negated.

ii. Double Negation (D.N.)

$p :: \sim\sim p$

A pair of tildes can be added to, or removed from, any statement.

iii. Wedge Equivalence (W.E.)

$p \supset q :: \sim p \lor q$

A conditional is logically equivalent to a disjunction in which the previous antecedent becomes negated.

iv. Commutation (Comm.)

$p \cdot q :: q \cdot p$
$p \lor q :: q \lor p$

The order of statements can be switched with either a dot or a wedge.

v. Association (Assoc.)

$p \cdot (q \cdot r) :: (p \cdot q) \cdot r$
$p \lor (q \lor r) :: (p \lor q) \lor r$

Parentheses (or brackets or braces) can be shifted in either a series of disjuncts or a series of conjuncts.

vi. Duplication (Du.)

$p :: p \lor p$
$p :: p \cdot p$

A statement is logically equivalent to a disjunction of it and itself. A statement is logically equivalent to a conjunction of it and itself.

vii. Material Equivalence (M.E.)

$p \equiv q :: (p \supset q) \cdot (q \supset p)$

A biconditional is logically equivalent to two conditionals, such that each statement combined in the biconditional is the antecedent of one of the two conditionals and is the consequent of the other of the two conditionals.

viii. Distribution (Dist.)

$p \lor (q \cdot r) :: (p \lor q) \cdot (p \lor r)$

$p \cdot (q \lor r) :: (p \cdot q) \lor (p \cdot r)$

A conjunct can be distributed across a disjunction. A disjunct can be distributed across a conjunction.

Exercises IV

Each of the following is a completed formal proof for the indicated argument. Indicate the inferential form or equivalence inference for each derived line.

*1.   1. $(B \lor V) \supset C$ $/C$
      2. V
      3. $V \lor B$
      4. $B \lor V$
      5. C

2.   1. $W \supset (W \supset C)$ $/W \lor C$
      2. $\sim W \lor (W \supset C)$
      3. $\sim W \lor (\sim W \lor C)$
      4. $(\sim W \lor \sim W) \lor C$
      5. $\sim W \lor C$

*3.   1. $\sim(O \cdot E)$ $/\sim E$
      2. O
      3. $\sim O \lor \sim E$
      4. $O \supset \sim E$
      5. $\sim E$

4.   1. $\sim D \supset (D \cdot S)$ $/D$
      2. $\sim\sim D \lor (D \cdot S)$
      3. $D \lor (D \cdot S)$
      4. $(D \lor D) \cdot (D \lor S)$
      5. $D \lor D$
      6. D

*5.   1. $(R \lor \sim P) \supset \sim S$ $/P$
      2. S
      3. $\sim(R \lor \sim P) \lor \sim S$
      4. $\sim S \lor \sim(R \lor \sim P)$
      5. $S \supset \sim(R \lor \sim P)$
      6. $\sim(R \lor \sim P)$
      7. $\sim R \cdot \sim\sim P$
      8. $\sim R \cdot P$
      9. P

6.   1. $S \supset (E \cdot S)$ $/S \supset E$
      2. $\sim S \lor (E \cdot S)$
      3. $(\sim S \lor E) \cdot (\sim S \lor S)$
      4. $\sim S \lor E$
      5. $S \supset E$

*7.   1. $\sim(D \cdot \sim A) \supset Z$ $/Z$
      2. A
      3. $A \lor \sim D$
      4. $\sim D \lor A$
      5. $\sim D \lor \sim\sim A$
      6. $\sim(D \cdot \sim A)$
      7. Z

8. *1.* $U \equiv R$ $\diagup I$
    2. $(U \cdot T) \vee (U \cdot S)$
    3. $I \vee \sim R$
    4. $(U \supset R) \cdot (R \supset U)$
    5. $U \supset R$
    6. $U \cdot (T \vee S)$
    7. U
    8. R
    9. $\sim R \vee I$
  10. $R \supset I$
  11. I

*9. *1.* $L \cdot B$ $\diagup B \equiv L$
    2. L
    3. $L \vee \sim B$
    4. $\sim B \vee L$
    5. $B \supset L$
    6. B
    7. $B \vee \sim L$
    8. $\sim L \vee B$
    9. $L \supset B$
  10. $(B \supset L) \cdot (L \supset B)$
  11. $B \equiv L$

Exercises V

For each of the following statements, apply distribution in the direction specified. Write down the statements that result.

*1. $A \vee (B \cdot C)$ *Apply from left to right.*
2. $B \cdot (R \vee S)$ *Apply from left to right.*
*3. $(\sim A \cdot R) \vee (\sim A \cdot Q)$ *Apply from right to left.*
4. $(S \vee K) \cdot (S \vee I)$ *Apply from right to left.*
*5. $(\sim A \cdot R) \vee (\sim A \cdot Q)$ *Apply from left to right.*
6. $(A \cdot \sim B) \vee (S \cdot I)$ *Apply from left to right.*
*7. $[(S \cdot R) \vee U] \cdot [(S \cdot R) \vee C]$ *Apply from right to left.*
8. $[(S \cdot R) \cdot U] \vee [(S \cdot R) \cdot C]$ *Apply from right to left.*

Exercises VI

Construct a formal proof of validity for each of the following arguments. None of these require the addition of more than two lines for their completion. Although some of our valid inferential forms are needed, these problems emphasize this chapter's equivalence inferential forms.

*1. $\sim(W \vee E)$
   $\therefore \sim E$

2. $\sim S \vee R$
   S
   $\therefore R$

3. $A \vee (I \cdot F)$
   $\therefore A \vee I$

4. $\sim(H \cdot \sim T)$
   $\therefore \sim H \vee T$

*5. $\sim E$
    $\sim B$
    $\overline{\therefore \sim (E \lor B)}$

6. $U \equiv I$
    $\overline{\therefore I \supset U}$

7. $Y \lor (Y \lor E)$
    $\overline{\therefore Y \lor E}$

8. $O \lor R$
    $\overline{\therefore \sim O \supset R}$

*9. $(\sim F \cdot \sim F) \lor T$
    $\overline{\therefore F \supset T}$

10. $A \lor \sim P$
    $\overline{\therefore P \supset A}$

11. $(I \cdot V) \lor (J \cdot I)$
    $\overline{\therefore I \cdot (V \lor J)}$

12. $(\sim G \lor S) \lor A$
    $\overline{\therefore G \supset (S \lor A)}$

*13. $(J \cdot U) \cdot (N \cdot V)$
    $\overline{\therefore U \cdot [J \cdot (N \cdot V)]}$

14. $O \supset (O \cdot R)$
    $(O \cdot R) \supset O$
    $\overline{\therefore (O \cdot R) \equiv O}$

V   Indirect-Proof Procedure

There are times when it is easier, both in standard English and in formal proofs, to argue for a statement by showing that its contradictory is absurd.

Contradictory statements must have opposite truth-values. If we can show that a statement leads to an absurdity, that it must be false, we know that its contradictory must be true. Arguments that use indirect proof are called "reductio ad absurdum" arguments. (The literal meaning of 'reductio ad absurdum' is "reduction to an absurdity.") We can outline our indirect proof strategy as follows.

1. Begin by assuming the contradictory of the statement to be proved.

2. Based on this assumption, derive an absurdity. In our artificial language, we can define an absurdity as an instance of '$p \cdot \sim p$', since this is a self-contradictory statement form. No instance of '$p \cdot \sim p$' can be true.

3. Conclude that the contradictory of the **assumption** must be true. The contradictory of our assumption will be logically equivalent to the statement that we set out to prove.

A. A Practical Example

Some people in our society are in favor of using animals in medical research experiments. Our society routinely uses a test, called "LD50," to determine the toxicity of pesticides, insecticides, and food additives. LD50 measures the amount of a substance that is required, when given in a single dose, to kill 50 percent of a group of experimental animals within a fourteen-day period. Some researchers have argued that it is more humane to conduct an experiment that kills 50 percent of a group of animals than to conduct an experiment that kills 50 percent of a group of people, since animals do not experience pain in the same way that we do.

Bernard Rollin, an advocate of moral rights for animals, has claimed that the argument that animals are different from people can be reduced to absurdity. The following reductio ad absurdum argument makes up a portion of Rollins' discussion.

> I recently debated a prominent neurophysiologist whose field of specialization is pain. During the course of his presentation, he brought forward an elaborate argument purporting to show that since the electrochemical activity in the cerebral cortex associated with pain is different in animals and human beings, animal pain is not *really* like human pain, since the cerebral cortex governs higher intellectual activity. My rebuttal was brief. I pointed out to him that his actions belied his rhetoric, since his own area of research was pain, and he used animal subjects and extrapolated the results to people![7]

Rollins is claiming that the neurophysiologist's position leads to an absurdity. If we accept the neurophysiologist's position, then animal pain *is* really like human pain; otherwise we would be unable to make inferences about human pain from studying animal pain. But if we accept the neurophysiologist's position, then animal pain is *not* really like human pain, since the cerebral cortex governs higher intellectual activity. The neurophysiologist's position leads to the absurdity that animal pain is, and is not, like human pain. Rollins argues that since the neurophysiologist's position implies an absurdity, it must be false.

B. Using Indirect Proof in Formal Proofs

The contradictory of a statement that we wish to prove may be assumed at any time in a formal proof. Since applying the tilde expresses the contradictory of an unnegated statement, we can do this by either applying one tilde to our desired statement or removing one tilde from it. This line should be indented, and it should be justified as an "indirect-proof assumption" (I.P.A.).

The formal proof is now continued. Within an indirect proof, its assumption may be used in the same ways as any other line.

When a line that is an instance of '$p \cdot \sim p$' has been derived, the indirect proof is boxed off and ended. The next line *must be the contradictory of the indirect proof's assumption*. It is justified by "indirect proof " (I.P.). The lines within the box should be specified.

---

[7]Bernard E. Rollin, *Animal Rights and Human Morality* (Buffalo: Prometheus Books, 1981), 31. (Rollin's italics.)

Restrictions

1. Every indirect proof that is started must be ended as stated in the third step, above. An instance of '$p \cdot \sim p$' must be derived, and the next line must be the contradictory of the indirect proof's assumption.

2. It is possible for a formal proof to contain a number of indirect proofs. Indirect proofs can be contained one within another, and can also follow one another. A formal proof can contain both conditional and indirect proofs. Indirect proofs and conditional proofs must be ended, however, so that boxes (from either or both types of proofs) do not partially overlap.

Example 1

We can use the following to summarize Rollin's argument against the neurophysiologist's position.

If the neurophysiologist's position is acceptable, then animal pain is like human pain.

If the neurophysiologist's position is acceptable, then animal pain is not like human pain.

Hence, the neurophysiologist's position is not acceptable.

Symbolically, we have:

$A \supset L$
$A \supset \sim L$
$\therefore \sim A$

We can use an indirect proof to construct a formal proof for this argument. Our indirect-proof assumption should be the contradictory of $\sim A$. Since the tilde is used to express the contradictory of a statement, we know that A and $\sim A$ are contradictories. We should begin the indirect proof by assuming A. Once we have derived an instance of '$p \cdot \sim p$,' we will be able to end our indirect proof and derive the argument's conclusion.

1. $A \supset L$ $\diagup \sim A$
2. $A \supset \sim L$

    3. A I.P.A.
    4. L M.P. 1, 3
    5. $\sim L$ M.P. 2, 3
    6. $L \cdot \sim L$ Conj. 4, 5

7. $\sim A$ I.P. 3–6

Example 2

The following example applies the method of indirect proof to derive a compound statement. Notice the required assumption. The contradictory of '$R \lor S$' is '$\sim(R \lor S)$', **not** '$\sim R \lor S$'.

1. $\sim(R \lor S) \supset (R \cdot S)$ $\underline{/R \lor S}$
2. $\sim(R \cdot S)$

> 3. $\sim(R \lor S)$ I.P.A.
> 4. $R \cdot S$ M.P. 1, 3
> 5. $(R \cdot S) \cdot \sim(R \cdot S)$ Conj. 4, 2

6. $R \lor S$ I.P. 3–5

Example 3

The following example has a conditional **and** an indirect proof. One subproof is contained entirely within the other.

1. $A \supset B$ $\underline{/(\sim B \lor \sim D) \supset (\sim A \lor \sim C)}$
2. $C \supset D$

> 3. $\sim B \lor \sim D$ C.P.A.
>
> > 4. $\sim(\sim A \lor \sim C)$ I.P.A.
> > 5. $\sim\sim A \cdot \sim\sim C$ D.M. 4
> > 6. $\sim\sim A$ Simp. 5
> > 7. A D.N. 6
> > 8. B M.P. 1, 7
> > 9. $\sim\sim C$ Simp. 5
> > 10. C D.N. 9
> > 11. D M.P. 2, 10
> > 12. $B \cdot D$ Conj. 8, 11
> > 13. $\sim(B \cdot D)$ D.M. 3
> > 14. $(B \cdot D) \cdot \sim(B \cdot D)$ Conj. 12, 13
>
> 15. $\sim A \lor \sim C$ I.P. 4–14

16. $(\sim B \lor \sim D) \supset (\sim A \lor \sim C)$ C.P. 3–15

C. Indirect-Proof Strategies

Although indirect proof can be very helpful when attempting to construct *some* formal proofs, it should be seen as a rule of last resort. Most problems can be more easily solved by not using indirect proof.

If we have worked with the goals approach and find that we are unable to get a problem going, *then* we should ask whether having the contradictory of a goal will help, and consider trying indirect proof. An indirect proof assumption should always be the contradictory of a goal-statement.

> *Indirect proofs should never be started unless a goal has been identified.*

Suppose that we attempt to provide a formal proof for the following argument.

> *If rats did not think like human beings and we had used them in experiments to learn about motivation, then our experiments would have been worthless.*
>
> *We have used rats in experiments to learn about motivation, and our experiments were not worthless.*
>
> *Hence, rats think like human beings.*

When this argument is symbolized, we have:

1. $(\sim T \cdot L) \supset W$ $/T$ **Goal: T**
2. $L \cdot \sim W$

There is no obvious way to begin a formal proof for this argument. T is negated in the argument's first premiss, but there is no obvious way to derive it. We should consider using indirect proof. Since our goal is T, our assumption for an indirect proof should be $\sim T$. T can be crossed off our goals list. Completing the indirect proof will derive T.

1. $(\sim T \cdot L) \supset W$ $/T$ **Goal: $\cancel{T}$**
2. $L \cdot \sim W$
   3. $\sim T$ *I.P.A.*

We should now derive an instance of '$p \cdot \sim p$'. But what statement will be an instance of p? Should we attempt to derive '$T \cdot \sim T$', or '$L \cdot \sim L$', or '$W \cdot \sim W$'? In example 1, both L and $\sim L$ were contained in usable lines after our indirect-proof assumption. The indirect proof was ended after we derived '$L \cdot \sim L$'. In example 2, both '$R \cdot S$' and '$\sim(R \cdot S)$' were contained in usable lines after our indirect-proof assumption. This indirect proof was ended after we derived '$(R \cdot S) \cdot \sim(R \cdot S)$'.

Most, but not all, indirect proofs are completed by conjoining negated and unnegated statements that appear in the problem after making the indirect-proof assumption.

In our example, both W and $\sim W$ are contained in usable lines. '$W \cdot \sim W$' will *likely* be the instance of '$p \cdot \sim p$' that ends our indirect proof. We should list '$W \cdot \sim W$' as a new goal:

1. $(\sim T \cdot L) \supset W$ $\underline{/T}$ ***Goals:*** $\cancel{T}$; $W \cdot \sim W$
2. $L \cdot \sim W$
       3. $\sim T$ I.P.A.

We can now apply our goals approach and complete the formal proof. '$W \cdot \sim W$' is a conjunction statement, and each conjunct appears in the problem. We can use simplification to obtain $\sim W$ from line 2. We can use modus ponens to obtain W from line 1, provided that we can derive line 1's antecedent. The antecedent of line 1 is a conjunction of $\sim T$ and L. We have $\sim T$ as line 3, and L can be simplified from line 2. Done! Our goals approach has outlined the following formal proof:

1. $(\sim T \cdot L) \supset W$ $\underline{/T}$ ***Goals:*** $\cancel{T}$; $\cancel{W} / \sim\cancel{W}$; $\cancel{W}$; $\sim\cancel{W}$; $\sim\cancel{T} / \cancel{L}$; $\sim\cancel{T}$; $\cancel{L}$
2. $L \cdot \sim W$

> 3. $\sim T$ I.P.A.
> 4. $\sim W$ Simp. 2
> 5. L Simp. 2
> 6. $\sim T \cdot L$ Conj. 3, 5
> 7. W M.P. 1, 6
> 8. $W \cdot \sim W$ Conj. 7, 4

9. T I.P. 3–8

Exercises VII

Use indirect proof to construct a formal proof of validity for each of the following arguments.

*1. $A \supset U$
    $\sim(A \cdot U)$
    $\therefore \sim A$

2. $L \supset W$
   $\sim W$
   $\therefore \sim(L \cdot Q)$

*3. $(\sim D \lor S) \supset E$
    $\sim D \supset \sim E$
    $\therefore D$

4. $\sim A \supset R$
   $\sim Y \supset \sim R$
   $\therefore A \lor Y$

*5. $F \equiv G$
    $\sim G$
    $\therefore \sim F$

6. $V \supset \sim(J \lor O)$
   $\sim J \supset \sim N$
   $\therefore \sim(V \cdot N)$

*7. $\sim U \cdot \sim H$
    $\therefore \sim[U \lor (H \cdot B)]$

8. $P \supset I$
   $I \supset \sim A$
   $\sim A \supset \sim T$
   $\therefore \sim P \lor \sim T$

Exercises VIII

Construct a formal proof for each of the following arguments. Use valid inferential forms, the conditional proof process, equivalence inferential forms, and indirect proof as needed. Should you become stuck with any of the first eight problems, there is a set of recipes following these problems. Before looking at the solutions, make a real effort, use the strategies and the goals approach, and look for indirect proofs.

*1. $P \supset \sim(N \cdot B)$
    P
    $(\sim N \lor \sim B) \supset R$
    $\therefore R$

2. $R \lor (W \cdot F)$
   $(R \lor W) \supset C$
   $\therefore C$

3. $V \equiv S$
   S
   $\therefore V$

4. $I \lor \sim H$
   $\therefore H \supset I$

*5. $B \supset R$
    $R \supset \sim B$
    $\therefore \sim B$

6. $(\sim K \lor G) \lor C$
   $\therefore K \supset (G \lor C)$

7. $(A \cdot I) \lor (A \cdot S)$
   $A \supset D$
   $\therefore D$

8. $G \lor W$
   $G \lor E$
   $\therefore G \lor (W \cdot E)$

*9. $U \lor (U \lor N)$
    $\therefore \sim U \supset N$

10. $A \supset (S \cdot Q)$
    $\sim Q$
    $\therefore \sim A$

11. $D \lor (O \cdot P)$
    $\therefore D \lor P$

12. $(M \cdot C) \supset I$
    $M \cdot \sim I$
    $\therefore \sim C$

*13. $M \lor \sim A$
     A
     $\therefore M$

14. $F \supset N$
    $N \supset P$
    $\therefore \sim F \lor P$

15. $\sim V \lor U$
     $\sim V \lor D$
     $(U \cdot D) \supset T$
     $\overline{\therefore V \supset T}$

16. $(W \lor J) \supset O$
     $\sim O$
     $\overline{\therefore \sim J}$

*17. $(R \cdot W) \lor (R \cdot F)$
      $\sim W$
      $\overline{\therefore F}$

18. $A \supset [(S \cdot T) \lor O]$
     $[O \lor (S \cdot T)] \supset R$
     $\overline{\therefore A \supset R}$

19. $R \supset L$
     $L \supset J$
     $\sim J \lor R$
     $\overline{\therefore R \equiv J}$

20. $G \lor \sim B$
     $\sim(\sim G \cdot B) \supset I$
     $\overline{\therefore I}$

*21. $R \supset K$
      $R \supset \sim K$
      $\overline{\therefore \sim R}$

22. U
     $\sim N$
     $\overline{\therefore \sim(U \equiv N)}$

23. $\sim D \lor \sim A$
     $D \lor \sim H$
     $\overline{\therefore A \supset \sim H}$

24. $\sim(M \supset T)$
     $(M \cdot Q) \cdot (\sim T \supset V)$
     $\overline{\therefore Q \supset V}$

*25. $W \supset (U \equiv G)$
      $\sim G$
      $\overline{\therefore W \supset \sim U}$

26. $\sim(A \cdot R) \equiv \sim C$
     $\sim(C \cdot O) \supset P$
     $\overline{\therefore \sim A \supset P}$

27. $K \supset A$
     $\overline{\therefore (A \cdot K) \equiv K}$

28. $Z \supset [(K \cdot A) \supset (L \lor T)]$
     $\sim L \cdot (L \lor A)$
     $\overline{\therefore Z \supset (K \supset T)}$

*29. $T \supset U$
      $\sim(U \cdot T)$
      $\sim R \supset T$
      $\overline{\therefore R}$

30. $J \supset (R \supset T)$
     $\sim U \supset (R \cdot V)$
     $(O \lor T) \supset S$
     $U \lor J$
     $\overline{\therefore U \lor S}$

31. $(R \equiv V) \supset W$
     $(M \lor R) \supset V$
     $R \lor \sim V$
     $\overline{\therefore W}$

32. $U \lor R$
     $U \lor \sim R$
     $(T \lor U) \supset W$
     $\overline{\therefore W}$

The following problems are challenging!

*33. $(B \cdot Q) \lor T$
      $(T \supset C) \cdot (C \supset Q)$
      $\overline{\therefore Q}$

34. $X \lor R$
     $Q \supset \sim B$
     $R \supset B$
     $(\sim Q \supset \sim O) \cdot (\sim O \supset \sim R)$
     $\overline{\therefore X}$

Recipes for the first eight problems of Exercises VIII:

1. Use modus ponens on lines 1 and 2 to produce line 4. Use
    De Morgan's laws on line 4 to produce line 5. Use modus ponens on
    lines 3 and 5 to produce line 6.

2. Use distribution on line 1 to produce line 3. Simplify line 3 to produce line 4. Use modus ponens on lines 2 and 4 to produce line 5.

3. Use material equivalence on line 1 to produce line 3. Simplify the second conjunct of line 3 to produce line 4. Use modus ponens on lines 4 and 2 to produce line 5.

4. Use commutation on line 1 to produce line 2. Use wedge equivalence on line 2 to produce line 3.

5. Make the contradictory of the conclusion an indirect-proof assumption. Use modus ponens on lines 1 and 3 to produce line 4. Use modus ponens on lines 2 and 4 to produce line 5. Conjoin lines 3 and 5 to produce line 6. End the indirect proof.

6. Use association on line 1 to produce line 2. Use wedge equivalence on line 2 to produce line 3.

7. Use distribution on line 1 to produce line 3. Simplify line 3 to produce line 4. Use modus ponens on lines 2 and 4 to produce line 5.

8. Conjoin lines 1 and 2 to produce line 3. Use distribution on line 3 to produce line 4.

Concept Reviews

1. Explain why applications of our equivalence inferential forms to portions of lines must preserve truth.

2. Our valid inferential forms can only be applied to instances of whole lines. Explain why, in contrast to our equivalence inferential forms, an application of a valid inferential form might not preserve truth if applied to a portion of a line. [Hint: valid inferential forms preserve truth, but they do not rule out inferences from false premisses to a true conclusion.]

3. Our equivalence inferential forms can be applied in either direction, whereas our valid inferential forms can only be applied from their premisses to their conclusions. Review the possibilities for valid forms, and explain why an application of a valid inferential form from its conclusion to its premisses might not preserve truth.

4. Indirect proofs require that the contradictory, not the contrary, of the desired statement be taken as the indirect proof assumption. Review the definition of 'contraries' in Chapter 2 and explain how

the justification of indirect proof fails if a contrary, rather than the contradictory, is used for the assumption.

D. Justification of Indirect Proof

Indirect proofs can be seen as abbreviated conditional proofs. As will become evident, any formal proof that can be completed with indirect proof can also be completed with conditional proof. Adding indirect proof as an inference process does not increase the number of arguments that can be proved valid. It does, however, reduce the length of some proofs and provide alternative strategies. Conditional proof is justified in Appendix B. If conditional proof is a legitimate inference, then indirect proof must also be a legitimate inference.

Suppose that we have an initial argument with premisses P_1, P_2, and P_3. The exact number of premisses is not important. (It is important that the justification is not based on a particular number.) Since any statement is an instance of p, we will write p to indicate some conclusion. In an indirect proof, the assumption must be the contradictory of the desired statement, and at some point we must be able to derive an instance of '$q \cdot \sim q$'. Justifying indirect proof now becomes a matter of showing why the following pattern must preserve truth.

$P_1 \qquad /p$
P_2
P_3

$$\boxed{\begin{array}{l} \sim p \quad I.P.A. \\ \vdots \\ q \cdot \sim q \end{array}}$$

p

But the above pattern can always be seen as an abbreviated conditional proof:

$P_1 \qquad /p$
P_2
P_3

$$\begin{array}{|l|}
\hline
\\
\sim p \quad C.P.A. \\
\qquad \vdots \\
q \cdot \sim q \\
\sim q \quad Simp. \\
\sim q \vee p \quad Add. \\
q \supset p \quad W.E. \\
q \quad Simp. \\
p \quad M.P. \\
\\
\hline
\end{array}$$

$\sim p \supset p \quad C.P.$
$\sim\sim p \vee p \quad W.E.$
$p \vee p \quad D.N.$
$p \quad Du.$

The contradictory of the desired statement can be seen as a conditional-proof assumption. (Remember that a conditional-proof assumption can be **any** statement.) Notice the steps from '$q \cdot \sim q$' on. The instance of '$q \cdot \sim q$' can always be simplified to the instance of $\sim q$. The conclusion can always be added to the instance of $\sim q$. All of the steps W.E., M.P., C.P., W.E., D.N., and Du. can always be carried out if we have a completed indirect proof.

In short, any argument for which we have completed an indirect proof could have been shown to be valid by using a conditional proof and following the above steps. Since a completed conditional proof shows that the argument is valid, and we know that a conditional proof can be completed for any argument which has a completed indirect proof, it follows that any argument for which we have a completed indirect proof must be valid.

Indirect proofs can follow one another and can be contained within one another, for the same reasons that conditional proofs can follow one another and be contained within one another. Showing that we are justified in placing one indirect proof within another has been left for you as a concept review problem.

Concept Review

1. Provide an argument that shows that if conditional proofs can be contained within one another, indirect proofs can also be contained within one another.

VI Optional Valid Inferential Forms

A. Rationale

We have developed what is called a system of "natural deduction." Our methods for deriving lines in formal proofs, called "rules of inference," make up our system. It is "natural" in the sense that it parallels reasoning processes that are used in everyday life. Reasoning in everyday life, as well as the system of this book, derives conclusions from accepted premisses.[8] It is called "deductive" for obvious reasons.

Not only is our present system deductively complete—capable of providing a formal proof for any valid argument of the kind that we have been considering; the system before we added indirect proof was also deductively complete. Our justification for indirect proof shows that any argument that can be proved valid by using it can also be proved valid without using it. We did not increase the number of arguments that our system is able to prove valid when we added indirect proof. Moreover, the system that results from subtracting De Morgan's laws, commutation, association, distribution, **and** indirect proof also remains deductively complete. We could eliminate all of these inferential forms from our deductive system and still not reduce the number of arguments that can be proved valid.

Adding indirect proof makes our deductive system more complex, but some arguments can be more easily proved valid in the resulting system. If we had developed a deductive system with a minimal number of inferential forms, then most arguments would have required complex formal proofs. On the other hand, we could add inferential forms to our system until every valid argument is an instance of a specific inferential form!

Logicians generally agree that systems with fewer inferential forms are more elegant than systems with more inferential forms. There is no general agreement, however, on how many inferential forms should be presented in an introductory logic course.

Each of the following inferential forms is used in everyday reasoning. If we add them to our deductive system, we will be able to construct shorter formal proofs for some arguments. Two of them, modus tollens and disjunctive syllogism, were used to complete enthymemes in Chapter 1. All of them can be considered optional; as with indirect proof, any argument

---

[8]Chapter 9 shows that our deductive system is capable of providing a formal proof for all valid arguments of the kind that we are considering. Chapter 9 also shows that our deductive system is capable of providing formal proofs for all truth-functional tautologies.

that can be proved valid by using them can also be proved valid without using them.

> *All of the following are valid inferential forms, not equivalence inferential forms. Hence, each of them must be used by forming instances from their premises to their conclusions.*

B. Modus Tollens, Disjunctive Syllogism, Hypothetical Syllogism, and Constructive Dilemma

i. Modus Tollens (M.T.)

$p \supset q$
$\underline{\sim q}$
$\therefore \sim p$

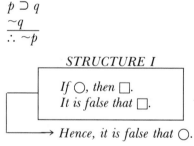

STRUCTURE I

If ○, then □.
It is false that □.

⟶ *Hence, it is false that ○.*

Using Modus Tollens in Formal Proofs

> *Modus tollens produces the negation of a conditional's antecedent. To be used, previous lines must include the conditional and a line that is the negation of the conditional's consequent.*

The following argument is an instance of modus tollens:

Premises: *If you can determine the position of a subatomic particle, then it is impossible to determine its momentum.*

   It is not impossible to determine its momentum.

Conclusion: *You cannot determine the subatomic particle's position.*[9]

---

[9]This example is based on the Heisenberg uncertainty principle. According to Werner Heisenberg, it is impossible to measure two "complementary" properties of a subatomic particle, such as its position and its momentum.

ii. Disjunctive Syllogism (D.S.)

Notice that disjunctive syllogism has two inferential forms:

$$p \lor q \qquad \text{and} \qquad p \lor q$$
$$\underline{\sim p} \qquad\qquad\qquad \underline{\sim q}$$
$$\therefore q \qquad\qquad\qquad\quad \therefore p$$

Disjunctive syllogism was also introduced in Chapter 1:

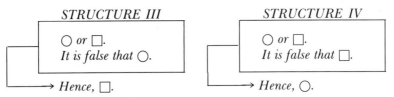

Using Disjunctive Syllogism in Formal Proofs

Disjunctive syllogism allows us to derive a disjunct, provided we have the disjunction and the negation of the other disjunct as usable lines.

Disjunctive syllogism allows us to produce a disjunct directly from a disjunction. The additional premiss must be the negation of the other disjunct. The following argument is an instance of disjunctive syllogism:

Premisses: *The tax increase would be imposed unless Lady Godiva rode naked through the town.*

               The tax increase was not imposed.

Conclusion: *Lady Godiva rode naked through the town.*[10]

iii. Hypothetical Syllogism (H.S.)

$$p \supset q$$
$$\underline{q \supset r}$$
$$\therefore p \supset r$$

Using Hypothetical Syllogism in Formal Proofs

Hypothetical syllogism allows us to derive a new conditional by eliminating a common consequent/antecedent statement that is present in two existing conditionals. To use hypothetical syllogism, we must have two conditionals, such that the consequent of one conditional is the same statement as the antecedent of the other conditional.

---

[10]Loefric, the Earl of Mercia (in England), imposed heavy taxes during the eleventh century. He agreed to rescind the tax increase only if his wife, Lady Godiva, would ride naked through the town of Coventry. She did, and he did.

Hypothetical syllogism arguments are also called "chain arguments." The two conditionals have a common antecedent/consequent link. Hypothetical syllogism derives the new conditional by eliminating the common link.

Premisses: *If science is to continue advancing, then potentially harmful experiments must be conducted.*

If potentially harmful experiments must be conducted, then animals should be used in scientific experiments.

Conclusion: *If science is to continue advancing, then animals should be used in scientific experiments.*

"Potentially harmful experiments must be conducted" is the common link.

iv. Constructive Dilemma (C.D.)

$(p \supset q) \cdot (r \supset s)$
$\underline{p \lor r}$
$\therefore q \lor s$

Using Constructive Dilemma in Formal Proofs

Constructive dilemma can be understood to be a disjunctive version of modus ponens. Notice that the disjuncts in the conclusion were each a consequent in the first premiss. This inference can be remembered by noticing that the second premiss is a disjunction of antecedents, and its conclusion is a disjunction of consequents. Since the second premiss is a disjunction, the conclusion is also a disjunction.

Constructive dilemma arguments tend to present "damned if you do and damned if you don't" perspectives. The following argument uses our constructive dilemma inferential form:

Premisses: *If animals are like us, then using them in scientific experiments is immoral; whereas if animals are not like us, then using them in scientific experiments is pointless.*

Either animals are like us or animals are not like us.

Conclusion: *Using animals in scientific experiments is either immoral or pointless.*

Exercises IX

Provide a formal proof for each of the following arguments. Use any of our inferential forms as needed.

*1. $K \lor U$
     $\sim K$
     $\overline{\therefore U}$

2. $R \supset C$
    $T \supset L$
    $R \lor T$
    $\overline{\therefore C \lor L}$

*3. $F \supset N$
     $N \supset P$
     $\overline{\therefore F \supset P}$

4. $J \supset O$
    $\sim O$
    $\overline{\therefore \sim J}$

*5. $E \supset P$
     $R \supset L$
     $\overline{\therefore (E \lor R) \supset (P \lor L)}$

6. $V \supset U$
    $U \supset D$
    $(V \supset D) \supset T$
    $\overline{\therefore T}$

7. $I \supset [(S \cdot L) \lor P]$
    $(S \cdot L) \supset C$
    $P \supset H$
    $\overline{\therefore I \supset (C \lor H)}$

8. $\sim A \supset (S \cdot I)$
    $\sim S$
    $\overline{\therefore A}$

*9. $U \supset (M \cdot T)$
     $(T \cdot M) \supset S$
     $B \supset S$
     $U \lor B$
     $\overline{\therefore S}$

10. $\sim M \lor \sim S$
     $(R \cdot B) \supset S$
     M
     $\overline{\therefore R \supset \sim B}$

11. $G \supset (L \lor Q)$
     $G \cdot \sim L$
     $\overline{\therefore Q}$

12. $(K \lor P) \cdot (K \lor A)$
     $(K \lor W) \equiv (M \supset C)$
     $\overline{\therefore \sim (P \cdot A) \supset \sim (M \cdot \sim C)}$

*13. $H \lor C$
      $I \supset U$
      $U \supset \sim I$
      $P \supset (H \supset T)$
      $P \supset (C \supset R)$
      $\overline{\therefore (P \lor I) \supset (T \lor R)}$

14. $(C \lor B) \supset T$
     $(\sim C \cdot \sim B) \supset O$
     $\sim O \lor S$
     $\sim T$
     $\overline{\therefore S}$

15. $Z \supset [(K \cdot A) \supset (L \lor T)]$
     $\sim L \cdot (L \lor A)$
     $\overline{\therefore Z \supset (K \supset T)}$

16. $H \supset (K \supset C)$
     $Y \supset (D \supset S)$
     $(H \lor Y) \cdot (K \cdot D)$
     $\overline{\therefore C \lor S}$

Exercises X

Use the italicized letters for the required statement constants, and symbolize each of the following arguments. Next, construct a formal proof for each of them. If you become bogged down when attempting to construct formal proofs, be sure to review your symbolizations. All of the following are valid arguments, but if you missymbolize them, you might wind up attempting to construct formal proofs for invalid arguments.

*1. Women either speak out *a*gainst the male-dominated society, or they are treated like *c*hildren. Women either speak out *a*gainst the male-dominated society, or they are treated like *s*ervants. Hence, women either speak out *a*gainst the male-dominated society, or they are treated like *c*hildren and *s*ervants.

2. Unless women receive equal *p*ay, they aren't equal to *m*en. Unless women receive equal *r*espect, they aren't equal to *m*en. So, only if women receive equal *p*ay and equal *r*espect, are they equal to *m*en.

3. If either North Vietnam was *d*efeated or South Vietnam continues to be an *i*ndependent country, then the U.S. war effort in Vietnam was *s*uccessful. The U.S. war effort in Vietnam wasn't *s*uccessful. Hence, North Vietnam wasn't *d*efeated.

4. If either the word 'broad' didn't *o*riginally mean "pregnant cow" or the word 'broad' isn't *d*emeaning to women for other reasons, then it is acceptable to refer to women as "*b*roads." It is not acceptable to refer to women as either "*b*roads" or "*c*hicks." So the word 'broad' *o*riginally meant "pregnant cow."

*5. Unless criminals *t*hink about their crimes before committing them, capital punishment does not *d*eter crime. If criminals *t*hink about their crimes before committing them and capital punishment *d*eters crime, then capital punishment is *j*ustified. Capital punishment is *j*ustified only if it *d*eters crime. Hence, capital punishment is *j*ustified if and only if it *d*eters crime.

6. Unless we *l*egalize drugs, we will have to spend more *m*oney on law enforcement, and a segment of our society will remain *a*ddicted to drugs. If we *l*egalize drugs, then a segment of our society will continue *u*sing them; and, if a segment of our society continues *u*sing them, then a segment of our society will remain *a*ddicted to drugs. Consequently, a segment of our society will remain *a*ddicted to drugs.

C. Justification of Our Optional Inferential Forms as Derived Rules

Our last four rules of inference can be justified by using truth tables to show that each of them is a valid argument form. They can also be justified as "derived rules," by showing, as we did for indirect proof, that all of their allowable derivations can be accomplished with our deductive system.

A rule of inference can be justified as a derived rule by showing that every derivation that it allows can be accomplished by the other rules of inference.

DEFINITION 5.5

A *derived inference rule*, in a deductive system that has a set of rules which are regarded as basic, is an inference rule that is justified by showing that all of its derivations can be accomplished with the set of basic inference rules.

We will regard our previously stated inference rules as our set of basic rules.

i. Justification of Modus Tollens

Suppose that we have a formal proof such that we are able to apply modus tollens. The proof must have a line that is an instance of '$p \supset q$', and another line that is an instance of $\sim q$. We need to show that it is possible to use our other rules of inference and derive a line that is an instance of $\sim p$.

Assume that a formal proof has lines that are instances of:

$p \supset q$

$\sim q$

Any problem can always employ the following steps:

1. $p \supset q$ *Assumed*
2. $\sim q$ *Assumed*
3. $\sim p \lor q$ *W.E. 1*
4. $q \lor \sim p$ *Comm. 3*
5. $\sim\sim q \lor \sim p$ *D.N. 4*
6. $\sim q \supset \sim p$ *W.E. 5*
7. $\sim p$ *M.P. 6, 2*

Hence, any potential application of modus tollens can be eliminated by following the series of steps outlined above. Modus tollens has been justified as a derived rule.

ii. Justification of Disjunctive Syllogism

Suppose that we have a formal proof such that we are able to apply disjunctive syllogism. Assume that a formal proof has lines that are instances of:

$p \lor q$

$\sim p$

or:

$p \lor q$

$\sim q$

Any problem can always employ the following steps:

1. $p \lor q$ *Assumed*	1. $p \lor q$ *Assumed*
2. $\sim p$ *Assumed*	2. $\sim q$
3. $\sim\sim p \lor q$ *D.N. 1*	3. $q \lor p$ *Comm. 1*
4. $\sim p \supset q$ *W.E. 3*	4. $\sim\sim q \lor p$ *D.N. 3*
5. q *M.P. 4, 2*	5. $\sim q \supset p$ *W.E. 4*
	6. p *M.P. 5, 2*

Disjunctive syllogism has been justified as a derived rule.

Concept Reviews

1. a. Provide justification for hypothetical syllogism as a derived rule.
    b. Provide justification for constructive dilemma as a derived rule.
2. Does adding a derived rule increase the number of arguments that can be proved valid? Explain why or why not.
3. Some systems have the rule of detachment as a valid inferential form. The rule of detachment is:

    $\sim(p \cdot q)$

    $\underline{p \qquad\qquad}$

    $\therefore \sim q$

    Prove that the rule of detachment can be established as a derived rule.

4. What does it mean to claim that if we eliminate conditional proof and indirect proof from our system of natural deduction, the resulting system is deductively incomplete? If this claim is true (it is), is it possible to establish conditional proof and indirect proof as derived rules in the new system? Why or why not?

6 Partial Truth Tables and Truth Trees

We have focused on valid arguments since the end of Chapter 3. Formal proofs provide a means for creating valid arguments and for proving that an argument is valid.

Suppose, however, that we are unable to complete a formal proof for a particular argument. The reason might be that the argument is invalid. There is also the possibility that the argument is valid and we have merely failed to find a way to derive its conclusion. We cannot construct a formal proof to show that an argument is *in*valid.

In principle, we can always resort to truth tables to determine whether an argument (of the kind that we have been considering) is valid. As developed in Chapter 3, however, truth tables can become tedious. Truth tables require 2^n number of lines, where n is the number of distinct variables in the form. An argument form with only eight variables requires a 256-line truth table, and super human patience!

This chapter presents shorter ways to accomplish some of the tasks that have been accomplished by using truth tables. If we either know how to apply the partial truth table method or know how to construct truth trees, we will be able to avoid a good deal of drudgery.

I Partial Truth Tables

January 30, 1948:

> As the first bullet struck, Gandhi's foot, which was in motion, descended to the ground, but he remained standing. The second bullet struck; blood began to stain Gandhi's white clothes. His face turned ashen pale. His hands, which had been in the touch-palm position, descended slowly, and one arm remained momentarily on Abha's neck.

Gandhi murmered, "Hey, Rama (Oh, God)." A third shot rang
out. The limp body settled to the ground. His spectacles dropped
to the earth. The leather sandals slipped from his feet.[1]

Nathuran Vinayak Godse had assassinated Mahatma Gandhi. Gandhi
had dedicated his life to the belief that all violence is senseless. Ironically,
his death proved to be senseless, even from the viewpoint of his assassin.
Godse's decision was based on his emotions rather than correct reasoning.

Gandhi and Godse were both Hindus. Godse was a Chitpowan
Brahman, the highest Hindu caste. Gandhi was born two caste levels beneath
him. Gandhi had spent years arguing in favor of equality and against the
caste system in India. Godse resented Gandhi's perspective.

Gandhi wanted to unify all Indians, both Hindus and Moslems.
He believed that human similarities are more important than religious
differences. He even permitted readings from the Koran, the Moslems'
holiest book, at Hindu services. Godse resented the Moslem influence.

The final straw came when Gandhi persuaded the Indian government
to pay 550 million rupees (approximately $180 million) to the Moslem nation
of Pakistan as a "peace offering." Godse was distressed by what he perceived
to be Moslem attacks on Hinduism. He was outraged that Gandhi, another
Hindu, would assist Moslems. As Godse testified at his trial, "I sat brooding
intensely on the atrocities perpetrated on Hinduism and its dark and deadly
future if left to face [Moslems] outside and Gandhi inside . . . I decided all
of a sudden to take the extreme step against Gandhi."[2]

Godse's reasoning can be outlined as follows:

*If Gandhi remained alive, then Hinduism would continue to be attacked
from the inside.*

*Hence, if Gandhi did not remain alive, then Hinduism would not con-
tinue to be attacked from the inside.*

When viewed from the standpoint of logic, Godse's decision was based
on an invalid argument.[3] We can symbolize the outline of Godse's "reasoning"
as follows:

$$\frac{G \supset A}{\therefore \sim G \supset \sim A}$$

---

[1]Louis Fischer, *The Life of Mahatma Gandhi*, (New York: Harper and Row, 1950), 4.

[2]Ibid., 504.

[3]Following events quickly confirmed that Godse had acted upon an invalid
inference. Gandhi's death caused a backlash in India against Hindus, many of
whom were subsequently viewed as anti-Moslem extremists.

Our interpretation of Godse's argument is a parallel-instance of the following invalid form:

$$\frac{p \supset q}{\therefore\ \sim p \supset \sim q}$$

Since this form has only two variables, we can verify that it is invalid with the following truth table:

p	$\supset$	q	$\sim p$	$\supset$	$\sim q$
T T T			FT T FT		
T F F			FT T TF		
F T T			**TF F FT**		
F T F			TF T TF		

Since line three shows the possibility of all true premisses and a false conclusion, the above table shows that the form is invalid. (Recall that all that it takes to show that a form is invalid is *one* line that has all true premisses and a false conclusion.)

Our partial-truth-table method attempts to show that a form has the possibility of all true premisses and a false conclusion without constructing the remainder of the table. There is no point in writing down the remainder of a truth table, if doing so cannot change the outcome.

> **The partial truth-table method for showing invalidity attempts to find a line of the complete truth table that shows an argument form to be invalid. It does this without constructing the remainder of the table.**

Notice that on line three of the complete truth table, p stands for a statement that is false and q stands for a statement that is true. When we apply our partial-truth-table method to this problem, we will assign p as false and q as true. Recognizing these values and being aware that the complete truth table has at least one line with all true premisses and a false conclusion is enough to justify claiming that the form is invalid. Our partial-truth-table method provides the following solution:

$$\frac{p \supset q}{\therefore\ \sim p \supset \sim q} \qquad \textit{Invalid: p F, q T}$$

Obviously, writing a *T* next to a variable fails to make anything true and writing an *F* next to a variable fails to make anything false. Writing a *T* next to a variable represents a decision to consider those lines of the complete truth table where statements that replace the variable are true. Writing an *F* next to a variable represents a decision to consider those lines of the complete truth table where statements that replace the variable are false.

In order to apply the partial-truth-table method effectively, it is important to notice and take "forced assignments."

DEFINITION 6.1

When we apply the partial-truth-table method, a variable has a *forced assignment* if and only if it must be specified as true or it must be specified as false so that the conclusion will be false or so that a premiss will be true.

Our example can be used to clarify the notion of forced assignments.

$$\frac{p \supset q}{\therefore \sim p \supset \sim q}$$

We want to assign values to p and q so that we designate at least one line of the complete truth table such that the premiss is true and the conclusion is false. There are three assignments that will make the premiss true: 'p true and q true', 'p false and q true', and 'p false and q false'. Since the first premiss can be true when p is either true or false and can also be true when q is either true or false, the premiss does not designate forced assignments for either of its variables.

Suppose that we look at the conclusion. The conclusion of the form is a conditional, and if a conditional is false, then its antecedent must be true and its consequent must be false. In order to make the form's conclusion false, we have the following forced assignments: 'p false', and 'q true'. We should list these values, since if the form has the possibility of all true premisses and a false conclusion, it must be when p and q have these values.

Is it possible to use these assignments and designate a line of the complete truth table with all true premisses? Since the premiss only contains the variables p and q and is true when p is false and q is true, we have proved that this form has the possibility of all true premisses and a false conclusion. The form must be invalid. Notice, again, that our assigned values for p and q are the same as those on line three of the complete table.

Suppose that we attempt to apply our partial truth table method on the following valid argument form:

$$\frac{\begin{array}{l} \sim(p \cdot q) \\ q \end{array}}{\therefore \sim p}$$

In order to make the conclusion false, we have the forced assignment of 'p true'. In order to make the second premiss true, we have the forced assignment 'q true'. But if p and q are both true, we cannot make the first premiss true. Since our assignments for p and q are both forced, we know that different assignments for these variables will result either in making the second premiss false or in making the conclusion true. We can see that it is impossible to assign truth-values to the variables so that all of the premisses are true and the conclusion is false. The complete truth table for this form must lack this possibility, and so this form is valid.

When a complete truth table is only four lines long, the partial-truth-table method is not much more efficient than constructing the complete truth table. But suppose that we had a problem with 256 (or more) lines. There are times when only having to designate one line of a complete truth table can be very helpful!

The partial-truth-table method cannot always be applied as straightforwardly as in our previous examples. Some applications require a bit of trial and error. Constructing partial truth tables requires skill, just as constructing formal proofs requires skill. The following guidelines will help solve most problems.

A. Guidelines for Partial Truth Tables

1. Use forced assignments whenever possible.
2. No argument form has more than one conclusion, and any line of a complete truth table that shows a form to be invalid *must* have truth-values such that the conclusion is false. Hence, most problems should be started by assigning truth-values so that the conclusion is false. (If, however, there are no forced assignments in the conclusion but there is a forced assignment in a premiss, then begin with the premiss's forced assignment.)
3. When making either the conclusion false or a premiss true, never assign truth-values to more variables than is necessary.

A premiss can often be made true without assigning truth-values to all of its variables. A conclusion can often be made false without assigning truth-values to all of its variables.

A conjunction is true if and only if both of its conjuncts are true. Hence, any conjunction can be made false by merely stipulating that *one* of its conjuncts is false:

$F \cdot ? = false$
$? \cdot F = false$

If a problem requires us to make a conjunction true, each conjunct has the forced assignment of 'true'.

A disjunction is false if and only if both of its disjuncts are false. Hence, any disjunction can be made true by merely stipulating that *one* of its disjuncts is true:

$T \lor ? = true$
$? \lor T = true$

If a problem requires us to make a disjunction false, each disjunct has the forced assignment of 'false'.

A conditional is false if and only if then its antecedent is true and its consequent is false. Hence, any conditional can be made true either by stipulating that its antecedent is false or by stipulating that its consequent is true:

$F \supset ? = true$
$? \supset T = true$

If a problem requires us to make a conditional false, the antecedent has the forced assignment of 'true', and the consequent has the forced assignment of 'false'.

Suppose that we apply our partial truth method to the following argument form:

$$\frac{p \lor q}{\therefore p \cdot q}$$

This problem lacks any initial forced assignments. There are a variety of ways to make the conclusion false and a variety of ways to make the premiss true. Our guidelines suggest that we begin with the conclusion. We can make the conclusion false either by designating that p is false or by designating that q is false. We are not going to assign values to more variables than is necessary, and we can make the conclusion false by assigning a value of 'false' to only one of the variables. But which one? Unless we can see further into the problem, we should assign a truth-value to some variable in order to get the problem started. Suppose that we decide to begin the problem by assigning p false:

p false   *Nonforced assignment*

We have made the conclusion false. Can p be false while the premiss is true? We can make the premiss true by taking the now forced assignment 'q true'. We have shown that the complete truth table for this form expresses the possibility of all true premisses and a false conclusion, the line where p is false and q is true. Hence, we have shown that this form is invalid.

If we make a nonforced assignment and are able to make all of the premisses true and the conclusion false, then the form is invalid. But suppose that, unlike our last example, we make a nonforced assignment and discover that we cannot make all of the premisses true. The form might still be invalid. A form is valid only if it is *impossible* to assign truth-values so that all of the premisses are true and the conclusion is false. A different initial guess might have enabled us to find a line that shows the form to be invalid.

> **If we make a nonforced assignment and we are unable to make**
> **all of the premisses true and the conclusion false, then we must**
> **go back and try an alternative assignment.**

Suppose that we apply our partial-truth-table method to the following argument form:

$$p \equiv (q \equiv r)$$
$$(\sim q \cdot r) \lor t$$
$$\underline{(s \cdot p) \supset t}$$
$$\therefore p \equiv t$$

Again we must do something to get the problem started. Suppose that we try the following:

> *p true*   *Nonforced assignment*
>
> *t false*   *Nonforced assignment*

Notice that if t is false, then in order to make the second premiss true, q is forced false and r is forced true. But these values make the first premiss, '$p \equiv (q \equiv r)$', false.

This form might still be invalid. We should go back to our nonforced assignment and make a different guess. We can view our second assignments as forced, since they complete all of the possibilities for making the conclusion false.

> *p false*
>
> *t true*

If t is true, then the second and third premisses are both true. (Why?) We can make the first premiss true by assigning q true and r false. We have a set of truth-value assignments that show that the form is invalid:

> *p false*
>
> *t true*
>
> *q true*
>
> *r false*

Our guidelines have us begin by making assignments so that the conclusion is false, unless none of the variables has a forced assignment in the form's conclusion and one (or more) of our variables has a forced assignment in a premiss. The next example points out this pattern.

$$p \supset (q \cdot r)$$
$$(r \lor s) \equiv (t \lor u)$$
$$\underline{p \cdot \sim(u \equiv s)}$$
$$\therefore u \cdot q$$

This problem's conclusion has a dot as the major connective. So we lack any forced assignments in order to make the conclusion false. In this case, we should look for forced assignments in the premises.

The major connective in the third premiss is the dot. Hence, this premiss will be true only if both of its conjuncts are true. *p must* be assigned true. We should begin the problem with this forced assignment.

Since *p* has been assigned true and we wish to make the first premiss true, we have the following forced assignments: '*q* true' and '*r* true'. Once *q* has been assigned true, we can now see that *u* must be made false so that the conclusion is false. By starting with a premiss rather than the conclusion, we have obtained a number of forced assignments. So far we have the following truth-value assignments:

p true

q true

r true

u false

u and *s* must have opposite truth-values for '~(*u* ≡ *s*)' to be true. Since *u* has been forced false, we have the forced assignment of '*s* true'.

Finally, given that *r* and *s* are true and *u* is false, *t* is forced true in order to make the second premiss true. This example is shown to be invalid by the fact that there is a line of its complete truth table with the following truth-values:

p true

q true

r true

u false

s true

t true

A few minutes were required in order to apply the partial-truth-table method to our last example, but having to construct the complete 64-line table would be a real hassle! Our partial-truth-table method usually does not require us to make nonforced assignments. Most of its applications are more straightforward than our last example.

B. Additional Suggestions

Check any partial truth table with the following steps:

1. Be certain that the same variable has not been assigned as both true and false.

2. If we are claiming that our assignments show that a form is invalid, then we should make sure that our assignments make all of its premises true and its conclusion false.

3. In order to claim that a form is valid, we must have examined all of the possibilities for showing invalidity. It is helpful to keep a running list of assignments, forced and nonforced, and of the premises that have been made true.

Exercises I

Suppose for the purpose of these exercises that A and B represent true statements, Y and Z represent false statements, and '?' represents a location of unknown truth-value. Which of the following statements must be true, which false, and which cannot be determined?

*1. $Y \supset ?$

*3. $\sim(A \lor ?)$

*5. $? \cdot A$

*7. $(? \cdot Y) \supset ?$

*9. $(A \lor ?) \cdot (? \lor B)$

11. $(A \cdot ?) \lor (A \cdot B)$

*13. $? \lor [? \lor (? \lor A)]$

15. $(? \supset A) \supset (? \cdot Y)$

2. $A \lor ?$

4. $Y \cdot ?$

6. $? \supset A$

8. $\sim(Y \cdot ?) \supset Z$

10. $(Y \lor ?) \cdot (? \lor Z)$

12. $(A \cdot ?) \lor (? \cdot B)$

14. $(? \supset ?) \supset (Y \supset ?)$

Exercises II

Each of the following argument forms is invalid. Use the partial-truth-table method, and specify a truth-table line that proves invalidity.

*1. $(\sim p \cdot \sim q) \supset r$
   $\therefore (p \cdot q) \supset \sim r$

3. $p \lor q$
   $p \supset \sim r$
   $r \lor s$
   $\overline{\therefore q}$

2. $p \supset q$
   $q \supset r$
   $\overline{\therefore r \supset p}$

4. $p \supset q$
   $q \supset r$
   $r \lor t$
   $\overline{\therefore p \supset t}$

*5. $(p \cdot q) \lor (r \cdot s)$
    $p \supset t$
    $\underline{s \supset u}$
    $\therefore q \supset u$

6. $(p \supset q) \cdot [r \supset (s \lor t)]$
    $\sim(r \supset s) \cdot (q \equiv u)$
    $\sim u \lor \sim v$
    $\underline{\sim p \supset (v \cdot w)}$
    $\therefore v \lor w$

7. $p \equiv \sim q$
    $r \lor (s \lor t)$
    $\sim p \supset \sim s$
    $\underline{q}$
    $\therefore r \cdot t$

8. $p \equiv (q \cdot r)$
    $(q \supset s) \cdot (r \supset t)$
    $\sim p \supset u$
    $\underline{\sim s \lor (\sim t \lor v)}$
    $\therefore p \supset (w \supset u)$

*9. $\sim(p \supset q)$
    $p \supset (r \lor s)$
    $\sim q \supset (s \supset t)$
    $\underline{\sim t \lor u}$
    $\therefore u$

10. $(p \supset q) \cdot (r \supset s)$
    $p \cdot \sim s$
    $\underline{(p \cdot \sim r) \supset (t \lor w)}$
    $\therefore t \supset w$

11. $p \supset (q \supset r)$
    $s \supset (t \supset u)$
    $\underline{(p \lor s) \cdot (q \cdot t)}$
    $\therefore r \cdot u$

12. $p \supset q$
    $(r \lor s) \supset (u \equiv v)$
    $(\sim p \cdot \sim q) \supset (u \equiv s)$
    $\sim q$
    $\underline{\sim v \lor \sim s}$
    $\therefore \sim u \cdot \sim r$

*13. $p \lor (q \cdot r)$
    $[(p \lor r) \cdot s] \supset (u \lor v)$
    $\underline{[(p \lor q) \lor t] \supset (\sim u \lor \sim v)}$
    $\therefore \sim u \equiv v$

14. $(p \cdot q) \lor (\sim p \cdot \sim q)$
    $(r \lor s) \supset \sim(p \equiv q)$
    $\sim(t \cdot \sim r)$
    $\sim t \supset v$
    $\underline{\sim s \supset (t \supset w)}$
    $\therefore v \cdot w$

15. $p \lor q$
    $r \supset s$
    $s \supset \sim r$
    $t \supset (p \supset u)$
    $\underline{t \supset (p \supset v)}$
    $\therefore (t \lor r) \supset (u \cdot v)$

Exercises III

Use the italicized letters for your statement constants, and symbolize each of the following with our artificial language. Write out the argument form that has the argument as a parallel-instance, and apply the partial truth table method to determine whether the argument form and argument are valid. If the argument is invalid, list a set of truth-value assignments that prove its invalidity. If the argument is valid, provide a formal proof.

*1. That the "I'm OK, you're OK" approach to life is correct implies that all desires are equal. All desires can be equal only if the thief's desire to have my car is as reasonable as my desire to have my car. Unless the thief's desire to have my car is not as reasonable as my desire to have my car, there's no point in calling it my car! So, if the "I'm OK, you're OK" approach to life is *incorrect*, then there is a point in calling it my car.

2. The United States has tried, ever since prohibition, to eliminate alcohol abuse. To try to eliminate alcohol abuse implies that the drinking-driving issue must be resolved. If we resolve the drinking-driving issue, then either the drinking age must be raised to 35 or the driving age must be raised to 35. Military obligations and the ability to drink are connected, if no sober person would want to go off to war. That the drinking age should not be raised to 35 is implied by a connection between the ability to drink and military obligations. Hence, If no sober person would want to go off to war then the driving age should be raised to 35.

3. "A dolphin was mistaken for an armed North Korean spy and shot to death by South Korean soldiers near the town of Samchonpo."[4] A dolphin could be mistaken for an armed North Korean spy if and only if the South Korean soldiers were either careless or drunk. That the dolphin was shot dead by South Korean soldiers implies that they weren't drunk. So, it must have happened at night and the South Korean soldiers were careless.

4. That Joan of Arc either heard voices or communicated with spirits implies that she was neither well-balanced nor found not guilty of heresy. Either Joan of Arc was found not guilty of heresy or she was burned at the stake. Although Joan of Arc is a saint of the Roman Catholic Church, she heard voices. Hence, she was burned at the stake.

*5. Gandhi could accept India's involvement in World War II if and only if Winston Churchill guaranteed India's independence. Churchill could guarantee India's independence if and only if he violated his ideals of a British empire; whereas Gandhi could accept India's involvement in world War II if and only if he sacrificed his belief in pacifism. Gandhi wanted India's independence even more than he valued pacifism, and if so, then he would sacrifice his belief in pacifism. Hence, Churchill guaranteed India's independence.

---

[4]"You Should Have Seen the One That Got Away," *The Progressive*, March 1985, 13.

6. Although 1,400 Cubans were *t*rained by the CIA, they *f*ailed to overthrow Fidel Castro at the Bay of Pigs. If 1,400 Cubans were *t*rained by the CIA, then we have *e*vidence of involvement on the part of the United States. President John F. Kennedy faced public *h*umiliation, if 1,400 Cubans *f*ailed to overthrow Fidel Castro at the Bay of Pigs and we have *e*vidence of involvement on the part of the United States. Hence, President John F. Kennedy *a*uthorized the Bay of Pigs invasion and faced public *h*umiliation.

7. Ireland was *p*redominately Roman Catholic, yet Henry VIII of England *c*losed the Catholic monasteries in Ireland and *d*eclared himself King of Ireland. If Henry VIII of England *c*losed the Catholic monasteries in Ireland, then if Ireland was *p*redominately Roman Catholic then Ireland *r*ebelled against English rule. Hence, Henry VIII of England *d*eclared himself King of Ireland and Ireland *r*ebelled against English rule.

8. The Olympic games of 1936 were *h*eld in Nazi Germany. Jesse Owens was *b*lack and *c*ompeted in the Olympic games of 1936. Therefore, Jesse Owens either did, or did not, *w*in four gold medals in the Olympic games of 1936.

*9. Only if carbon dioxide levels are *c*ontinuing to increase and our planet is continuing to become *w*armer, must we *a*ccept current beliefs regarding the greenhouse effect. That carbon dioxide levels are *c*ontinuing to rise implies that *i*ndustrial pollution is increasing; unless we do not *a*ccept current beliefs regarding the greenhouse effect. If the summer of 1988 was exceptionally *h*ot, then either the jet stream was *p*ushed farther north than usual in 1988 or we must *a*ccept current beliefs regarding the greenhouse effect. *I*ndustrial pollution is not increasing, our planet is continuing to become *w*armer, and the summer of 1988 was exceptionally *h*ot. Hence, we must *a*ccept current beliefs regarding the greenhouse effect.

Concept Reviews

1. Successfully completing a partial truth table for an argument form shows that it is invalid. Why is it impossible to provide a line of a complete truth table that shows that a form is valid?

2. Suppose that we are able to produce a set of partial-truth-table assignments that will make all of the premises true and the conclusion false, without assigning a truth-value to one of the variables. What does the unneeded variable assignment indicate about the complete truth table for the form?

3. How can an invalid argument have all true premisses and a true conclusion, when the partial-truth-table method has us assign values so that the form has all true premisses and a false conclusion? (If necessary, review the relationship between invalid forms and invalid instances.)

II   Truth Trees

KEY TERMS FOR THIS SECTION

Use the glossary as necessary, and review the definitions of these terms prior to a second reading of this section.

Set   **Inconsistent set of statement**
Member of a set   **forms**
Consistent set of statement forms

A. Consistent and Inconsistent Sets of Statement Forms

We will construct truth trees for collections of statement forms. Collections of objects, including statement forms, are called "sets."

DEFINITION 6.2

A *set* is any clearly defined collection of objects.

DEFINITION 6.3

An object within a set is called a *member* or element of the set.

Objects can be seen as collected into a set on the basis of almost any characteristic, but not on the basis of a characteristic such that an object is a member of a set if and only if it is not a member of the set. We can talk about the set of all students, about the set of all students in a particular room, or about the set of all female or male students in a particular room.

Parts of the members of a set are not, as such, members of the set.

Students in a particular room have chins, arms, legs, and so on. Their chins, arms, and legs are not members of the set of students in the room. Chins, arms, and legs are not students. Body parts fail to meet the characteristic that defines this set's membership. Arms are not students, and so they are not considered to be members of the set.

Our concern in this chapter is with sets of statement forms. Sets of statement forms are written out by placing the members within braces, '{ }'. Commas are used to separate the members. The set containing the statement forms '$p \supset q$', p, and $\sim q$ is written out as:

$$\{p \supset q, p, \sim q\}$$

Although '$p \supset q$' is a member of the above set, q is not a member, even though q is a part of '$p \supset q$'. Just as parts of students are not members of sets that only contain students, parts of statement forms are not automatically members of the set that contains the whole statement form. p is a member of the above set, not because it is part of '$p \supset q$', but because it is specified as a member.

The collection of statement forms that contains '$p \supset (q \supset r)$', p, $\sim q$, and r is written out as:

$$\{p \supset (q \supset r), p, \sim q, r\}$$

The collection of statement forms that contains '$p \supset (q \supset r)$' and p is written out as:

$$\{p \supset (q \supset r), p\}$$

DEFINITION 6.4

A set of statement forms is *consistent* if and only if it is possible for all of its members to be true.

DEFINITION 6.5

A set of statement forms is *inconsistent* if and only if it is impossible for all of its members to be true.

As discussed in Chapter 3, truth tables can be used to express possibilities for statement forms. We can use them to determine whether a set of statement forms is consistent.

> **A set of statements forms is consistent if and only if there is at least one line of a truth table such that all of the members of the set are true.**

> **A set of statement forms is inconsistent if and only if there is no line of a truth table such that all of the members of the set are true.**

Suppose that we wish to determine whether the following set of statement forms is consistent:

$$\{p \supset q, p, \sim q\}$$

We can construct the following truth table for the elements of this set:

$p \supset q$	p	$\sim q$
T T T	T	F
T F F	T	T
F T T	F	F
F T F	F	T

Notice that there is no line of the truth table for the elements of this set such that all of them are true. Hence, this set is inconsistent.

Suppose that we consider the following set of statement forms:

$$\{p \supset (q \supset r), p, \sim q, r\}$$

We can create the following truth table for the elements of this set:

$p \supset (q \supset r)$	p	$\sim q$	r
T T T T T	T	F	T
T F T F F	T	F	F
T T F T T	T	T	T
T T F T F	T	T	F
F T T T T	F	F	T
F T T F F	F	F	F
F T F T T	F	T	T
F T F T F	F	T	F

Clearly it is possible for all of the elements of this set to be true. Hence, this set is consistent.

We can now specify an alternative method, the method of constructing "truth trees," that can be used to determine whether a set of statement forms is consistent. The truth-tree method is mechanical, in that it can be described with a list of rules; and it is efficient, in that it eliminates the need for constructing complete truth tables. Once we are aware of how to construct truth trees and can determine whether sets of statement forms are consistent, we will be able to use them to determine whether argument forms are valid. We will also use truth trees to determine whether statement forms are tautologous, self-contradictory, or contingent.

B. Constructing Truth Trees

Truth trees systematically use the definitions of our truth-functional connectives to determine whether the members of a set of statement forms can all be true. If they can all be true, the set is consistent. If they cannot all be true, the set is inconsistent.

We will explain the method by first considering some relatively simple examples. The following example shows how conjunctions are expressed with truth trees:

$$\{p \cdot q, q \cdot r\}$$

The first step in creating a truth tree requires the construction of the tree's "trunk." The trunk is produced by writing the elements of the set in a column:

$$p \cdot q$$
$$q \cdot r$$

Truth tree construction is based on the initial ***pretense*** that it is possible for all of the elements of a set to be true. Truth trees are started on the pretense that the set is consistent. Given this, each element is treated as true when it is first written. The above trunk treats '$p \cdot q$' and '$q \cdot r$' as though they are both true.

Any conjunction is true if and only if each of its conjuncts is true. '$p \cdot q$' is true if and only if p is true and q is true. We can express this by adding them to the tree:

$$p \cdot q$$
$$q \cdot r$$

Added by treating p as true
and q as true
$$\begin{array}{|l} p \\ q \end{array}$$

'$q \cdot r$' is also a conjunction. Hence, if we are treating '$q \cdot r$' as though it is true, then we should add q and r to the tree:

$$p \cdot q$$
$$q \cdot r$$
$$p$$
$$q$$

Added by treating q as true
and r as true

$$q$$
$$r$$

Notice that the elements of the set have been reduced to individual statement variables. Asking whether the original set is consistent is equivalent, in this case, to asking whether it is possible for all of the statement variables in the tree to be true. Obviously, they can. Since all of the elements of our set are true when p, q, and r are true, we know that the set is consistent.

Suppose that we compare the above truth tree with the complete truth table for this set of statement forms:

p	$\cdot$	q	q	$\cdot$	r
T	T	T	T	T	T
T	T	T	T	F	F
T	F	F	F	F	T
T	F	F	F	F	F
F	F	T	T	T	T
F	F	T	T	F	F
F	F	F	F	F	T
F	F	F	F	F	F

Our truth tree shows consistency by finding line one of the complete truth table—the line where p, and q, and r are all true—without constructing the entire truth table.

Our next example shows how disjunctions are expressed with truth trees:

$$\{p \lor q, \sim p, q\}$$

As before, we create the tree's trunk by arranging the set's elements in a column:

$$p \lor q$$
$$\sim p$$
$$q$$

Again we will begin with the initial pretense that this set is consistent and that all of its elements can be true. To this end, q must be regarded as true. Since we are to regard ~*p* as true, we must consider *p* to be false. To determine whether it is possible for all of the elements to be true, we need a way to express truth-functional aspects of the disjunction '*p* V *q*'.

A disjunction is true if and only if at least one of its disjuncts is true. Truth-functional conditions for disjunctions are expressed by splitting the disjuncts into two branching tree "paths." '*p* V *q*' will be interpreted with a path for *p* and a path for *q*:

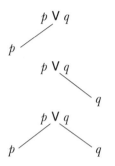

Expresses the possibility that *p* is true.

Expresses the possibility that *q* is true.

Expresses the possibility that either *p* or *q* is true.

Obviously, '*p* V *q*' is true if either path is true. We can add the above interpretation of disjunction to our example:

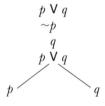

(Restatement of first member)

How can we determine whether the set of statement forms is consistent? For it to be possible for all of the initial elements to be true, there must be a possible assignment of truth-values to the variables such that each statement form contained along at least one path (including the trunk) of the tree is true.

Any variable can be designated either as true or as false. No variable can be designated as both true and false. Hence, if there is at least one path, combined with the trunk, that does not have both a statement form and its negation, then there must be a possible assignment of truth-values such that all of the elements of the set are true.

We can determine whether a set of statement forms is consistent by determining whether a statement form and its negation appears on every path leading up through the trunk. If the completed tree has a path without both a statement and its negation, then the set is consistent.

To return to our example:

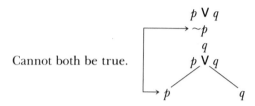

Cannot both be true.

The left path, ***beginning at the bottom of the tree*** with p, fails to show the possibility of all true statement forms. p could be true, of course, but not when $\sim p$ in the trunk is also true. This path fails to express a possibility where the statement forms can all be true. Remembering that '$p \vee q$' will also be true if the path beginning at the bottom with q is true, we can examine this path to see if it expresses the possibility of all true statement forms.

Notice that this path, leading up through the trunk, does not contain any statement form ***and*** its negation. Hence, there must be an assignment of truth-values for the variables such that all of the elements in the initial set are true. The initial set must be consistent. Examining the right path and trunk, we can see that assigning q true and p false, will make all of the statement forms along the path (and trunk) true.

The complete truth table for this example shows the set of statement forms to be consistent owing to the truth-values on line three. Notice that this line has the same truth-values that we obtained by examining the completed tree.

$p \vee q$	$\sim p$	q
T T T	F	T
T T F	F	F

F T T T	T	All elements true. p is false and q is true.

| F F F | T | F |

Our truth tree method established the existence of line three without writing out all of the truth-value possibilities!

From now on, we will place a check mark, '$\checkmark$', next to those statement forms that have been reduced. Doing this will enable us to keep track of which statement forms have been reduced. Our next example shows how check marks are used. It also shows what happens when truth trees are applied to an inconsistent set of statement forms.

$\{p \vee q, \sim p \cdot \sim q\}$

Setting up the trunk:

$$p \lor q$$
$$\sim p \cdot \sim q$$

The statement forms in our trunk include both a conjunction and a disjunction. We can apply our truth-functional operations as follows. Reducing the conjunction, we obtain:

$$p \lor q$$
$$\sim p \cdot \sim q\surd$$
$$\sim p$$
$$\sim q$$

Next we can add two branching paths to express the disjunction:

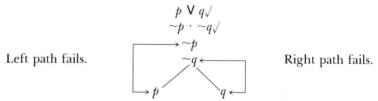

Left path fails.   Right path fails.

Having completed the truth tree, we can examine it to see whether there is at least one path leading up through the trunk that does not contain both a statement form and the negation of the same statement form. Notice that starting at the left path and proceeding up fails. This path has both p and $\sim p$. There is no possibility of assigning truth-values to the variables so that all of the statement forms along this path (including the trunk) of the tree are true. Beginning with the right path and proceeding up fails as well. This path has both q and $\sim q$.

We have entirely reduced all of our compound statement forms and found that all paths contain both a statement form and its negation. There can be no assignment for p so that all of the statement forms on the left path are true. Similarly, there can be no assignment for q so that all of the statement forms on the right path are true. The original collection of statement forms cannot all be true at once. Hence, this set is inconsistent.

Truth-tree construction is clearly based on our truth-functional definitions of conjunction and disjunction. Obviously, however, not every set that we might wish to check for consistency will consist only of conjunctions and disjunctions. For every compound statement form that is not either a conjunction or a disjunction, there is a logically equivalent statement form that can be used to reduce it when constructing truth trees.

i. Logical Equivalences

Some of our Chapter 5 equivalence inferential forms are based on logical equivalences that can be used to construct truth trees.

a. Double Negation (D.N.)

$p :: \sim\sim p$

Suppose that a truth tree contains a doubly negated statement form. We can remove the pair of tildes and add the logically equivalent statement form to our tree:

$$\sim\sim p \surd$$
$$p$$

b. Wedge Equivalence (W.E.)

$p \supset q :: \sim p \lor q$

Suppose that we wish to reduce a conditional. We can treat a conditional as though it were the logically equivalent disjunction. As with any disjunction, we will divide the disjuncts into two branching tree paths:

$$p \supset q \surd$$

$$\sim p \qquad\qquad q$$

c. De Morgan's Laws (D.M.)

$\sim(p \cdot q) :: \sim p \lor \sim q$

$\sim(p \lor q) :: \sim p \cdot \sim q$

Suppose that we wish to reduce a negated conjunction. We can treat a negated conjunction as though it were the logically equivalent disjunction:

$$\sim(p \cdot q) \surd$$

$$\sim p \qquad\qquad \sim q$$

Suppose that we wish to reduce a negated disjunction. We can treat a negated disjunction as though it were the logically equivalent conjunction:

$$\sim(p \lor q) \surd$$
$$\sim p$$
$$\sim q$$

There are three other kinds of compound statement forms that we might want to reduce when constructing a truth tree: biconditionals, negated biconditionals, and negated conditionals.

d. Biconditionals   The following complete truth table verifies that '$p \equiv q$' is logically equivalent to '$(p \cdot q) \lor (\sim p \cdot \sim q)$'.

$$(p \equiv q) \equiv [(p \cdot q) \lor (\sim p \cdot \sim q)]$$

| T T T T T T T T F F F |
| T F F T T F F F F F T |
| F F T T F F T F T F F |
| F T F T F F F T T T T |

└────same────┘

Suppose that we wish to reduce a biconditional. We can treat a biconditional as though it were the logically equivalent disjunction, and divide the disjuncts into two branching tree paths. Each disjunct is a conjunction. Hence, each new path will include both conjuncts:

e. Negated Biconditionals   A truth table can also be constructed to verify that '$\sim(p \equiv q)$' is logically equivalent to '$(p \cdot \sim q) \lor (\sim p \cdot q)$'.

Suppose that we wish to reduce a negated biconditional. We can treat the negated biconditional as though it were the logically equivalent disjunction, and divide the disjuncts into two branching tree paths. Each disjunct is a conjunction. Hence, each new path will include both conjuncts:

f. Negated Conditionals   A truth table can be constructed to verify that '$\sim(p \supset q)$' is logically equivalent to '$p \cdot \sim q$'.

Suppose that we wish to reduce a negated conditional. We can treat a negated conditional as though it were the logically equivalent conjunction:

$$\sim(p \supset q)\surd$$
$$p$$
$$\sim q$$

ii. Summary of Truth-Tree Reduction Patterns

When constructing a truth tree, any compound statement form can be reduced by applying one of the following reduction patterns. All reduction patterns must be applied on a statement form's major connective.

$$\sim\sim p\surd \qquad p \cdot q\surd \qquad p \vee q\surd \qquad p \equiv q\surd \qquad p \supset q\surd$$

$$\begin{array}{ccccc}
p & p & & & \\
& q & p \quad\quad q & p \quad\quad \sim p & \sim p \quad\quad q \\
& & & q \quad\quad \sim q &
\end{array}$$

$$\sim(p \supset q)\surd \qquad \sim(p \cdot q)\surd \qquad \sim(p \vee q)\surd \qquad \sim(p \equiv q)\surd$$

$$\begin{array}{cccc}
p & & \sim p & \\
\sim q & \sim p \quad\quad \sim q & \sim q & p \quad\quad \sim p \\
& & & \sim q \quad\quad q
\end{array}$$

iii. Closed and Open Paths

Before giving a recipe for constructing truth trees, we need a way to refer to a path that has a statement and its negation.

DEFINITION 6.6

A truth tree path is *closed* if and only if it contains, including the statement forms in the tree's trunk, a statement form and the negation of the same statement form.

For example, a path is closed when it contains p and $\sim p$, or '$p \cdot q$' and '$\sim(p \cdot q)$', or '$r \supset s$' and '$\sim(r \supset s)$'.

DEFINITION 6.7

A truth tree path is *open* if and only if it is not closed.

When a path is closed, there can be no assignment of truth-values that will make all of the statement forms along the path (including the trunk) true.

iv. Recipe for Constructing Truth Trees

Step 1   Write the elements of the set to be tested in a column. (The order in which they are written makes no difference.) Doing this creates the trunk of the tree.

Step 2   Check the trunk to see whether elements, considered as wholes, have a statement form and the negation of the same statement form. If so, the set is inconsistent. If not, place a check mark next to a statement form, and apply one of the reduction patterns *to all of the open paths* below *it*. Add statement forms to the trunk or split disjuncts, as indicated by the pattern. Examine all paths from the bottom of the tree to the top of the trunk to determine whether any paths contain a statement form and the negation of the same statement form. Place a cross, '**X**', below any closed paths.

Step 3   Continue the process in step 2 until *either*

a. All paths leading through the trunk to the top of the tree are closed. In this case the set of statement forms is inconsistent. All of the potential paths will have a **X** below them. It is impossible for all of the elements to be true.

or

b. Every statement form that has not been check-marked is either a statement variable or the negation of a statement variable. In this event, the patterns have been applied as far as possible. If there is an open path leading through the trunk to the top of the tree, the set of statement forms is consistent. It is possible for all of the elements of the set to be true.

For the most part, the above recipe merely states the process that was followed with our three examples in this section. It does, however, note two new aspects of constructing truth trees.

First, paths that have become closed—those containing a statement form and its negation—are to have a **X** placed below them. Closed paths cannot have all of the statement forms in them true.

Second, when we apply a reduction pattern we must do so with all open paths below it.

> **When one of the patterns is used to reduce a statement form, the results must be placed under each open path below it.**

Our next example points out these requirements:

$$\{p \lor q, p \lor \sim q\}$$

Step 1 has us create the trunk of the tree:

$$p \lor q$$
$$p \lor \sim q$$

The trunk does not have a statement form and the negation of the same statement form, so we should apply our reduction patterns and check-mark the statement forms that we have reduced:

Next, we should examine our tree to see if any paths have a statement form and the negation of the same statement form. Neither path does. The second statement form in the trunk is still more compound than a statement variable or the negation of a statement variable, so we should continue applying our reduction patterns. Since the second statement form is a disjunction, it must also be split.

If '$p \lor q$', the first element of our set, is true, then either p is true or q is true. Either of our paths might enable us to show that the set is consistent. We are not justified in ignoring one of the paths. Hence, when we apply a reduction pattern to '$p \lor \sim q$', we must do so to *all open paths below it.*

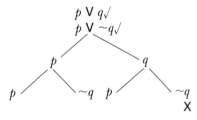

X   Indicates this path is closed.

The far right path closes, but the remaining paths are open. There are no more possible applications of our reduction patterns. Each remaining statement form is either a statement variable or the negation of a statement variable. The truth tree is completed. Since it contains at least one open path, the original set of statement forms is consistent.

Our last example suggests a bit of strategy. When we have a choice, our trees will be shorter and less cumbersome if we apply the nonsplitting patterns first. It is more important to construct truth trees than to worry about constructing the most efficient ones, but if we can see more than one approach for solving a problem, we might as well take the shortest one.

We need a set of statement forms:

$$\{p \supset q,\ r \supset p,\ \sim(\sim q \lor \sim r)\}$$

First, we should create the trunk:

$$
\begin{array}{ll}
p \supset q & \qquad\qquad p \supset q \\
r \supset p & \qquad\qquad r \supset p \\
\sim(\sim q \lor \sim r) & \qquad\quad \sim(\sim q \lor \sim r)
\end{array}
$$

Reducing the third statement form in the tree on the left and the first statement form in the tree on the right:

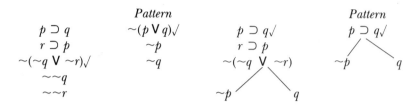

	Pattern		*Pattern*
$p \supset q$	$\sim(p \lor q)\checkmark$	$p \supset q\checkmark$	$p \supset q\checkmark$
$r \supset p$	$\sim p$	$r \supset p$	
$\sim(\sim q \lor \sim r)\checkmark$	$\sim q$	$\sim(\sim q \lor \sim r)$	$\sim p \qquad q$
$\sim\sim q$			
$\sim\sim r$		$\sim p \qquad q$	

Notice that '$\sim(\sim q \lor \sim r)$' is reduced to $\sim\sim q$ and $\sim\sim r$, *not* q and r. Each application of a reduction pattern should be carried out as a separate step. Next, we will apply the double-negation reduction pattern to the left-hand tree, and reduce the second element of the right-hand tree:

$p \supset q$
$r \supset p$
$\sim(\sim q \lor \sim r)\checkmark$
$\sim\sim q\checkmark$
$\sim\sim r\checkmark$
q
r

$p \supset q\checkmark$
$r \supset p\checkmark$
$\sim(\sim q \lor \sim r)$

$\sim p \qquad q$
$\sim r \quad p \quad \sim r \quad p$
$\quad\ \ \textbf{X}$

The left-hand tree lacks any closed paths, while the second path of the right-hand tree has closed. Both problems still have open paths and contain statement forms that can be further reduced. Let us continue and completely reduce the statement forms:

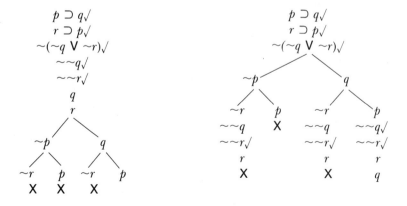

$p \supset q\checkmark$
$r \supset p\checkmark$
$\sim(\sim q \lor \sim r)\checkmark$
$\sim\sim q\checkmark$
$\sim\sim r\checkmark$
q
r

$\sim p \qquad q$
$\sim r \quad p \quad \sim r \quad p$
$\textbf{X} \quad \textbf{X} \quad \textbf{X}$

$p \supset q\checkmark$
$r \supset p\checkmark$
$\sim(\sim q \lor \sim r)\checkmark$

$\sim p \qquad\qquad q$
$\sim r \quad p \qquad \sim r \qquad p$
$\sim\sim q \quad \textbf{X} \quad \sim\sim q \quad \sim\sim q\checkmark$
$\sim\sim r\checkmark \qquad \sim\sim r\checkmark \quad \sim\sim r\checkmark$
$r \qquad\qquad r \qquad\quad r$
$\textbf{X} \qquad\qquad \textbf{X} \qquad\quad q$

Although the left-hand tree provides a somewhat more efficient solution than the right-hand tree, both are equally correct.

Our next example has compound forms contained within compound forms. Notice that *our reduction patterns are always applied to major connectives.* The forms that result from the first set of reductions are broken down as though they had been part of the original trunk.

Set of statement forms:

$$\{(p \cdot q) \equiv (r \cdot s), \sim p \cdot (r \cdot s)\}$$

Creating the trunk and applying the available nonsplitting reduction step (on the second element) produces:

$(p \cdot q) \equiv (r \cdot s)$
$\sim p \cdot (r \cdot s)\surd$
$\quad \sim p$
$\quad r \cdot s$

The *compound* '$r \cdot s$' has been brought down. Again, each application of a reduction pattern should be written as a separate step. Let us continue:

$(p \cdot q) \equiv (r \cdot s)$
$\sim p \cdot (r \cdot s)\surd$
$\quad \sim p$
$\quad r \cdot s\surd$
$\quad r$
$\quad s$

Biconditionals, when reduced, are represented as disjunctions. Applying the pattern we obtain:

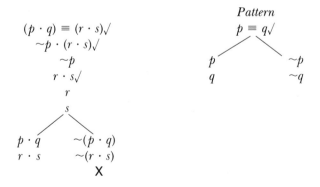

Since '$\sim(r \cdot s)$' is the negation of '$r \cdot s$', the right-hand path contains a statement form and the negation of the same statement form. Hence, the right-hand path is closed. Since we can still have an open path and can apply our reduction patterns, we must do so:

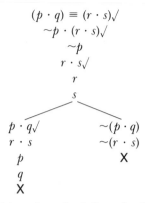

At this point, the left path closes as well. Both paths contain a statement form and the negation of the same statement form. Hence, our initial set is inconsistent.

We can summarize the relationship between truth trees and set consistency as follows:

> *A set of statement forms is consistent if and only if a completed truth tree for its elements has at least one open (not closed) path.*

> *A set of statement forms is inconsistent if and only if a completed truth tree for its elements has only closed paths.*

Our last group of explanations has been rather involved. You likely sense that it is time to *do* something. V. I. Lenin, one of the leaders of the Bolshevik party and the leader of the Soviet Union from 1917 until his death in 1924, once claimed that: "It is more pleasant and useful to go through 'the experience of the revolution' than to write about it."[5]

It is more pleasant and certainly more useful to go through the experience of truth trees than to read about them.

v. Summary of Truth Tree Reduction Patterns

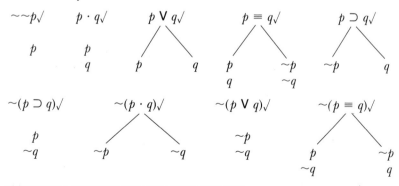

---

[5]V. I. Lenin, *State and Revolution* (New York: International Publishers, 1932), 101.

Exercises IV

Construct truth trees for each of the following sets of statement forms to determine whether it is consistent.

*1. $\{p \cdot q, \sim q\}$ 2. $\{p \lor q, \sim q \cdot p\}$

*3. $\{p \lor q, \sim(p \cdot q)\}$ 4. $\{p \cdot \sim q, p \equiv q\}$

*5. $\{p \supset q, p \cdot \sim q\}$ 6. $\{\sim(p \equiv q), p \cdot q\}$

*7. $\{\sim(p \lor q), \sim p \supset \sim q, \sim p\}$

8. $\{p \supset (q \lor r), s \supset (t \cdot \sim q), p \lor s\}$

Concept Reviews

1. Does *every* set of false statements have to be inconsistent? Explain the basis for your answer. Does a set of all true statements have to be consistent? Explain the basis for your answer.

2. The truth tree method as presented in the last section *pretends*, when writing statement forms, that they can be true. Disjunctions create split paths, since there are two possibilities that will ensure their truth. Had we wished, however, we could have set up truth trees based on the opposite assumption. In writing statement forms, we could have pretended that they can be false. How would truth trees based on this opposite assumption have expressed path splitting for conjunctions and disjunctions?

3. How should an approach based on the opposite assumptions, given in the last question, relate set consistency to completed trees?

C. Determining Whether Argument Forms Are Valid

Truth trees can be readily used to determine whether an argument form is valid. All that we have to do is clarify the connection between set consistency and argument-form validity. We will begin with a brief review of some concepts that were first presented in Chapter 3.

An argument form is deductively valid if and only if it is impossible for it to have all true premises and a false conclusion. (Definition 3.13).

An argument form is deductively invalid if and only if it is possible for it to have all true premises and a false conclusion. (Definition 3.14).

Negating a statement produces one that has the opposite truth-value.

If a statement is true, then its negation must be false. If a statement is false, then its negation must be true. If it is impossible for an argument form to have all true premisses and a false conclusion, then it must be impossible for the set of statement forms that consists of its premisses, and the *negation* of its conclusion, to have all true members. Hence:

> **An argument form is valid if and only if the set of statement forms that consists of its premisses and the negation of its conclusion is inconsistent.**

Suppose that we consider the following argument form:

$$p \lor (q \supset r)$$
$$\underline{\sim r}$$
$$\therefore p \cdot \sim q$$

The argument form is valid if and only if the following set of statement forms is inconsistent:

$$\{p \lor (q \supset r),\ \sim r,\ \sim(p \cdot \sim q)\}$$

Notice that our set of statement forms has the negation of the argument form's conclusion as a member. The negation of '$p \cdot \sim q$' is '$\sim(p \cdot \sim q)$', *not* '$\sim p \cdot \sim q$'.

Comparing the complete truth table for the argument form with the complete truth table for the set of statement forms will help us to see how they are related:

Argument Form			Corresponding Set		
$p \lor (q \supset r)$	$\sim r$	$p \cdot \sim q$	$p \lor (q \supset r)$	$\sim r$	$\sim(p \cdot \sim q)$
T T T T T	F	T F F	T T T T T	F	T T F F
T T T F F	T	T F F	T T T F F	T	T T F F
T T F T T	F	T T T	T T F T T	F	F T T T
T T F T F	T	T T T	T T F T F	T	F T T T
F T T T T	F	F F F	F T T T T	F	T F F F
F F T F F	T	F F F	F F T F F	T	T F F F
F T F T T	F	F F T	F T F T T	F	T F F T
F T F T F	T	F F T	F T F T F	T	T F F T

The argument form is *invalid* and its corresponding set of statement forms is *consistent*. Lines two and eight show that the form can have all true premisses and a false conclusion. Notice that the same lines, two and eight, show that all of the members of the set can be true. The form is shown to be invalid and the set is shown to be consistent when p is true, q is true, and r is false; and when p is false, q is false, and r is false.

Rather than construct a complete truth table, we could have constructed a truth tree to determine whether the set of statement forms is consistent:

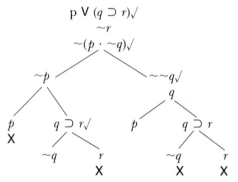

Our completed truth tree shows that the set is consistent, since it has two open paths. The open path on the left side of the tree shows that all of the members of the set are true when p, q, and r are false, the same truth-values as are present on line eight of the complete truth table. The open path on the right side of the tree designates the same truth-values as are present on line two of the complete truth table.

Suppose that we construct a truth tree to determine whether the following argument form is valid:

$$p \equiv q$$
$$\underline{\sim p \cdot r}$$
$$\therefore \sim q \cdot r$$

We know that this argument form is valid if and only if the following set of statement forms is inconsistent:

$$\{p \equiv q, \sim p \cdot r, \sim(\sim q \cdot r)\}$$

We can construct the following truth tree:

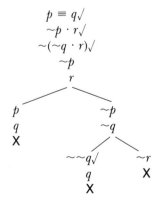

Our truth tree for this set of statement forms has only closed paths. Hence, the set of statement forms is *inconsistent* and the argument form is *valid*.

We can summarize the relationship between completed truth trees and valid argument forms as follows:

> ***An argument form is valid if and only if the completed truth tree for the set of statement forms that has the argument form's premisses and the negation of its conclusion as members has only closed paths.***

Exercises V

Write out the set of statement forms that must be inconsistent if each of the following argument forms is valid. Next, construct a truth tree for each set, and determine whether it is consistent and whether the initial argument is valid.

*1. $p \supset q$
$q \supset \sim p$
∴ $\sim q$

2. $\sim(p \lor q)$
$\sim p$
∴ q

*3. $p \equiv q$
$\sim p$
∴ q

4. $p \lor \sim q$
$q \supset \sim p$
∴ p

*5. $\sim(\sim p \cdot q)$
p
∴ $\sim q$

6. $p \supset q$
$\sim q \supset r$
$\sim r \lor p$
∴ $\sim p$

*7. $\sim p \supset \sim(p \lor q)$
$\sim q \equiv \sim r$
∴ $r \lor \sim p$

8. $(p \supset q) \lor r$
$\sim q \lor \sim r$
∴ $\sim p$

*9. $p \equiv q$
$r \equiv q$
q
∴ $p \cdot r$

10. $(p \equiv q) \cdot (r \equiv s)$
$q \lor r$
∴ $p \lor s$

11. $(p \cdot q) \lor (r \cdot s)$
$p \supset t$
$s \supset u$
∴ $q \supset u$

12. $(p \supset q) \cdot [r \supset (s \lor t)]$
$\sim(r \supset s) \cdot (q \equiv u)$
$\sim u \lor v$
$\sim p \supset (v \cdot w)$
∴ $v \lor w$

*13. $p \equiv \sim q$
$r \lor (s \lor t)$
$\sim p \supset \sim s$
q
∴ $r \lor t$

14. $p \equiv (q \cdot r)$
$(q \supset s) \cdot (r \supset t)$
$\sim p \supset u$
$\sim s \lor (\sim t \lor v)$
∴ $p \supset (w \supset u)$

15. $\sim(p \supset q)$
     $p \supset s$
     $\sim q \supset (s \supset t)$
     $\underline{\sim t \lor u}$
     $\therefore u$

16. $(p \supset q) \cdot (r \supset s)$
     $p \cdot \sim s$
     $\underline{(p \cdot \sim r) \supset (t \cdot w)}$
     $\therefore t \supset w$

*17. $p \supset (q \supset r)$
      $s \supset (t \supset u)$
      $\underline{(p \cdot q) \lor (s \cdot t)}$
      $\therefore r \lor u$

18. $p \supset q$
     $(r \lor s) \supset (u \equiv v)$
     $(\sim p \cdot \sim q) \supset (u \equiv s)$
     $\sim q$
     $\underline{\sim v \lor \sim s}$
     $\therefore \sim u \cdot \sim r$

Exercises VI

Use the italicized letters for your statement constants, and symbolize each of the following with our artificial language. Write out the argument form that has the argument as a parallel-instance, and construct a truth tree to determine whether the argument form and argument are valid.

*1. If a layer of warm air *l*ies over a layer of cool air and air *p*ollutants are present, then there is *s*mog. Air *p*ollutants are present. Hence, if a layer of warm air *l*ies over a layer of cool air, then there is *s*mog.

2. Either Oliver Hazard *P*erry or Francis Scott *K*ey wrote "The Star-Spangled Banner." *K*ey didn't write "The Star-Spangled Banner" unless he was in *M*aryland during the war of 1812. *P*erry didn't write "The Star-Spangled Banner" unless Key wasn't in *M*aryland during the war of 1812. So Francis Scott *K*ey wrote "The Star-Spangled Banner."

3. Either "*w*agon" or "*w*aggon" is the correct way to spell the name of a toy that children pull behind them. Either "*c*enter" or "*c*entre" is the correct way to spell the name of a point that is equidistant from all points on the circumference of a circle. Hence, if Noah Webster worked for an *A*merican version of English, then Noah Webster worked for an *A*merican version of English.

4. It is false that: there was *o*ne lantern if and only if the British came by *s*ea. Therefore, there was *o*ne lantern if and only if the British did not come by *s*ea.

*5. Triceratops could *e*at plants and *r*aise her young, unless Tyrannosaurus was *h*ungry. If Triceratops was *s*afe, then she could *e*at plants and *r*aise her young. If Triceratops was *s*afe, then Tyrannosaurus was not *h*ungry. So Triceratops was not *s*afe.

6. If we continue to abuse our *e*nvironment and continue to use *F*reon, then there will be less *o*zone in the atmosphere and the number of *c*ancer patients will increase. If we continue to abuse our *e*nvironment but do not continue to use *F*reon, then *s*mog levels will increase. If *s*mog levels increase, then the number of *c*ancer patients will increase. If we continue to use *F*reon, then we continue to abuse our *e*nvironment. Hence, the number of *c*ancer patients will increase.

7. If the Bolshevik investigators wanted a *c*onfession, then if the prisoners *r*efused to talk, then the investigators were *p*ersuasive. Rats were forced to *g*naw through the prisoners' intestines, if the Bolshevik investigators were being *p*ersuasive. Hence, rats were not forced to *g*naw through the prisoners' intestines only if the Bolshevik investigators either didn't want a *c*onfession or the prisoners didn't *r*efuse to talk.

8. If *G*od exists, then He is *o*mnipotent and supremely *b*enevolent. If God is *o*mnipotent, then He is *a*ble to abolish evil. If God is supremely *b*enevolent, then He *w*ishes to abolish evil. If God *w*ishes to abolish evil and is *a*ble to abolish evil, then *e*vil does not exist. *E*vil exists. Therefore, *G*od does not exist.

D. Determining Whether a Statement Form Is Tautologous, Self-contradictory, or Contingent

Truth trees can be readily applied to determine whether statement forms are tautologous, self-contradictory, or contingent.

Sets can have any number of members. The set of all persons legally married to Ms. Jones can have, at most, one member. If Ms. Jones is unmarried, the set of all persons married to her will not have any members. (A set without any members is called the "null set.") Similarly, sets of statement forms can have any number of members. We can construct a truth tree for a set that consists of only one statement form and determine whether it is possible for the statement form to be true. The statement form will be self-contradictory if and only if the set that has the statement form as its sole member is inconsistent.

A statement form is self-contradictory if and only if its completed truth tree has only closed paths.

Determining whether '$\sim[(p \cdot q) \supset q]$' is self-contradictory is equivalent to determining whether the following set is inconsistent:

$$\{\sim[(p \cdot q) \supset q]\}$$

We can construct a truth tree as follows:

$$\sim[(p \cdot q) \supset q]\surd$$
$$p \cdot q\surd$$
$$\sim q$$
$$p$$
$$q$$
$$\mathsf{X}$$

Since the truth tree for this statement form has only a closed path, it cannot possibly be true. Hence, this statement form is self-contradictory.

The negation of any true statement is a false statement. A tautologous statement form is true on every line of its truth table. The negation of a tautologous statement form must have the opposite truth-value; it must be false on every line of its truth table. If a statement form lacks any possibility of being false, its negation must lack any possibility of being true. A statement is tautologous if and only if its negation is self-contradictory.

> *A statement form is tautologous if and only if the statement form that results from negating it has only closed paths on its completed truth tree.*

Suppose we wish to determine whether '$(p \supset q) \equiv [p \supset (p \cdot q)]$' is a tautology. We know that it will be a tautology if and only if the following statement form is self-contradictory:

$$\sim\{(p \supset q) \equiv [p \supset (p \cdot q)]\}$$

The following truth tree shows that this is a self-contradictory statement form. Hence, our initial statement form must be a tautology.

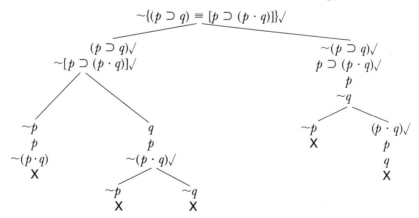

If a statement form is neither self-contradictory nor tautologous, then it must be contingent. It must be possible for a contingent statement form to be true; otherwise, it would be self-contradictory. It must be possible for the negation of a contingent statement form to be true; otherwise, it would be tautologous. Combining these ideas with our truth tree method we have:

A statement form is contingent if and only if the completed truth trees for both it and its negation have at least one open path.

Exercises VII

First, construct a truth tree for each of the following statement forms and determine which are self-contradictory. Next, for those that are not self-contradictory, construct a truth tree for each corresponding negated statement form, and determine which are tautologous. What do you know about statement forms that are neither contradictory nor tautologous?

*1. $\sim p \supset \sim p$
 2. $(p \lor q) \supset p$
 3. $(p \cdot q) \equiv p$
 4. $(p \cdot q) \cdot (\sim p \lor \sim q)$
*5. $(p \supset q) \lor (p \supset \sim q)$
 6. $p \lor (q \supset r)$
 7. $[p \lor (q \cdot r)] \cdot [\sim(p \lor q) \lor \sim(p \lor r)]$
 8. $[(p \supset q) \cdot (r \supset s)] \supset [(\sim q \lor r) \supset (\sim p \lor s)]$

E. Similarities between Truth Tables and Truth Trees

Clearly, truth trees can be used to accomplish all of the tasks that were accomplished in Chapter 3 by using complete truth tables. There are a number of additional similarities. Since both examine possibilities, not actualities, both are applied on statement forms rather than statements. Actual statements, as abbreviated by statement constants, have definite truth-values.

Our truth-tree reduction patterns specify exactly the same conditions for truth as are specified in a complete truth table. Any line of a truth table in which a conjunction is true must be a line that has both conjuncts true. Our truth-tree method has us list each conjunct as potentially true. Any line of a truth table in which a disjunction is true must be a line that has one of the disjuncts true. Our truth trees have us list each disjunct as a potentially true branch.

Truth trees show inconsistency when all of their paths are closed. In this case, the corresponding truth table for the statement forms, if expressed (by using our logical equivalences) as negations, conjunctions, and disjunctions, must contain a statement form and the negation of the same statement form; otherwise, there would be a line of the complete truth table such that all of the statement forms are true.

If a complete truth table determines that a set of statement forms is consistent, then there must be an assignment of truth-values to the variables such that all of the statement forms are true. With truth trees, a set of statement forms is not considered consistent unless all of our reduction patterns have been applied whenever possible. The complete application of the reduction patterns reduces every statement form to an examination of statement variables and the negations of statement variables. All truth-table possibilities for a statement form's variables are considered by truth trees when determining whether a set of statement forms is consistent.[6]

---

[6]This section makes a number of intuitive comparisons between truth-table and truth-tree methods. For a rigorous comparison, see Richard Jeffery, *Formal Logic: Its Scope and Limits* (New York: McGraw-Hill, 1967), 81–90.

7 Monadic Predication

Our earlier chapters have presented an account of propositional logic. We have considered arguments that have propositions linked by connectives such as 'if . . . then . . .', 'or', and 'and'. Some arguments, however, cannot be correctly expressed solely in terms of these connectives. The symbolization methods that we developed in previous chapters do not adequately express the connections that are present in the following arguments.

Shakespeare's Julius Caesar (JC) claimed:

Yond Cassius has a lean and hungry look;
He thinks too much: such men are dangerous.[1]

Caesar's argument can be summarized as follows:

ARGUMENT JC
Men who have a lean and hungry look are dangerous.
Cassius has a lean and hungry look.
Hence, Cassius is dangerous.

Milne's Winnie the Pooh (WP) claimed:

"That's funny," thought Pooh. "I said 'Ow!' without really oo'ing."

"Help" said a small, high voice.

"That's me again," thought Pooh. "I've had an Accident, and fallen down a well, and my voice has all gone squeaky and works before I'm ready for it, because I've done something to myself inside, Bother!"[2]

---

[1] William Shakespeare, *Julius Caesar*, act 1, scene 2, lines 193–94.

[2] A. A. Milne, *The House at Pooh Corner* (New York: Dutton, 1961), 3. Pooh had fallen on Piglet, and it was Piglet who was saying "Ow!" and "Help!"

Pooh's reasoning can be summarized as follows:

ARGUMENT WP

Any time that I'm injured, I hear "Ow!"
I hear "Ow!" now.
Hence, I'm injured now.

JC is valid and WP is (intentionally) invalid. With our earlier methods of symbolization, however, both arguments appear to be invalid. Argument JC, as summarized, consists of three different propositions.

'Men who have a lean and hungry look are dangerous' makes a claim about *all* men who have a lean and hungry look.

'Cassius *h*as a lean and hungry look' attributes the quality of having a lean and hungry look to Cassius.

'Cassius is *d*angerous' attributes another quality, the quality of being dangerous, to Cassius.

Given the method of symbolizing arguments that we developed in Chapter 2, each different statement should be abbreviated with a different statement constant. Using the italicized letters for our statement constants, our summary of JC can be expressed as follows:

M.
H.
Hence, D.

But this symbolization seems to make the argument invalid. The truth table for the following form will have a line that assigns p as true, q as true, and r as false.

p.
q.
Hence, r.

If we apply our symbolization as developed in Chapter 2 to the argument WP, it also appears to be invalid. WP has three different statements, and our symbolization methods of Chapter 2 will use three different statement constants. Our present symbolization methods represent arguments JC and WP as being parallel-instances of the same invalid form.

Neither JC nor WP has been adequately represented. The general terms 'have/has a lean and hungry look' and 'are/is dangerous' each appear twice in JP. The general terms 'I'm injured' and 'I hear "Ow!" ' each appear twice in WP. Our present symbolization fails to notice that the same predicates, or general terms, are repeated in each argument.

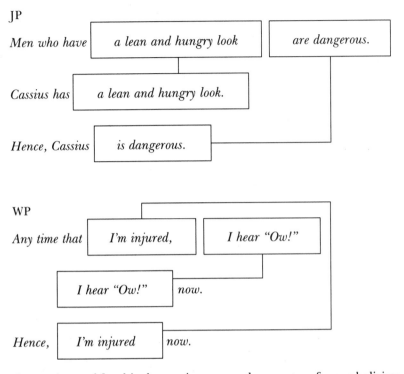

Our major goal for this chapter is to expand our system for symbolizing statements so that we are able to represent predicates. Once our system is capable of expressing predicates, many of our principles from earlier chapters will be applicable to arguments that are expressed with them. We will be able to show that JP is valid and that WP is invalid.

KEY TERMS FOR THIS CHAPTER

Use the glossary as necessary, and review the definitions of these terms prior to a second reading of this chapter.

Singular statement	**Universal statement**
Individual	**Individual variable**
Predicate	**Universal quantifier**
Individual constant	**Existential statement**
Predicate constant	**Existential quantifier**
Monadic predicate	**Existential import**
General statement	

I   Symbolization

A. Singular Statements

DEFINITION 7.1

A *singular statement* asserts or denies that an individual has a particular quality.

All of the following sentences are singular statements.

Beethoven wrote the *Moonlight* Sonata.

The Civil War began abruptly.

Alan Shepard was the first man to walk on the moon.

Cassius is not trustworthy.

Each of the above statements either asserts or denies a quality of a particular individual. The word 'individual' has a much broader meaning in logic than in standard English. In normal usage, 'individual' designates a person. In logic, an individual is anything that can be considered a thing.

DEFINITION 7.2

An *individual* is any particular thing that can be discussed in an argument.

Tables, cats, persons, and salamanders are all things that can be discussed. Hence, all can be considered individuals. What we decide to count as a thing depends on the context. When discussing amusement parks, we might refer to Disney World as a thing. When discussing amusement park rides, we might refer to the Space Mountain roller coaster as a thing, even though it is obviously part of Disney World. When concerned about maintenance, we might refer to a wheel bearing of the Space Mountain roller coaster. What we count as a thing depends on the discussion. Since different discussions can be about different things, what counts as a thing varies from discussion to discussion. In the same way, what logic considers to be an individual may vary.

DEFINITION 7.3

A *predicate* is an expression that is used to attribute a quality to an individual.

In this chapter, predicates specify qualities or properties that things may or may not have. (Some predicates express relationships between individuals. Predicates of this type are covered in Chapter 8.) English has four major ways of attributing qualities to individuals.

1. A verb-noun combination can attribute a quality. In 'Beethoven wrote the *Moonlight* Sonata', the phrase 'wrote the *Moonlight* Sonata' attributes a quality—being the writer of the *Moonlight* Sonata—to an individual, Beethoven. Less frequently, a verb by itself can indicate a quality, as in 'Beethoven wrote'.

2. A verb-adverb combination can attribute a quality. In 'the Civil War began abruptly', the phrase 'began abruptly' attributes a quality—having an abrupt beginning—to an individual, the Civil War.

3. A form of the verb 'to be' and a noun phrase can attribute a quality. In 'Alan Shepard was the first man to walk on the moon', the word 'was', a form of the verb 'to be', attributes the quality—being the first man to walk on the moon—to an individual, Alan Shepard. This is an example of a predication statement that is false. Neil Armstrong was the first man to walk on the moon. Alan Shepard made the first suborbital flight as part of the Mercury program.

4. A form of the verb 'to be' and an adjective can attribute a quality. 'Cassius is not trustworthy' denies that the quality of being trustworthy applies to Cassius. 'Trustworthy' is an adjective that attributes the quality. As this example shows, singular statements can deny, as well as affirm, that a quality applies to an individual.

The following table summarizes these four forms.

	Individual	*Quality*	*English Construction*
Beethoven wrote the *Moonlight* Sonata.	Beethoven	being the writer of the *Moonlight* Sonata.	verb + noun
The Civil War began abruptly.	the Civil War	having an abrupt beginning	verb + adverb
Alan Shepard was the first man to walk on the moon.	Alan Shepard	being the first man to walk on the moon	form of 'to be' + noun phrase
Cassius is not trustworthy.	Cassius	not being trustworthy	form of 'to be' + adjective

i. Artificial-Language Notation

We need to be able to represent individuals and predicates with our artificial language.

DEFINITION 7.4

An *individual constant* is any lower-case letter, from *a* to *w*, used to identify a particular individual.

DEFINITION 7.5

A *predicate constant* is any capital letter, from *A* to *Z*, used to identify a particular predicate.

Just as we used statement constants to represent particular statements, we will use individual constants to represent particular individuals. Notice that it is the *lower-case* letters that are individual constants. English frequently capitalizes the first letter of a word that indicates an individual, but lower-case letters are used in the artificial language. Any lower-case letter, from *a* to *w*, may be used to stand for any individual. Simplicity has us choose a letter that we can identify with the corresponding English. Each individual must be represented by a unique individual constant. For example:

'Beethoven' can be represented with *b*.

'The Civil War' can be represented with *w*.

'Alan Shepard' can be represented with *s*.

'Cassius' can be represented with *c*.

Any predicate constant can be used to represent a particular predicate. Simplicity, again, has us choose letters that remind us of the English. Each predicate must be represented by a unique predicate constant. For example:

'Being the writer of the *Moonlight* Sonata' can be represented with *W*.

'Having an abrupt beginning' can be represented with *B*.

'Being the first man to walk on the moon' can be represented with *F*.

'Being trustworthy' can be represented with *T*.

Finally, to indicate in the artificial language that an individual has a given quality, the individual constant is placed to the right of the predicate constant. Using the above abbreviations, the first three examples can be expressed as follows:

Wb   <u>B</u>eethoven *w*rote the *Moonlight* Sonata.

Bw   The Civil <u>W</u>ar *b*egan abruptly.

Fs   Alan <u>Sh</u>epard was the *f*irst man to walk on the moon.

To symbolize the fourth example, which is the negation of 'Cassius is trustworthy', we can use the tilde as in Chapter 2:

~*Tc*   <u>C</u>assius *is* not *t*rustworthy.

As before, the negation of a statement is expressed by placing the tilde before its symbolic representation. In fact, all of the symbols that we developed in Chapter 2 can be combined with our method of expressing singular statements. Suppose that someone claimed:

If the Civil War began abruptly, then it started with a major assault.

Using *S* to abbreviate the quality of starting with a major assault, we can write:

Bw ⊃ *Sw*

ii. Suggestions for Symbolizing Singular Statements

1. Identify the individuals and predicates. Use the tilde as necessary, and express the predication statements.
2. Use our connectives of Chapter 2, as needed, to symbolize compound statements.

iii. A Complex Example

If carbon is present in plants and animals, then it forms a basis for life.

In this example, the individual, carbon, is identified with three qualities: being present in plants, being present in animals, and forming a basis for life. If we use *c* to abbreviate the individual 'carbon', and the italicized letters for our predicate constants, this example contains three predication statements: *Pc*, *Ac*, and *Bc*. When we add our connectives of Chapter 2, we obtain:

(*Pc* · *Ac*) ⊃ *Bc*

As always, practice in using the system will help in learning it!

Exercises I

Symbolize each of the following predication statements with our predicate notation. Use the underlined letters for individual constants and the italicized letters for predicate constants. Be sure to use lower-case and capital letters as necessary. All of the following statements relate to the Civil War.

*1. The Civil War began with an attack on Fort Sumter.

2. Robert E. Lee was a Confederate general.

3. The Battle of Bull Run did not end the war.

4. The Civil War began in 1861 and ended in 1865.

*5. If the Confederacy had won at Gettysburg, then it would have won the war.

6. Abraham Lincoln was not a well-known orator, but he wrote the Gettysburg address.

7. The Confederacy was determined either to secede from the Union or to change it.

8. If the Confederacy had won at Gettysburg, then it would have won the war and seceded from the Union.

*9. Either Grant or Lee was the winning general.

10. If Lincoln had not signed the Emancipation Proclamation, then if the Confederacy had won at Gettysburg then the Union would not have won the war.

Concept Review

1. In Chapter 2, there was a danger in seeing the letters as abbreviating words rather than statements. In this chapter, there is a danger in seeing the letters as abbreviating words rather than specifying individuals and predicates. For exercises 1, 4, 7, and 10 above, indicate the predicates that are specified by the predicate constants.

B. Types of Predication Statements

Before proceeding to develop additional methods for symbolizing statements, it is helpful to have a preview of the types of predication statements that will be considered in this chapter. Notice that this chapter is titled "Monadic Predication."

Predicate constants in this chapter can be used to create meaningful sentences in the artificial language when one individual is being described. Suppose that we let the predicate constant R indicate the quality of being a road. Ra, Rb, and so on are all meaningful, provided that the individual constants designate individuals. Not all attributions of a given quality will result in true statements, however. If a abbreviates 'Afghanistan', then Ra, the claim that 'Afghanistan is a road', is meaningful, but false. If *i* abbreviates 'Interstate 75', then *Ri*, the claim that 'Interstate 75 is a road', is meaningful and true. The prefix 'mon-', derived from the Greek, means "one." Predicates that take one individual in order to form a meaningful expression are called "monadic predicates."

DEFINITION 7.6

A *monadic predicate* is a predicate which claims that an individual has a particular quality.

Not all predicates are monadic. Some predicates require at least two individuals. One politician, for example, cannot be more liberal than another unless there are at least two politicians. Predicates that require more than one individual in order to express a meaningful statement are covered in Chapter 8.

Even though the predicates in this chapter are monadic, they can be used to make statements about groups of individuals. In 400 A.D., during the Roman Empire, it was more or less true that 'All roads lead to Rome'. This claim is expressed with monadic predicates. It does not, however, make a claim about a particular road. 'All roads lead to Rome' defines a group of individuals, those that are roads, and claims that all members of this group lead to Rome. General statements make claims about the individuals of a group.

DEFINITION 7.7

A *general statement* makes a claim about members of a group (rather than about a particular individual).

'All roads lead to Rome' is about all things that are roads. General statements that are about *all* things of a certain kind, are called "universal statements."

The previous section discussed symbolizing singular statements. The next two sections discuss symbolizing two kinds of general statements: universal statements and existential statements, respectively. "Monadic predication arguments" are arguments that involve singular, universal, and existential statements that contain only monadic predicates.

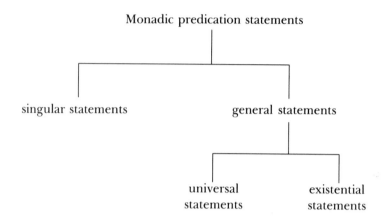

C. Universal Statements

i. Symbolizing Universal Statements

DEFINITION 7.8

A *universal statement* affirms or denies a predicate of all individuals of a certain kind.

Typical universal statements contain at least two predicates. One or several predicates define the group at issue, and one or several additional predicates apply an attribute or attributes to members of the group. The arguments JC and WP each have a universal statement that fits this pattern. The example in the last section does so as well.

In 'all roads lead to Rome', 'being a road' defines the group, and 'lead to Rome' applies an attribute. In 'men who have a lean and hungry look are dangerous', 'being a man with a lean and hungry look' defines the group, and 'being dangerous' applies the attribute. In 'any time that I'm injured, I hear "Ow!",' 'being a time I'm injured' defines the group, and 'I hear "Ow!" ' applies the attribute.

Universal statements are not about one particular thing. We need a way to identify individuals in a general sense. The lower-case letters x, y, and z serve this function.

DEFINITION 7.9

The lower-case letters *x*, *y*, and *z*, called *individual variables*, are placeholders for individual constants.

Recall that statement constants identify a particular statement, and statement variables are placeholders for some statement or other. Similarly, individual constants identify particular individuals, and individual variables are placeholders for some individual constant or other. These variables do not, however, indicate a particular *quantity* of individuals. Quantifiers are used for that purpose.

DEFINITION 7.10

∀x, ∀y, and ∀z are *universal quantifiers*. They abbreviate "for any individual in the universe, call it *x* (or *y*, or *z*), ..."

Since all of the symbolizations in this chapter involve monadic predicates and each monadic predicate takes only one individual, only the variable, *x* and the universal quantifier ∀x are needed in this chapter. Chapter 8 will require us to use *y* and *z*.

We now have enough machinery to express universal statements, but we need to assemble it. We can use *R* to indicate the quality of being a road, and *L* to indicate the quality of *l*eading to Rome. Our example claims that all individuals (things) that have the quality of being a road, also have the quality of leading to Rome. Symbolically, we have the following:

All roads lead to Rome.

For any individual	*if the individual, x,*	*then the individual,*
in the universe, call	*has the quality of*	*x, has the quality of*
it x:	*being a road,*	*leading to Rome.*
∀x	(Rx ⊃	Lx)

Or, in a more condensed form:

∀x(Rx ⊃ Lx)

The expression '*Rx* ⊃ *Lx*' has been placed in parentheses. The full significance of doing this will be explained later. For now, the parentheses merely indicate that the quantifier applies to *all* of '*Rx* ⊃ *Lx*'. Notice that the quantifier and both predicates all have the variable x. This indicates that the same individual is being talked about throughout the statement. Pronouns in English serve this function when they are used to refer back to a noun. For example:

The Berlin wall was torn down in 1989. It was built in 1961.

'It' refers to the subject of the previous sentence, 'the Berlin wall'. For the present, whatever follows the quantifier will be placed in parentheses, brackets, or braces, as needed.

ii. Symbolization Patterns

P and Q indicate predicates.

   a. Universal Affirmative Statements   A universal affirmative statement claims (or affirms) that all members of the group at issue have a particular attribute. 'All roads lead to Rome' is a universal affirmative statement, since it claims that all things that are roads have the quality of leading to Rome. English has a number of constructions that are commonly used to express universal affirmative statements.

1. All Ps are Qs.   Universal affirmative statements are often expressed in English with 'all Ps are Qs', symbolized as

   $\forall x(Px \supset Qx)$

   'All presidential candidates are publicity hounds' is symbolized as '$\forall x(Cx \supset Hx)$': "For anything in the universe, if it is a presidential candidate, then it is a publicity hound."

2. Any P is a Q.   'Any P is a Q' is frequently used in English to assert that all Ps are Qs. 'Any P is a Q' is symbolized as

   $\forall x(Px \supset Qx)$

   'All presidential candidates are publicity hounds' has approximately the same meaning as 'any presidential candidate is a publicity hound'. Hence, 'any presidential candidate is a publicity hound' is also symbolized as '$\forall x(Cx \supset Hx)$': "For anything in the universe, if it is a presidential candidate, then it is a publicity hound."

3. The only Ps are Qs.   'The only' is often used to characterize the group at issue. Hence, 'the only Ps are Qs' is often symbolized as

   $\forall x(Px \supset Qx)$

   'The only efficient governments are dictatorships' has approximately the same meaning as 'all efficient governments are dictatorships'. Accordingly, it should be symbolized as '$\forall x(Ex \supset Dx)$': "For anything in the universe, if it is an efficient government, then it is a dictatorship."

4. **The *P* is *Q*.** *Not all English usages of this pattern express universal statements.* When a universal statement is intended, 'the *P* is *Q*' is symbolized as

$\forall x(Px \supset Qx)$

'The *d*og is a human's best *f*riend' is symbolized as '$\forall x(Dx \supset Fx)$': "For anything in the universe, if it is a dog, then it is a human's best friend." When symbolizing this English construction, be sure to compare the translation and the English to verify that both have (roughly) the same meaning.

5. ***P*s are *Q*s.** *Not all English usages of this pattern express universal statements.* There are times when the word 'all' is intended, but not explicitly stated. In these cases, the statement should be translated the same as 1 above. Try reading the sentence with 'all' to see if it was intended. If so, '*P*s are *Q*s' is symbolized as

$\forall x(Px \supset Qx)$

'*N*ice guys finish *l*ast' is symbolized as '$\forall x(Nx \supset Lx)$': "For anything in the universe, if it is a nice guy then it finishes last." Be sure to compare the translation and the English to verify that both have (roughly) the same meaning.

Consequent predicate indicators:

6. **Only *P*s are *Q*s.** *'Only' serves a different logical function from 'the only'.* 'Only if' in Chapter 2 indicated the consequent statement. 'Only, *but not 'the only'*, indicates the consequent predicate. 'Only *P*s are *Q*s' is symbolized as

$\forall x(Qx \supset Px)$

'Only the well *e*ducated are college *p*rofessors' is symbolized as '$\forall x(Px \supset Ex)$': "For anything in the universe, if it is a college professor then it is well educated."

The last example points out how the order in which the predicates are placed around the horseshoe is important. The statement that 'only the well-educated are college professors' is more or less true. '$\forall x(Ex \supset Px)$', however, claims that all well-educated people are college professors. Since neurosurgeons, engineers, and Supreme Court justices are well educated but are not college professors, '$\forall x(Ex \supset Px)$' is false.

7. **None but *P*s are *Q*s.** 'None but' has the same logical function as 'only'. Accordingly, 'none but' also specifies the consequent predicate. 'None but *P*s are *Q*s' is symbolized as

$\forall x(Qx \supset Px)$

'None but the *foolish* fall in *love*' is symbolized as '$\forall x(Lx \supset Fx)$': "For anything in the universe, if it falls in love then it is foolish."

b. Universal Negative Statements   Universal negative statements assert that the *denial* of an attribute applies to all members of a group.

1. No *P*s are *Q*s.   Beginning a sentence with 'no' expresses a universal statement, but the *negation* of the second predicate is applied to members of the group. 'No *P*s are *Q*s' is symbolized as

$\forall x(Px \supset \sim Qx)$

'No *person* can *serve* two masters' is symbolized as '$\forall x(Px \supset \sim Sx)$': "For anything in the universe, if it is a person then it cannot serve two masters."

2. Not any *P*s are *Q*s.   'Not any' can also be used to express a universal statement where the negation of the second predicate is applied to members of the group. 'Not any *P*s are *Q*s' is also symbolized as

$\forall x(Px \supset \sim Qx)$

'Not any *hostages* are *safe*' is symbolized as '$\forall x(Hx \supset \sim Sx)$': "For anything in the universe, if it is a hostage then it is not safe."

All of the universal statements that we have symbolized so far have had the horseshoe as their major connective. The reason for this lies in the significance of the universal quantifier. The universal quantifier is *entirely* universal. It specifies all individuals in the universe. Using the universal quantifier in connection with symbols other than the horseshoe typically states either more or less than sane people wish to say.

Suppose that we let *R* abbreviate the quality of being a road, and let *L* abbreviate the quality of leading to Rome. Suppose as well that we connect the predicate constants with the dot:

$\forall x(Rx \cdot Lx)$

This does *not* correctly symbolize 'All roads lead to Rome'. Rather, it symbolizes the claim that every individual in the universe is both a road and leads to Rome. For the expression '$\forall x(Rx \cdot Lx)$' to be true, every single thing in existence, including logic professors and pet parakeets, would have to be roads that lead to Rome.

There are a few exceptions, but universal statements should generally be expressed by using the universal quantifier with the horseshoe. The antecedent of the conditional typically indicates the group being talked about, and the consequent expresses the quality that is asserted or denied of the group's members.

SYMBOLIZATION PATTERNS FOR UNIVERSAL STATEMENTS
P and *Q* indicate predicates

English	*Symbolization*
All *P*s are *Q*s. Any *P* is a *Q*. The only *P*s are *Q*s. *When expressing a universal statement:* The *P* is *Q*. *P*s are *Q*s.	$\forall x(Px \supset Qx)$
Only *P*s are *Q*s. None but *P*s are *Q*s.	$\forall x(Qx \supset Px)$
No *P*s are *Q*s. Not any *P*s are *Q*s.	$\forall x(Px \supset \sim Qx)$

Exercises II

Symbolize each of the following by using the italicized letters for the required predicate constants. Each sentence is a universal statement that fits one of the above patterns.

*1. All *p*oliticians have *r*ead Machiavelli.
2. All *s*hoplifters will be *p*rosecuted.
*3. Any presidential *c*andidate is a publicity *h*ound.
4. 'Every *r*evolution is *b*ased on love.' (Che Guevara)
*5. Not any *r*evolutions are *b*ased on love.
6. No *w*eather forecasts are *a*ccurate.
*7. The only place *l*ike home is *h*ome.
8. Not any *m*utts are *p*urebreds.
*9. No *b*icycles *p*ollute the environment.
10. None but the *s*trong *s*urvive.
11. Only *c*apitalists *b*elieve in private ownership of the means of production.
12. Only *n*onprofit corporations are *c*onsidered tax exempt.
*13. The *p*yramids were *c*reated by alien civilizations.
14. The only *n*oble savage is an *i*magined savage.
15. "Whatever doesn't *k*ill a person *m*akes them stronger." (Friedrich Nietzsche)

16. Not any *p*recipitation is *e*xpected.

*17. Every *f*orm of refuge *h*as its price.

18. *A*cts of violence *b*eget violence.

iii. Complex Symbolizations: Universal Statements

Complex universal statements are usually expressed as quantified conditionals, but the antecedent and consequent expressions are compound.

When an individual (thing) must have more than one quality to be a member of the group being discussed, the antecedent in the symbolization is typically a conjunction.

Benjamin Franklin once claimed that "a *p*enny *s*aved is a *p*enny *e*arned." Franklin no doubt intended his statement to be universal, so we should begin with the universal quantifier. We should also expect the horseshoe to be the major connective in the quantified expression. What things was Franklin making a claim about? Obviously, things that are **both** pennies and saved. Since his claim is only about things with both qualities, members of the group at issue must have both qualities. The symbolization's antecedent will be a conjunction of the predicate constants. Using the italicized letters to provide our predicate constants, Franklin's saying can be symbolized as follows:

$$\forall x[(Px \cdot Sx) \supset (Px \cdot Ex)]$$

Not every English sentence can be translated this cleanly, however. Consider '*s*wordtails and *a*ngelfish are *f*in nippers'. If we use the italicized letters for the required predicate constants, the correct symbolization might seem to be:

$$\forall x[(Sx \cdot Ax) \supset Fx]$$

Reading the artificial-language symbols back into English, however, gives us the following:

> *For anything in the universe, if it is **both** a swordtail **and** an angelfish, then it is a fin nipper.*

The attempted symbolization, but not the original English, is about things that are **both** swordtails and angelfish (a sword-angel fish?). 'And' in this example is used to indicate two groups, not two characteristics that define one group. 'Swordtails and *a*ngelfish are *f*in nippers' expresses the conjunction of the two sentences: '*s*wordtails are *f*in nippers' and '*a*ngelfish are *f*in nippers'. Accordingly, it can be symbolized as:

$$\forall x(Sx \supset Fx) \cdot \forall x(Ax \supset Fx)$$

The above symbolization is correct, but we do not have to express this example as the conjunction of two sentences. Truth tables as developed in Chapters 3 and 4 can be constructed to show that '$(p \supset r) \cdot (q \supset r)$' is logically equivalent to '(p V q) ⊃ r'. Our discussion of inference relationships for universal statements in section II of this chapter will enable us to show that '∀x(Sx ⊃ Fx) · ∀x(Ax ⊃ Fx)' is logically equivalent to '∀x[(Sx V Ax) ⊃ Fx]'. Rather than symbolize this example as the conjunction of two sentences, we can have our symbolization refer to members of more than one group by making the conditional's antecedent a *disjunction* of the predicates that define the groups.

For anything in the universe, if it is either a swordtail or an angelfish, then it is a fin nipper.

When an English sentence is about all of the members of two (or more) groups, it can be symbolized by making the conditional's antecedent a disjunction of the predicates that define the groups.

Although '∀x[(Sx · Ax) ⊃ Fx]' is *incorrect*, our example can be correctly symbolized as either '∀x(Sx ⊃ Fx) · ∀x(Ax ⊃ Fx)' or '∀x[(Sx V Ax) ⊃ Fx]'.

Any attempted symbolization should always be read back into English to make sure that the symbolization and the English have (roughly) the same meaning.

Finally, some sentences cannot be correctly expressed by following *any* set of rules. There are times when we should make symbolization attempts and compare them to the English until we obtain similar meanings.

Playwright Noël Coward (1899–1973) wrote a revue, *The Third Little Show*, that was first produced in 1931. Coward's intent was to satirize the British leisure class. One of the songs in the show contains the following sentence:

Mad dogs and Englishmen go out in the midday sun.

Suppose that we attempt to symbolize Coward's statement. Although Coward may have thought that mad dogs and Englishmen have much in common, a mad dog is not a kind of Englishman. Coward was not making a claim about a group of things that are both mad dogs and Englishmen.

Coward's statement can be interpreted as the conjunction of two sentences: 'Mad dogs go out in the midday sun', and 'Englishmen go out in the midday sun'. Alternatively, as with 'swordtails and angelfish are fin nippers', we can view Coward's assertion as a conditional that has as its antecedent the disjunction of the predicates that specify the two groups. Since Coward's statement is fairly complex, it will be helpful to symbolize it in stages.

For anything in the universe, if it is either a mad dog or an Englishman, then it goes out in the midday sun.

For any x *in the universe, if* x *is either a mad dog or an Englishman, then* x *goes out in the midday sun.*

∀x[(x *is either a mad dog or an Englishman*) ⊃ x *goes out in the midday sun*].

∀x{[(Mx · Dx) ∨ Ex] ⊃ Gx}

If we express Coward's statement as the (logically equivalent) conjunction of two sentences, we obtain the following:

∀x[(Mx · Dx) ⊃ Gx] · ∀x(Ex ⊃ Gx)

Imagine, however, that the statement was made by someone obligated to go out in the midday sun. Imagine that troops stationed in the Arabian desert claim that "Mad dogs and Englishmen go out in the midday sun." In this context, the sentence claims that *only* mad dogs and Englishmen go out in the midday sun. For anything in the universe, if it goes out in the midday sun then it is either a mad dog or an Englishman. *This* meaning can be symbolized as:

∀x{Gx ⊃ [(Mx · Dx) ∨ Ex]}

Which of these symbolizations is correct depends on whether the sentence is understood as making a statement about things that are either mad dogs or Englishmen, or about things that go out in the midday sun.

iv. Specifying Predicate Constants

Predicate constants must be specified so that they indicate attributes of individuals.

Consider:

Alleged murderers are entitled to a fair trial.

'Alleged murderer', not 'alleged', indicates a kind of individual. 'Fair' indicates a kind of trial, not a quality that an alleged murderer is entitled to. Hence, this example should be symbolized as '∀x(Mx ⊃ Tx)', not as

∀x[(Ax · Mx) ⊃ (Fx · Tx)]'.

'∀x[(Ax · Mx) ⊃ (Fx · Tx)]' claims that for anything in the universe, if it is alleged and a murderer then it is entitled to a fair and entitled to a trial.

Ernest Hemingway once claimed that "the most essential gift for a good writer is a built-in, shockproof shit detector." 'Most essential' describes a kind of gift, not an aspect of individuals who are good writers. Hemingway claimed that those things that have the quality of being a "most essential gift for a good writer" are those things that are "built in," "shockproof," and "shit detectors." Hemingway's assertion should *not* be rendered as 'for anything in the universe, if it is most essential and a gift for a good writer . . . .' (This example is number 17 in the following exercises.)

Exercises III

Symbolize each of the following universal statements. Each problem has suggested predicate-constant interpretations. For example, number 1 suggests that *Px* = 'x is a person'. Use the predicate constant *P* to indicate the quality of being a person. Be sure to compare your symbolizations back to the English.

*1. No *person* can serve *Mammon* [riches] and *God*. [*Px* = 'x is a person'; *Mx* = 'x serves Mammon'; *Gx* = 'x serves God'.]

2. *Apples* and *oranges* are *nutritious*. [*Ax* = 'x is an apple'; *Ox* = 'x is an orange'; *Nx* = 'x is nutritious'.]

3. *Apples* and *oranges* are *nutritious* unless they're *rotten*. [As number 2; plus *Rx* = 'x is rotten'.]

4. "An *idle* *mind* is the devil's *playground*." (Ben Franklin, *Poor Richard's Almanac*) [*Ix* = 'x is idle'; *Mx* = 'x is a mind'; *Px* = 'x is a playground for the devil'.]

*5. *Cocaine*', *heroin*, and "*ice*" are all *addictive*. [*Cx* = 'x is cocaine'; *Hx* = 'x is heroin'; *Ix* = 'x is "ice"'; *Ax* = 'x is addictive'.]

6. The only *Englishmen* who *go* out in the midday sun are *mad*. [*Ex* = 'x is an Englishman'; *Gx* = 'x goes out in the midday sun'; *Mx* = 'x is mad'.]

7. *Soap* operas *pale* when *compared* to life. [*Sx* = 'x is a soap opera'; *Px* = 'x pales'; *Cx* = 'x is compared to life'.]

8. Not any *friends* or *Romans* *listened* to Mark Antony. [*Fx* = 'x is a friend'; *Rx* = 'x is a Roman'; *Lx* = 'x listened to Mark Antony'.]

*9. Neither *eggs* nor *brains* should be *fried*. [*Ex* = 'x is an egg'; *Bx* = 'x is a brain'; *Fx* = 'x should be fried'.]

10. *Lilliputians* have a *human* form, but they are *six* inches tall. [*Lx* = 'x is a Lilliputian'; *Hx* = 'x has a human form'; *Sx* = 'x is six inches tall'.]

11. *People* with an "*oral* personality" satisfy their *sexual* and *aggressive* drives orally. [*Px* = 'x is a person'; *Ox* = 'x has an oral personality'; *Sx* = 'x satisfies sexual drives orally'; *Ax* = 'x satisfies aggressive drives orally'.]

12. A *proton* is an *elementary* particle, has a positive *charge*, and can be *found* in the nucleus of an atom. [*Px* = 'x is a proton'; *Ex* = 'x is an elementary particle'; *Cx* = 'x has a positive charge'; *Fx* = 'x can be found in the nucleus of an atom'.]

*13. Left-wing *believers* who are *politicians* are either *Democrats*', *Communists*, or *Libertarians*. [*Bx* = 'x is a left-wing believer';

Px = 'x is a politician'; Dx = 'x is a Democrat'; Cx = 'x is a Communist'; Lx = 'x is a Libertarian.']

14. A *person* should either *love* America or *leave* it. [Px = 'x is a person'; Lx = 'x should love America'; Ex = 'x should leave America'.]

15. *B*MWs, *S*aabs, *A*udis, and *V*olkswagens are all *i*mported, and are either *e*fficient or *l*uxurious. [Bx = 'x is a BMW'; Sx = 'x is a Saab'; Ax = 'x is an Audi'; Vx = 'x is a Volkswagen'; Ix = 'x is imported'; Ex = 'x is efficient'; Lx = 'x is luxurious'.]

16. Any *s*hip *i*n a storm is *d*oomed, unless it can *f*ind a port. [Sx = 'x is a ship'; Ix = 'x is in a storm'; Dx = 'x is doomed'; Fx = 'x can find a port'.]

*17. "The most essential *g*ift for a good writer is a *b*uilt-in, *s*hockproof shit *d*etector." (Ernest Hemingway) [Gx = 'x is the most essential gift for a good writer'; Bx = 'x is built in'; Sx = 'x is shockproof'; Dx = 'x is a shit detector'. Hint: This is a biconditional.]

Concept Reviews

1. Is it possible to confuse a predicate constant with a statement constant? Why or why not?

2. We have seen that the major connective in a universally quantified expression is usually the horseshoe. Under what conditions will the antecedent be a disjunction? Under what conditions will the antecedent be a conjunction?

3. p in previous chapters was used as a statement variable. x in this chapter is used as an individual variable. Explain how the two usages are similar. Explain how they are different.

4. Universal statements are about all individuals of a certain kind. Singular statements are about a particular individual. Are there any possible situations where a singular statement and a universal statement will be equivalent in meaning? Indicate the basis for your answer.

D. Existential Statements

General statements make claims about members of a group. As was mentioned earlier, not all general statements are universal statements. A general statement can also make claims about *some* members of a group.

DEFINITION 7.11

An *existential statement* affirms or denies a predicate of some individuals of a certain kind.

Suppose we know that Copernicus, who claimed that the earth revolves around the sun, was in opposition to beliefs of the 16th-century Roman Catholic Church. We are justified in claiming that

> *Some 16th-century astronomers were opposed to beliefs of the Roman Catholic Church.*

Existential statements are often expressed with two or more predicates, though less frequently than universal statements are. As with universal statements, one predicate typically defines the group at issue, and the other predicate applies an attribute to its members. In the above example, the group at issue is defined by the quality of being a 16th-century astronomer. *Some* members of this group were opposed to beliefs of the Roman Catholic Church.

Our predicate constants enable us to express qualities. We are able to indicate individuals (indeterminately) by using our individual variables. We need a way, a quantifier, to indicate 'some'.

Just as all of our previous artificial-language symbols have had precise and unchanging meanings, the expression of 'some' in the artificial language also has a precise and unchanging meaning. 'Some' will be understood to indicate "at least one."

DEFINITION 7.12

$\exists x$, $\exists y$, and $\exists z$ are *existential quantifiers*. They abbreviate "there is at least one individual in the universe, call it x (or y, or z), ..."

By assembling our machinery and using the italicized letters for predicate constants, our example for this section can be symbolized as follows:

> *Some 16th-century astronomers were opposed to beliefs of the Roman Catholic Church.*

There is at least one individual in the universe, call it x, such that:	the individual, x, has the quality of being a 16th-century astronomer,	and	the individual, x, has the quality of opposing beliefs of the Roman Catholic Church.
$\exists x$	$(Ax$	$\bullet$	$Ox)$

Or, in a more condensed form:

$\exists x(Ax \cdot Ox)$

As with the universal quantifier, whatever follows the existential quantifier should be placed in parentheses (or brackets, or braces).

i. Existential Import

Notice that with the existential quantifier, our quantified expression has had the dot as the major connective. Most symbolizations of existential statements have the dot as the major connective. Suppose that we had attempted to symbolize the example for this section as follows:

$\exists x(Ax \supset Ox)$

The above does not correctly express 'Some 16th-century astronomers opposed beliefs of the Roman Catholic Church'. Rather, this symbolization claims that 'There is at least one thing in the universe (it could be a chair), such that *if* it is a 16th-century astronomer, *then* it opposed beliefs of the Roman Catholic Church'. Statements about 'some' things are called "existential statements." They claim that things of the kind being discussed exist. The statement about 16th-century astronomers has, as part of its meaning, the claim that there were 16th-century astronomers.

DEFINITION 7.13

A statement has *existential import* if and only if it claims that things of a given kind exist.

Existential quantifiers assert the existence of at least one thing, but they do not indicate which thing. The thing claimed to exist can be any "call-it-x" thing.

Conditionals do not assert their antecedents. '$\exists x(Ax \supset Ox)$' does not claim that there were 16th-century astronomers. It claims that there is at least one thing in the universe, such that *if* it was a 16th-century astronomer, *then* it opposed beliefs of the Roman Catholic Church. Since the English sentence claims that 16th-century astronomers existed, using our existential quantifier with the horseshoe is incorrect.

Conjunctions, as expressed with the dot, do assert both conjuncts. Hence, '$\exists x(Ax \cdot Ox)$', which claims that 'there is at least one thing, x, such that x was a 16th-century astronomer *and* x was opposed to beliefs of the Roman Catholic Church', is the correct translation. '$\exists x(Ax \cdot Ox)$' asserts that there is at least one thing with both qualities.

There are times when universal statements, as expressed in English, are intended to have existential import, and there are times when they are not. Suppose that a car dealership displays the following message:

All complaints will be handled promptly.

The dealership is not intending to claim that there are complaints. A person who, upon seeing the sign, refused to leave her car because she did not wish to leave it where there are complaints, would have misinterpreted the sentence.

From 1918 to 1921, the All-Russian Extraordinary Commission to Combat Counterrevolution and Sabotage, better known as the Cheka, brutalized Soviet citizens who opposed the Bolshevik revolution. Historians have compared the Cheka's brutality in quality, if not quantity, to Nazi exploits of World War II. Many Soviet citizens realized that

The Cheka brutalized all of its prisoners.

In a suitable context, the above sentence will convey the idea that there were brutalized prisoners. It will be understood as claiming that brutalized prisoners existed.

Our earlier symbolizations of universal statements have not claimed that things of the kind at issue exist. '$\forall x(Cx \supset Px)$', using obvious predicate-constant abbreviations, does not claim that there are promptly handled complaints. All of our symbols in this chapter, as in earlier chapters, have a constant meaning. Accordingly, '$\forall x(Px \supset Bx)$' does not claim that there were prisoners who were brutalized by the Cheka. Rather, it claims that for anything in the universe, *if* it was a prisoner of the Cheka then it was brutalized by the Cheka.

We will continue to use the horseshoe, as explained in the previous section, to express *universal* statements. We will do so regardless of whether the English sentence might be considered to imply that things of the kind at issue exist. It is certainly incorrect to regard all universal statements as claiming that things of the kind at issue exist. The example from the car dealer does *not* intend existential import. In some contexts we assume that things of the kind at issue exist. When this assumption is essential for an argument, perhaps for the construction of a formal proof in the next section, we can easily indicate that things of a given kind exist. '$\exists x Px$' can be used to indicate that there has been at least one thing that was a Cheka prisoner. Rather than debate whether existential import is a reasonable assumption when expressing a given statement, we can make any such assumptions explicit in the context of an argument.

ii. Symbolization Patterns

P and *Q* indicate predicates.

  a. Existential Affirmative Statements An existential affirmative statement claims (or affirms) that some members of the group at issue have a particular attribute. 'Some 16th-century astronomers were opposed to beliefs of the Roman Catholic Church' is an existential affirmative statement, since it claims that some things that were 16th-century astronomers had the quality of being opposed to beliefs of the Roman Catholic Church. English has a number of constructions that are commonly used to express existential affirmative statements.

1. Some *P*s are *Q*s.   This is the most common pattern in English for expressing existential statements. 'Some *P*s are *Q*s' is symbolized as

$\exists x(Px \cdot Qx)$

'Some *s*cientists *b*elieve in God' is symbolized as '$\exists x(Sx \cdot Bx)$': "There is at least one thing in the universe that is a scientist, and it believes in God."

2. At least one *P* is a *Q*.   This English expression most closely expresses the meaning of the existential quantifier. 'At least one *P* is a *Q*' is symbolized as

$\exists x(Px \cdot Qx)$

'At least one *a*thlete is *t*ired' is symbolized as '$\exists x(Ax \cdot Tx)$': "There is at least one thing in the universe such that it is an athlete and it is tired."

3. There are *P*s (that are) *Q*s.   Since there are Ps that are Qs, there must be at least one *P* that is a *Q*. 'There are *P*s that are *Q*s' is symbolized as

$\exists x(Px \cdot Qx)$

'There are *A*fro-American *c*ongressmen' is symbolized as '$\exists x(Ax \cdot Cx)$': "There is at least one thing in the universe such that it is Afro-American and a congressman."

4. Many *P*s are *Q*s.   Our artificial language does not distinguish between 'many' and 'some'. 'Many' is ambiguous in English. It is unclear how many parts must be defective before we can truly say that "many parts are defective." For our present purposes, we will symbolize 'many' with the 'at least one' meaning of our existential quantifier. 'Many *P*s are *Q*s' is symbolized as

$\exists x(Px \cdot Qx)$

'Many *p*arts are *d*efective' is symbolized as '$\exists x(Px \cdot Dx)$': "There is at least one thing in the universe such that it is a part and defective."

5. *P*s are *Q*s   *Not all English usages of this pattern express existential statements.* There are times where the quantity of 'some' is intended, but not explicitly stated. In cases where 'some' is intended, '*P*s are *Q*s' should be expressed as

$\exists x(Px \cdot Qx)$

'Students are *present*' likely means that some students are present. If so, it can be symbolized as '$\exists x(Sx \cdot Px)$': "There is at least one thing such that it is a student and present." Be sure to compare the translation back to the English, to verify that both have (roughly) the same meaning.

6. There are *P*s. Some things are *P*s. Few qualities reasonably apply to all things in the universe, and so most universal statements have at least two predicates: one to define the group and one to apply a quality to its members. In contrast, many qualities can reasonably be asserted for *some* things. 'There are *P*s' and 'some things are *P*s' are both symbolized as

$\exists x Px$

'There are things that are *best* forgotten' is symbolized as '$\exists x Bx$': "There is at least one thing in the universe such that it is best forgotten."

b. Existential Negative Statements   Existential negative statements assert that the *denial* of an attribute applies to some members of a group.

All of the above patterns can be used to express existential negative statements.

The tilde can be used to deny that a predicate applies to a group when we are symbolizing existential statements, just as it was used to deny that a predicate applied to a group when we were symbolizing universal statements.

1. Some *P*s are not *Q*s. 'Some *P*s are not *Q*s' is symbolized as

$\exists x(Px \cdot \sim Qx)$

'Some *politicians* are not *honest*' is symbolized as '$\exists x(Px \cdot \sim Hx)$': "There is at least one thing in the universe such that it is a politician and is not honest."

Any of the following, given the restrictions noted above, can also be symbolized as '$\exists x(Px \cdot \sim Qx)$':

At least one *P* is not a *Q*.
There are *P*s that are not *Q*s.
Many *P*s are not *Q*s.
*P*s are not *Q*s.

2. Not all *P*s are *Q*s. 'Not all *P*s are *Q*s' generally has the same meaning as 'some *P*s are not *Q*s'. Accordingly, 'not all *P*s are *Q*s' is symbolized as

$\exists x(Px \cdot \sim Qx)$

'Not all *d*ogs are *v*icious' is symbolized as '∃x(Dx · ~Vx)': "There is at least one thing in the universe such that it is a dog and not vicious."

Exercises IV

Symbolize each of the following by using the italicized letters for the required predicate constants. Each of the following is an existential statement that fits one of the above patterns. All of the statements are based on recent research regarding the aging process. People tend to complain about getting older. But, while not the ideal, getting older is better than the other alternative!

*1. There are *o*ctogenarians.
2. There are *s*cientists who are studying the *a*ging process.
3. At least one *c*hemical (aminoguanidine) *p*revents cell deterioration.
4. Many *s*cientists *b*elieve that aging has a genetic component.
*5. Cell *a*ctivities *p*roduce destructive particles.
6. Some *g*enes *c*ontrol the aging process.
7. Some *g*enes do not *c*ontrol the aging process.
8. Not all *s*cientists are studying the *a*ging process.
*9. Excess *p*rotein from cell division *r*esults in clogged arteries.
10. There are *b*abies born with Werner's *s*yndrome. [Werner's syndrome causes premature aging.]
11. Not all of the *e*lderly *c*an memorize lists of unrelated words.
12. Not all of the *e*lderly *w*ant to memorize "dumb lists."
*13. At least one *s*cientist *b*elieves that human chromosome #1 accounts for aging.

iii. More Complex Symbolizations: Existential Statements

Although less predictable than universal statements, complex existential statements are frequently expressed as quantified conjunctions. Most complex symbolizations can be seen as variations of the patterns that have already been presented.

Suppose that we attempt to symbolize:

Not all households headed by women are living below the poverty level.

This assertion is a variant of the 'not all *P*s are *Q*s' pattern. As we have seen, these sentences are usually expressed as '∃x(Px · ~Qx)'. This example contains three predicates, rather than two predicates as in the pattern. The sentence mentions the quality of being a household, the quality of being headed by a woman, and the quality of living below the poverty level.

Obviously, the statement is about those households that are headed by women; *they* make up the group being described. Accordingly, we should expect the symbolization to begin with '∃x[(Hx · Wx) . . .]'. The statement claims that some of these households are *not* living below the poverty level. Our symbolization becomes:

∃x[(Hx · Wx) · ~Lx]

Political scientists have noted that the United States, more than most democracies, has a pool of voters without a major party affiliation. There are voters who are neither Democrats nor Republicans. How can we express this claim? First, the claim is about voters; *they* make up the group at issue. Some members of this group are neither Democrats nor Republicans. We can use the following steps to develop our symbolization:

> *There is at least one thing that is a voter, and it is neither a Democrat nor a Republican.*
>
> *There is at least one individual, x, such that x is a voter and x is neither a Democrat nor a Republican.*
>
> ∃x [x is a voter and (x is neither a Democrat nor a Republican)].

As in Chapter 2, 'neither one nor the other' has the meaning of "not the first and not the second." When a person is neither a Democrat nor a Republican, she is *not* a Democrat *and not* a Republican. The statement should be symbolized as:

∃x[Vx · (~Dx · ~Rx)]

Also, of course, some voters do have a major party affiliation. There are voters who are either Democrats or Repubicans. Again, the group at issue is voters. Moreover, some of them are *either* Democrats *or* Republicans. In symbols, we have:

∃x[Vx · (Dx ∨ Rx)]

As with universal statements, some existential statements fail to fit any of our standard symbolization patterns. 'Some things are either worthwhile expenditures or a waste of money' is symbolized as '∃x(Ex ∨ Wx)'.

Finally, some English sentences are ambiguous. They fail to express a meaning that warrants one symbolization rather than another. In these cases, the best we can do is review the context and, if necessary, look at an argument in terms of reasonable possibilities.

In response to fears of poisons in the food chain, one can note that:

> *Some chemicals are essential for plant and animal life.*

Since the statement is about *some* chemicals, it is an existential statement. Our symbolization should begin with the existential quantifier. Some members of the group of chemicals have the quality of being essential for plant and animal life. At this point, the ambiguity of the English becomes apparent. Is the sentence claiming that some chemicals serve both functions—that there are chemicals that are needed for *both* plant and animal life? We can symbolize this claim as:

$$\exists x[Cx \cdot (Px \cdot Ax)]$$

Or is it claiming that there are chemicals that are needed for plant life, and there are chemicals, but perhaps different ones, that are needed for animal life? We can symbolize this claim as:

$$\exists x(Cx \cdot Px) \cdot \exists x(Cx \cdot Ax)$$

'$\exists x[Cx \cdot (Px \cdot Ax)]$' is *not* logically equivalent to '$\exists x(Cx \cdot Px) \cdot \exists x(Cx \cdot Ax)$'. The differences in meaning between these artificial-language expressions is discussed in section III.

Obviously, we can express either meaning, but which is correct? Context might provide an answer, but perhaps both meanings will have to be considered.

Exercises V

Symbolize each of the following existential statements. Be sure to compare your symbolizations back to the English.

*1. Some *n*uclear power plants *e*xperienced enormous cost overruns and went on to *p*roduce harmful wastes. [Nx = 'x is a nuclear power plant'; Ex = 'x has experienced enormous cost overruns'; Px = 'x went on to produce harmful wastes'.]

2. Some *h*ouses are *c*onsidered to be churches by the IRS, and are *t*ax exempt. [Hx = 'x is a house'; Cx = 'x is considered to be a church by the IRS'; Tx = 'x is tax exempt'.]

3. There are *s*cientists who *p*roclaim equality but *d*iscriminate against women. [Sx = 'x is a scientist'; Px = 'x proclaims equality'; Dx = 'x discriminates against women'.]

4. "The Marines are *l*ooking for a few *g*ood men." [Lx = 'x has the quality of being looked for by the Marines'; Gx = 'x is a good man'.]

*5. Many *c*ongresspersons *w*ish to deal with the deficit, but cannot find a *r*easonable solution. [Cx = 'x is a congressperson'; Wx = 'x wishes to deal with the deficit'; Rx = 'x can find a reasonable solution'.]

6. There are *p*lays that *u*se acts of nudity and *d*ramatize the tension of sexual repression. [Px = 'x is a play'; Ux = 'x is an act of nudity'; Dx = 'x dramatizes the tension of sexual repression'.]

7. At least one *F*ounding Father was a *d*eist who did not believe that God either *c*ares about the world or takes an *a*ctive role with it. [*Fx* = '*x* was a Founding Father'; *Dx* = '*x* was a deist'; *Cx* = '*x* believed that God cares about the world'; *Ax* = '*x* believed that God takes an active role with the world'.]

8. Some *d*octors do not accept either *w*elfare patients or *M*edicaid patients. [*Dx* = '*x* is a doctor'; *Wx* = '*x* accepts welfare patients'; *Mx* = '*x* accepts Medicaid patients'.]

*9. Not all doctors accept both welfare and Medicaid patients. [As number 8.]

10. Many *e*mergency rooms were not planned with *d*rug abuse and *A*IDS patients in mind. [*Ex* = '*x* is an emergency room'; *Dx* = '*x* was planned with drug abuse patients in mind'; *Ax* = '*x* was planned with AIDS patients in mind'.]

11. Some things are either *e*xpensive and of high *q*uality or inexpensive and of low quality. [*Ex* = '*x* is expensive'; *Qx* = '*x* is of high quality'.]

12. At least one *p*erson either *e*ats to live or *l*ives to eat. [*Px* = '*x* is a person'; *Ex* = '*x* eats to live'; *Lx* = '*x* lives to eat'.]

*13. Some *p*eople are *u*nusual, not because they *t*ry to be, but because being so comes *n*aturally. [*Px* = '*x* is a person'; *Ux* = '*x* is unusual'; *Tx* = '*x* is unusual because *x* tries to be unusual'; *Nx* = '*x* is unusual because *x* is naturally unusual'.]

iv. Suggestions for Symbolizing Statements in Predicate Logic

1. First, determine the quantity of the statement to be translated. If it is a singular statement, use individual constants. If it is a universal statement, begin with the universal quantifier. If it is an existential statement, begin with the existential quantifier.

2. If the statement is either universal or existential, decide what group is being described. If it is a universal statement, use predicate constants, as needed, to identify the group being described. The major connective will likely be the horseshoe. The group at issue will be expressed by the antecedent, and the attributes of its members will be expressed by the consequent. If it is an existential statement, use predicate constants, as needed, to identify the groups being described. The major connective will likely be the dot. The group at issue will be expressed as one conjunct, and the attributes of its members will be expressed as the other conjunct.

SYMBOLS FOR PREDICATE LOGIC

	Symbol	*Purpose*
Individual constants	a–w	To identify a particular individual
Predicate constants	A–Z	To identify a particular predicate
Individual variables	x, y, z	To provide placeholders for individual constants
Universal quantifiers	$\forall x, \ \forall y, \ \forall z$	To express universal statements: "For any individual in the universe, call it x, (or y or z), ..."
Existential quantifiers	$\exists x, \ \exists y, \ \exists z$	To express existential statements: "For at least one individual in the universe, call it x, (or y, or z), ..."

SYMBOLIZATION PATTERNS FOR GENERAL STATEMENTS
P and Q indicate predicates

English	*Symbolization*
All Ps are Qs. Any P is a Q. The only Ps are Qs. *When a universal statement is expressed:* The Ps are Qs. Ps are Qs.	$\forall x(Px \supset Qx)$
Only Ps are Qs. None but Ps are Qs.	$\forall x(Qx \supset Px)$
No Ps are Qs. Not any Ps are Qs.	$\forall x(Px \supset {\sim}Qx)$
Some Ps are Qs. At least one P is a Q. There are Ps (that are) Qs. Many Ps are Qs.	$\exists x(Px \cdot Qx)$

SYMBOLIZATION PATTERNS FOR GENERAL STATEMENTS
P and *Q* indicate predicates (*continued*)

English	*Symbolization*
Some *P*s are not *Q*s. At least one *P* is not a *Q*. There are *P*s that are not *Q*s. Many *P*s are not *Q*s. *P*s are not *Q*s. Not all *P*s are *Q*s.	$\exists x(Px \cdot \sim Qx)$
There are *P*s. Some things are *P*s.	$\exists x Px$
*P*s are *Q*s.	$\forall x(Px \supset Qx)$ or $\exists x(Px \cdot Qx)$
The *P* is *Q*.	$\forall x(Px \supset Qx)$ or a singular statement

In 1770, Captain James Cook claimed the continent of Australia for Great Britain. Faced with inadequate prison facilities at home, Britain proceeded to make Australia a penal colony. Prisoners, many convicted of only petty crimes, were shipped to Australia to serve their sentences. From the arrival of the first shipment in 1788 until the arrival of the last shipment in 1867, over 160,000 prisoners were transported. In addition to killing aborigines for sport and dog food, the ruling British created concentration camps for Irish rebels.[3] The following exercises are all based on such acts.

Exercises VI

Symbolize each of the following into the predicate notation. Some are singular statements, some are universal statements, and some are existential statements. Use the suggested predicate constants. You will have to designate individual constants as needed.

---

[3]For a detailed account, written from prisoner and aborigine perspectives, see Robert Hughes, *The Fatal Shore: The Epic of Australia's Founding* (New York: Alfred A. Knopf, 1987).

*1. Captain Arthur Phillip entered Port Jackson [Sydney Harbor] on January 26, 1788. [Ex = 'x entered Port Jackson on January 26, 1788'.]

2. All of the Iora (a tribe of Aborigines) covered themselves with fish oil to ward off mosquitoes. [Ix = 'x was an Iora'; Cx = 'x covered himself or herself with fish oil to ward off mosquitos'.]

3. Not all of the aborigines were killed. [Ax = 'x was an aborigine'; Kx = 'x was killed'.]

4. Many aborigines died from cholera and influenza. [Ax = 'x was an aborigine'; Cx = 'x died from cholera'; Ix = 'x died from influenza'.]

*5. King George III authorized the voyage, and Captain Phillip set out for Australia. [Ax = 'x authorized the voyage'; Sx = 'x set out for Australia'.]

6. A few of the prisoners in Van Diemen's Land were well treated. [Px = 'x was a prisoner in Van Diemen's Land'; Tx = 'x was well treated'.]

7. Many convicts had been found guilty of minor thefts. [Cx = 'x was a convict'; Gx = 'x was found guilty of a minor theft'.]

8. At times, the aborigine men would lend their wives to respected visitors. [Ax = 'x was an aborigine'; Lx = 'x would lend his wife to respected visitors'.]

*9. Any prisoner who escaped was assured of death. [Px = 'x was a prisoner'; Ex = 'x escaped'; Dx = 'x was assured of death'.]

10. If a prisoner on Norfolk Island was found guilty of getting a light to smoke, then he was sentenced to 50 lashes. [Px = 'x was a prisoner on Norfolk Island'; Fx = 'x was found guilty of getting a light to smoke; Sx = 'x was sentenced to 50 lashes'.]

11. Major Joseph Anderson (1790–1877), a pious Scot, planned a new jail on Norfolk Island; and if a prisoner was found guilty by Major Anderson of striking an overseer who pushed him, he would administer 100 lashes before breakfast. [Px = 'x was pious'; Sx = 'x was a Scot'; Jx = 'x planned a new jail on Norfolk Island'; Gx = 'x was found guilty by Major Anderson of striking an overseer who pushed him'; Ax = 'x would administer 100 lashes before breakfast'.]

12. All of the aborigines living in Tasmania were killed. [Ax = 'x was an aborigine'; Tx = 'x lived in Tasmania'; Kx = 'x was killed'.]

*13. There can be no slavery in a free land. [Sx = 'x is a case of slavery'; Fx = 'x is in a free land'.]

14. Many early settlers died of starvation and disease. [Ex = 'x was an early settler'; Sx = 'x died of starvation'; Dx = 'x died of disease'.]

15. There were no slaves in Australia. [Sx = 'x was a slave'; Ax = 'x was in Australia'.]

16. No Catholic could sit in Parliament, on the bench, or in a jury. [Cx = 'x was a Catholic'; Px = 'x could sit in Parliament'; Bx = 'x could sit on the bench'; Jx = 'x could sit in a jury'.]

*17. The aborigines were classified as British subjects in 1836. [Ax = 'x was an aborigine'; Cx = 'x was classified as a British subject in 1836'.]

18. The Irish were classified as traitors, given vicious punishments, and kept under constant scrutiny. [Ix = 'x was Irish'; Tx = 'x was classified as a traitor'; Px = 'x was given vicious punishments'; Sx = 'x was kept under constant scrutiny'.]

19. Philip Cunningham led an unsuccessful rebellion by the "Rum Corps," refused to surrender to Major Johnson, and was sentenced to death by hanging. [Lx = 'x led an unsuccessful rebellion by the "Rum Corps" '; Rx = 'x refused to surrender to Major Johnson'; Sx = 'x was sentenced to death by hanging'.]

In a more modern vein:

20. Sydney is located in New South Wales. [Lx = 'x is located in New South Wales'.]

*21. Although still part of the British Commonwealth, Australia became an independent nation in 1901. [Px = 'x is part of the British Commonwealth'; Ix = 'x became an independent nation in 1901'.]

22. Canberra is the present capital of Australia. [Cx = 'x is the present capital of Australia'.]

23. Any Australian who has a right to vote is required by law to vote, and is subject to a fine for failure to do so. [Ax = 'x is an Australian'; Rx = 'x has a right to vote'; Lx = 'x is required by law to vote'; Sx = 'x is subject to a fine'; Fx = 'x fails to vote'.]

24. Not all Australians are like Crocodile Dundee. [Ax = 'x is an Australian'; Lx = 'x is like Crocodile Dundee'.]

*25. There are sheep in Australia. [Sx = 'x is a sheep in Australia'.]

26. Some parts of Australia are accessible by plane, but only at a risk to both passengers and crew. [Px = 'x is a part of Australia'; Ax = 'x is accessible by plane'; Sx = 'accessing x involves a risk to passengers'; Cx = 'accessing x involves a risk to the crew'.]

27. Some Australians are uncertain about how to perceive their convict heritage. [Ax = 'x is an Australian'; Ux = 'x is uncertain about how to perceive the convict heritage'.]

28. Some Australians do not wish to remember their felon origins. [Ax = 'x is an Australian'; Wx = 'x wishes to remember x's felon origins'.]

*29. Most Australians are of either British or European descent. [Ax = 'x is Australian'; Bx = 'x is of British descent'; Ex = 'x is of European descent'.]

30. There are Australians who are not happy about their convict origins. [Ax = 'x is an Australian'; Hx = 'x is happy about his or her convict origins'.]

31. Some Australians of respectable British descent have furthered the myths of convict blood and convict evil. [Ax = 'x is an Australian'; Bx = 'x is of respectable British descent'; Cx = 'x has furthered the myth of convict blood'; Ex = 'x has furthered the myth of convict evil'.]

32. Most convicts wished to stay in Australia and rejected the idea of going back to England. [Cx = 'x was a 'convict,' Wx = 'x wished to stay in Australia'; Rx = 'x rejected the idea of going back to England'.]

*33. Only Australians would have paid the price at Gallipoli. [Ax = 'x is an Australian'; Px = 'x would have paid the price at Gallipoli'.]

34. All convict-descendant communities have shown respect for law and have not shown criminal tendencies. [Cx = 'x is a convict-descendant community'; Rx = 'x has shown respect for law'; Sx = 'x has shown criminal tendencies'.]

Concept Reviews

1. 'All complaints will be handled promptly' should be symbolized as '∀x(Cx ⊃ Px)'. 'Some complaints will be handled promptly' should be symbolized as '∃x(Cx · Px)'. Is it possible for the universal statement to be true while the existential statement is false? Under what conditions might this happen? Explain your answer by noting whether both statements claim that things of the kind at issue exist.

2. Conversely, can you think of any situations where '∃x(Cx · Px)' should be considered true and '∀x(Cx ⊃ Px)' should be considered false? From number 1, should we consider arguments from a universal statement to the corresponding existential statement to be valid? Should we consider an argument from an existential statement to the corresponding universal statement to be valid?

3. Suppose that someone symbolized 'some complaints will be handled promptly' as '∃x(Cx ⊃ Px)'. Explain how and why this attempted symbolization would misconstrue the existential import of 'some complaints will be handled promptly'.

4. Suppose that someone symbolized 'only real vegetarians eat dill pickles' as: '∀x{[(Ex · Dx) · Px] ⊃ (Rx · Vx)}', using the italicized letters for predicate constants. Explain what is wrong with this symbolization. How should predicates be chosen, and how should the sentence be symbolized?

E. Requirements for Well-Formed Formulas (WFFs)

In Chapter 2 we noticed that there are restrictions that must be met for an expression to be a proper expression in the artificial language. An acceptable expression must have enough punctuation to define the statements that are connected to form the compound statement. '$D \cdot S \vee L$' cannot correctly symbolize *any* English sentence. Expressions that are acceptably constructed in the artificial language are called "well-formed formulas," or WFFs.

We have placed quantified expressions in parentheses (or brackets or braces). Doing so placed the quantified expression within the scope of the quantifier.

DEFINITION 7.14

The *scope of a quantifier* consists of the entire expression, as defined by parentheses, brackets, or braces, that directly follows it.

Quantifiers apply to the expressions that follow them, in the same way as the tilde applies to the expression that follows it. In '$\exists x[(Cx \cdot Px) \cdot Ax)]$', the scope of the existential quantifier consists of the entire expression that is contained within the brackets: '$(Cx \cdot Px) \cdot Ax$'. In '$\forall x[Gx \supset (Mx \vee Ex)]$', the scope of the universal quantifier again consists of the entire expression that is contained within the brackets: '$Gx \supset (Mx \vee Ex)$'.

In the following expression, however, only Gx is within the scope of the universal quantifier:

$\forall x Gx \supset (Mx \vee Ex)$

Similarly, in the following expression, only '$Cx \cdot Px$' is within the scope of the existential quantifier:

$\exists x(Cx \cdot Px) \cdot Ax$

Now we can state a requirement for quantified expressions.

For an expression to be a well-formed formula (WFF), each variable within the quantified expression must be within the scope of a quantifier that has the same variable.

'$\forall x Gx \supset (Mx \vee Ex)$' is not a WFF, since x in '$(Mx \vee Ex)$' is not within the scope of a quantifier that has this variable. '$(Mx \vee Ex)$' is beyond the scope of the universal quantifier. '$\exists x(Cx \cdot Px) \cdot Ax$' is not a WFF, since the *x* in '*Ax*' is not within the scope of a quantifier that has this variable. *Ax* is beyond the scope of the existential quantifier.

'∀*x*[*Gy* ⊃ (*Mx* ∨ *Ex*)]' is also not a WFF. All of the variables are within the scope of a quantifier, but the variable *y* is not within the scope of a quantifier that has this variable.

Notice that well-formed formulas do not require that the entire expression be within the scope of a quantifier. Our requirement only states that any *variable* must be within the scope of a quantifier that has the same variable. '∀*xGx* ⊃ (*Ma* ∨ *Ea*)' *is* a WFF in our artificial language. The only variable in '*Gx*' is within the scope of a (universal) quantifier that has the same variable.

II Formal Proofs

This section assumes that you have a working knowledge of the system for constructing formal proofs that was developed in Chapters 4 and 5.

If we add three inferences to our present formal proof system, we will be able to construct formal proofs of validity for arguments in predicate logic.

All of the equivalence inferential forms of Chapter 5 can already be applied to quantified expressions. Suppose that someone argued as follows:

> *Premiss:*   No person can serve Mammon and God.
> *Hence:*   If a person serves Mammon, then that person doesn't serve God.

The equivalence inferential forms from Chapter 5 enable us to construct the following formal proof:

1. ∀*x*[*Px* ⊃ ~(*Mx* · *Gx*)]   ⟋∀*x*[(*Px* · *Mx*) ⊃ ~*Gx*]
2. ∀*x*[~*Px* ∨ ~(*Mx* · *Gx*)] W.E. *1*
3. ∀*x*[~*Px* ∨ (~*Mx* ∨ ~*Gx*)] D.M. *2*
4. ∀*x*[(~*Px* ∨ ~*Mx*) ∨ ~*Gx*] Assoc. *3*
5. ∀*x*[~(*Px* · *Mx*) ∨ ~*Gx*] D.M. *4*
6. ∀*x*[(*Px* · *Mx*) ⊃ ~*Gx*] W.E. *5*

To apply our inferential forms of Chapter 4, however, we need ways to eliminate quantifiers. Our valid inferential forms can only be applied when instances consist of whole lines.

In addition, formal proofs in predicate logic will often require us to relate universal and existential statements to one another. We will need to be able to manipulate quantifiers. First, we will formally define universal and existential statements in the artificial language. Next, we will add rules of inference for quantified statements to our deductive system.

DEFINITION 7.15

A well-formed formula (WFF) is a *universal quantification* if and only if it begins with a universal quantifier whose scope is the entire remainder of the WFF.

DEFINITION 7.16

A well-formed formula (WFF) is an *existential quantification* if and only if it begins with an existential quantifier whose scope is the entire remainder of the WFF.

'$\forall x(Sx \supset Ix) \supset Ib$' is a WFF, but it is *not* a universal quantification, since 'Ib' is outside the scope of the universal quantifier. The scope of $\forall x$ is not the entire remainder of the WFF. Similarly, '$\exists xFx \cdot Fm$' is not an existential quantification, since Fm is outside the scope of the existential quantifier. '$\exists xGx \supset \forall x{\sim}Ex$' is neither a universal nor an existential quantification.

Each of the following is a universal quantification:

$\forall x[(Sx \lor Ix) \supset Gx]$ $\forall x{\sim}Ex$

Each of the following is an existential quantification:

$\exists xGx$ $\exists x[Sx \cdot (Ix \lor Gx)]$

A. Universal Instantiation (U.I.)

A universal quantification is true if and only if its claim is true of every member in the universe.[4] The rule of universal instantiation is based on the fact that what is true for every member of the universe must be true for each member of the universe. Hence:

We may derive a singular statement from a universal quantification by dropping the quantifier and uniformly replacing the individual variable with any individual constant. We must replace the variable with the same individual constant throughout.

---

[4]Or restricted domain as later defined.

Suppose that we let '$\forall x(\ldots Px \ldots)$' represent any universal quantification. Universal instantiation can now be stated as follows.

UNIVERSAL INSTANTIATION (U.I.)

Where '$\forall x(\ldots Px \ldots)$' indicates a universal quantification, we may infer '$(\ldots Pa \ldots)$' (or b, or c, etc.), as long as all occurrences of x are uniformly replaced with a (or b, or c, etc.).

From 'no person can serve Mammon and God' we can infer that 'If Smitty is a person, then he cannot serve Mammon and God'. In the artificial language:

1. $\forall x[Px \supset \sim(Mx \cdot Gx)]$ (*premiss*)
2. $Ps \supset \sim(Ms \cdot Gs)$ U.I. 1

Notice that line 2 has been justified by U.I. (Universal Instantiation), and that line 1 has been listed as the premiss.

The following are *not* legitimate uses of universal instantiation.

1. $\forall x[Px \supset \sim(Mx \cdot Gx)]$
2. $Py \supset \sim(My \cdot Gy)$ **Error**; *must be replaced with a **constant**.*

1. $\forall x[Px \supset \sim(Mx \cdot Gx)]$
2. $Pa \supset \sim(Mb \cdot Gb)$ **Error**; *must be uniformly replaced with the same constant.*

The introduction to this chapter claimed that JC is a valid argument. We can finally provide a formal proof to show this.

ARGUMENT JC

Men who have a lean and hungry look are dangerous.
Cassius [a man] has a lean and hungry look.[5]
Hence, Cassius is dangerous.

Symbolization and formal proof:

1. $\forall x[(Mx \cdot Lx) \supset Dx]$ $/Dc$
2. $Mc \cdot Lc$
3. $(Mc \cdot Lc) \supset Dc$ U.I. 1
4. Dc M.P. 3, 2

Line 4 is a permissible use of modus ponens. Mc, Lc, and Dc each abbreviate a statement. In Chapter 4, we would have used statement constants to express them. Hence, the application of modus ponens in this case is not

---

[5]"Yond Cassius has a lean and hungry look; He thinks too much: such men are dangerous." "Lean and hungry" likely indicates one particular kind of look.

any different from its application in Chapter 4. The same reasoning justifies using all of the inferences that were developed in Chapters 4 and 5, including conditional-proof and indirect-proof procedures. Conditional and indirect proofs in predicate logic, however, usually require an additional rule of inference for quantifiers, quantifier negation.

B. Quantifier Negation (Q.N.)

Indirect-proof assumptions in predicate logic frequently produce negated quantifications. '$\sim\forall xCx$' is *not* a universal quantification, since it begins with a tilde rather than a universal quantifier. Hence, universal instantiation cannot be applied to a line that is '$\sim\forall xCx$'. Quantifier negation will enable us to derive either a universal quantification or an existential quantification from a negated quantification.

'$\forall x$' abbreviates "for any individual in the universe, call it x." '$\exists x$' abbreviates "there is at least one individual in the universe, call it x."

Suppose that C stands for the predicate 'is *caused*', and that we consider some examples that use this predicate in order to discover logical equivalences for negated quantifications. '$\forall xCx$' claims that everything is caused. '$\exists xCx$' claims that there is at least one thing that is caused. '$\sim\forall xCx$' expresses the contradictory of '$\forall xCx$', and claims that it is false that everything is caused. '$\sim\exists xCx$' expresses the contradictory of '$\exists xCx$', and claims that it is false that there is at least one thing that is caused. These negated quantifications can be more colloquially translated as follows:

$\sim\forall xCx$ Not everything is caused.

$\sim\exists xCx$ There is nothing that is caused.

Under what conditions will not everything have a cause? Not everything is caused if and only if there is at least one thing that is not caused. And there will be nothing that is caused if and only if everything is not caused. We have discovered the following logical equivalences:

$$\sim\forall xCx \ :: \ \exists x\sim Cx$$

and

$$\sim\exists xCx \ :: \ \forall x\sim Cx$$

The logical equivalence pattern that we discovered in the above examples holds for all quantification statements. It can be expressed as follows:

$$\sim\forall x(\ldots Px \ldots) \ :: \ \exists x\sim(\ldots Px \ldots)$$

and

$$\sim\exists x(\ldots Px \ldots) \ :: \ \forall x\sim(\ldots Px \ldots)$$

> *A negated quantification statement is equivalent to the statement formed by switching quantifiers and placing the tilde after the new quantifier.*

QUANTIFIER NEGATION (Q.N.)

Where '∀x(. . . Px . . .)' indicates a universal quantification and '∃x(. . . Px . . .)' indicates an existential quantification: any occurrence of '~∃x(. . . Px . . .)' can be replaced with '∀x~(. . . Px . . .)' (and conversely), and any occurrence of '~∀x(. . . Px . . .)' can be replaced with '∃x~(. . . Px . . .)' (and conversely).

Since they express logical equivalences, the rules of quantifier negation can be applied in either direction, and on portions of lines as well as whole lines. The use of quantifier negation in formal proofs is almost entirely confined to eliminating tildes from in front of quantifiers.

Formal proofs that derive quantification statements normally begin with an indirect-proof assumption that has the negation of a quantifier. Quantifier negation is used to remove the tilde.

We can now provide a formal proof for the following valid argument:

Any Nathaniel Hawthorne novel explores guilt.
The Scarlet Letter *is a Nathaniel Hawthorne novel.*
Hence, there are Nathaniel Hawthorne novels that explore guilt.

The inference from the first premiss alone to the conclusion is invalid, since the universal statement lacks the required existential import. The second premiss claims that at least one Nathaniel Hawthorne novel, *The Scarlet Letter*, exists. The resulting inference is valid.

1. ∀x(Nx ⊃ Gx)   /∃x(Nx · Gx)
2. Ns

3. ~∃x(Nx · Gx) I.P.A.
4. ∀x~(Nx · Gx) Q.N. 3
5. Ns ⊃ Gs U.I. 1
6. Gs M.P. 5, 2
7. ~(Ns · Gs) U.I. 4
8. Ns · Gs Conj. 2, 6
9. (Ns · Gs) · ~(Ns · Gs) Conj. 8, 7

10. ∃x(Nx · Gx) I.P. 3–9

Guidelines for Constructing Formal Proofs

1. After setting up the problem for a formal proof by numbering the premises and so forth, notice the kind of conclusion that is to be proved. None of our inferences derives a quantification statement. Hence, if the conclusion is a quantification statement, the proof should be started with an indirect-proof assumption. Quantification statements can only be derived by assuming their negations and deriving a contradiction.

2. If there is a negated quantifier, use quantifier negation to derive a line that is either a universal quantification or an existential quantification.

3. Use universal instantiation on all universal quantifications. Derive singular statements by instantiating to individual constants that are already in the problem. (If the problem lacks any individual constants, instantiate to *some* constant in order to continue the proof.)

4. If the problem has an indirect-proof assumption, use the inferential forms from Chapters 4 and 5 to derive a contradiction and end the proof. If the problem does not have an indirect-proof assumption, use the inferential forms from Chapters 4 and 5 to derive the conclusion.

As suggested in number 3, there are times when universal instantiation must be used, although there are no individual constants in the problem. The following is such a case.

Suppose that someone claims that something is either *m*aterial or *s*piritual, since all things are either material or spiritual.

> *1.* $\forall x(Mx \lor Sx)$ $/\exists x(Mx \lor Sx)$

We know that this should be treated by using indirect proof, since the conclusion is a quantification statement. We also know that quantifier negation will be needed to eliminate the tilde that results from the indirect-proof assumption:

> *1.* $\forall x(Mx \lor Sx)$ $/\exists x(Mx \lor Sx)$
> 2. $\sim\exists x(Mx \lor Sx)$ *I.P.A.*
> 3. $\forall x \sim (Mx \lor Sx)$ *Q.N.* 2

To complete the proof, we have to derive a contradiction after removing the universal quantifiers. There are no individual constants that are already in the problem. At this point, we should pick some constant, so that the proof can be continued. In the following problem, *a* has been used in line 4, so that the proof can be finished.

1. ∀x(Mx ∨ Sx)   /∃x(Mx ∨ Sx)

> 2. ~∃x(Mx ∨ Sx) I.P.A.
> 3. ∀x~(Mx ∨ Sx) Q.N. 2
> 4. Ma ∨ Sa U.I. 1
> 5. ~(Ma ∨ Sa) U.I. 3
> 6. (Ma ∨ Sa) · ~(Ma ∨ Sa) Conj. 4, 5

7. ∃x(Mx ∨ Sx) I.P. 2–6

Exercises VII

Provide a formal proof for each of the following valid arguments.

*1. ∀x(Lx ⊃ Ex)
     Lj
     ──────
     ∴ Ej

2. ∀x(Ax ⊃ Rx)
    ~Rs
    ──────
    ∴ ~As

3. ∀x(Mx ⊃ Sx)
    Mo
    ──────
    ∴ Mo · So

4. Sk
    ──────
    ∴ ∃xSx

*5. ∀x(Ex ⊃ Mx)
     Es
     ──────
     ∴ ∃xMx

6. ∀x[~Dx ⊃ (Dx · Cx)]
    ──────
    ∴ ∃xDx

7. ∀x(Ux ⊃ Rx)
    ∀x(Rx ⊃ Lx)
    Up
    ──────
    ∴ Rp · Lp

8. ∀x(Bx ≡ Vx)
    Vb
    ──────
    ∴ Vb · Bb

*9. ∀x[(Yx ∨ Px) ⊃ (~Tx ⊃ Ox)]
     Yl · ~Tl
     ──────
     ∴ ∃xOx

10. ∀x[Hx ⊃ (Kx ⊃ Cx)]
     Ha · ~Ca
     ──────
     ∴ ∃x(~Kx ∨ Nx)

Exercises VIII

Symbolize each of the following arguments, and prove that each argument is valid by providing a formal proof.

*1. All *a*nimals *e*xperience pain. Nothing that *e*xperiences pain should be *h*armed. Fido is an *a*nimal. Hence, Fido should not be *h*armed.

2. Nothing without *l*anguage has *c*oncepts. Nothing without *c*oncepts can have a *r*ight to life. Fido is an *a*nimal, but Fido lacks *l*anguage. Hence, some *a*nimals cannot have a *r*ight to life.

C. Existential Instantiation (E.I.)

Universal instantiation provides a way to derive singular statements from universal quantifications, but we are still unable to apply our valid inferential forms when we have existential quantifications. If the conclusion of an argument is a universal quantification and we begin the formal proof with an indirect proof assumption and apply quantifier negation, we will have derived an existential quantification. We will have derived a line that is beyond our present inferences. Existential instantiation provides a way to derive singular statements from existential quantifications.

An existential quantification is true if and only if what it claims is true for at least one member of the universe. It would be invalid, however, to infer that a particular individual that is referred to elsewhere in the problem is that individual.

> *We may derive a singular statement from an existential quantification by dropping the quantifier and uniformly replacing the individual variable with an individual constant. The same variable must be replaced with the same constant throughout, and the constant must not appear anywhere previously in the problem.*

The following invalid argument could be "proved" without the restriction against picking individual constants that appear in the problem.

Some citizens of the USSR are patriotic.
Some citizens of the United States are patriotic.
Hence, some citizens of the USSR are citizens of the United States.

1. $\exists x(Ux \cdot Px)$ / $\exists x(Ux \cdot Sx)$
2. $\exists x(Sx \cdot Px)$

> 3. $\sim\exists x(Ux \cdot Sx)$ I.P.A.
> 4. $\forall x \sim(Ux \cdot Sx)$ Q.N. 3
> 3. $Ua \cdot Pa$ E.I. 1 *(This step is acceptable.)*
> 4. $Sa \cdot Pa$ E.I. 2 **Error!**
> 5. Sa Simp. 4
> 6. Ua Simp. 3
> 7. $\sim(Ua \cdot Sa)$ U.I. 4
> 8. $Ua \cdot Sa$ Conj. 6, 5
> 9. $(Ua \cdot Sa) \cdot \sim(Ua \cdot Sa)$ Conj 8, 7

10. $\exists x(Ux \cdot Sx)$ I.P. 3–9

EXISTENTIAL INSTANTIATION (E.I.)

Where '$\exists x(\ldots Px \ldots)$' indicates an existential quantification, we may infer '$(\ldots Pa \ldots)$' (or b, or c, etc.), as long as all occurrences of x are uniformly replaced with a (or b, or c, etc.) and a (or b, or c, etc.) does not appear anywhere previously in the problem.

The following prochoice and antiabortion arguments exhibit typical and correct usages of existential instantiation. Both positions have been simplified, perhaps to the point of being offensive to their adherents.

If a woman chooses to have an abortion, then she should be able to have an abortion.

Some women choose to have an abortion.

Hence, some women should be able to have an abortion.

  1. $\forall x[(Wx \cdot Cx) \supset Ax]$ $/\underline{\exists x(Wx \cdot Ax)}$
  2. $\exists x(Wx \cdot Cx)$

---

  3. $\sim\exists x(Wx \cdot Ax)$ I.P.A.
  4. $\forall x \sim(Wx \cdot Ax)$ Q.N. 3
  5. $Wa \cdot Ca$ E.I. 2
  6. $(Wa \cdot Ca) \supset Aa$ U.I. 1
  7. $\sim(Wa \cdot Aa)$ U.I. 4
  8. Aa M.P. 6, 5
  9. Wa Simp. 5
  10. $Wa \cdot Aa$ Conj. 9, 8
  11. $(Wa \cdot Aa) \cdot \sim(Wa \cdot Aa)$ Conj. 10, 7

---

  12. $\exists x(Wx \cdot Ax)$ I.P. 3–11

Existential instantiation was applied to an existential quantification. Notice that the E.I. step was taken before the universal instantiation steps. Had universal instantiation been applied first, a would have been present in the problem prior to the use of existential instantiation. E.I. would have had to derive an instance by using a new individual constant. The U.I. steps would have had to be repeated.

The following shows what happens if we attempt a formal proof for our previous example by using U.I. before E.I.

  1. $\forall x[(Wx \cdot Cx) \supset Ax]$ $/\underline{\exists x(Wx \cdot Ax)}$
  2. $\exists x(Wx \cdot Cx)$

---

  3. $\sim\exists x(Wx \cdot Ax)$ I.P.A.

4. ∀x~(Wx · Ax) Q.N. 3
5. (Wa · Ca) ⊃ Aa U.I. 1
6. ~(Wa · Aa) U.I. 4
7. Wb · Cb E.I. 2

Since *a* already appears in the problem, in lines 5 and 6, existential instantiation requires us to introduce a new constant, other than *a*, on line 7. But unless all of the instances that are derived in the proof have the same constant, it will be impossible to derive a contradiction and end the indirect proof. To finish the above proof, we would have to repeat the U.I. steps by using *b*.

E.I. requires us to derive an instance by using a constant that does not already appear in the problem, but U.I. allows us to derive an instance by using any constant, whether or not it already appears in the problem. Hence:

If a problem requires using both existential instantiation and universal instantiation, the E.I. step(s) should be taken first.

The next example uses E.I. when the argument's conclusion is a universal quantification.

A fetus is a person.

A person has a right to life.

Hence, a fetus has a right to life.

We have the following symbolization and proof. Notice that E.I. has been applied prior to U.I.

1. ∀x(Fx ⊃ Px)   ⟋∀x(Fx ⊃ Lx)
2. ∀x(Px ⊃ Lx)

3. ~∀x(Fx ⊃ Lx) I.P.A.
4. ∃x~(Fx ⊃ Lx) Q.N. 3
5. ~(Fa ⊃ La) E.I. 4
6. Fa ⊃ Pa U.I. 1
7. Pa ⊃ La U.I. 2
8. ~(~Fa ∨ La) W.E. 5
9. ~~Fa · ~La D.M. 8
10. Fa · ~La D.N. 9
11. Fa Simp. 10
12. Pa M.P. 6, 11
13. La M.P. 7, 12
14. ~La Simp. 9
15. La · ~La Conj. 13, 14

16. ∀x(Fx ⊃ Lx) I.P. 3–15

The above formal proofs show that both the prochoice and antiabortion arguments are valid. Here, as in Chapters 4 and 5, formal proofs show that an argument is valid. They do not determine whether the argument's premises are all true, and they do not determine whether an argument is sound. If the fetus has a right to life that would be violated by an abortion, then a woman should not be able to have an abortion. The conclusions of both arguments cannot be true. One or both arguments must be unsound. One or both of them lacks all true premises. Whether either of these is sound is for you to decide!

D. Negation of a Conditional (N.C.)

Suppose that we wish to construct a formal proof for an argument whose conclusion is '$\forall x(Ax \supset Bx)$'. Most formal proofs for an argument whose conclusion is a universal quantification, such as '$\forall x(Ax \supset Bx)$', require us to go through the following steps as part of the formal proof:

$\sim\forall x(Ax \supset Bx)$ I.P.A.

$\exists x \sim(Ax \supset Bx)$ Q.N.

$\sim(Aa \supset Ba)$ E.I.   *Provided that a has not appeared previously.*

$\sim(\sim Aa \vee Ba)$ W.E.

$\sim\sim Aa \cdot \sim Ba$ D.M.

$Aa \cdot \sim Ba$ D.N.

Given our present inferential forms, we must frequently apply wedge equivalence, De Morgan's laws, and double negation in order to derive a conjunction such as the one above. Since these steps can be taken in any problem that has the negation of a conditional, derivations from an instance of '$\sim(p \supset q)$' to an instance of '$p \cdot \sim q$' can be established as a derived rule. (A truth table could be constructed to verify that '$\sim(p \supset q)$' and '$p \cdot \sim q$' are logically equivalent.)

Adding the following equivalence inferential form, called "negation of a conditional," to our deductive system does not increase the number of arguments for which formal proofs are possible. Adding it merely simplifies some of our formal proofs. Negation of a conditional can be used in the same fashion as any of the equivalence inferential forms that were developed in Chapter 5.

Negation of a Conditional (N.C.)

$\sim(p \supset q) :: p \cdot \sim q$

The negation of a conditional is logically equivalent to a conjunction, in which the previous consequent is negated.

Notice how using negation of a conditional simplifies the previous example.

~∀x(Ax ⊃ Bx) I.P.A.

∃x~(Ax ⊃ Bx) Q.N.

~(Aa ⊃ Ba) E.I.   *Provided that a has not appeared previously.*

Aa · ~Ba N.C.

The following provides another example of negation of a conditional, and points out a series of steps that will provide a formal proof for most arguments in predicate logic.

Step 1   Symbolize, if necessary.

Every revolution is based on love.

Nothing based on love is intended to be harmful.

Hence, no revolution is intended to be harmful.

　1. ∀x(Rx ⊃ Bx)　　　／∀x(Rx ⊃ ~Ix)

　2. ∀x(Bx ⊃ ~Ix)

Step 2   If the conclusion is a quantified statement, make an indirect-proof assumption and apply quantifier negation.

　3. ~∀x(Rx ⊃ ~Ix) I.P.A.

　4. ∃x~(Rx ⊃ ~Ix) Q.N. 3

Step 3   Use existential instantiation first, and eliminate quantifiers.

　5. ~(Ra ⊃ ~Ia) E.I. 4

　6. Ra ⊃ Ba U.I. 1

　7. Ba ⊃ ~Ia U.I. 2

Step 4   Use our inferential forms, and derive either the conclusion of the argument or a contradiction.

　8. Ra · ~~Ia N.C. 5

　9. Ra Simp. 8

　10. Ba M.P. 6, 9

　11. ~Ia M.P. 7, 10

　12. ~~Ia Simp. 8

　13. Ia D.N. 12

　　　·

　14. Ia ~Ia Conj. 13, 11

Step 5   If indirect proof has been used, derive the conclusion.

　15. ∀x(Rx ⊃ ~Ix) I.P. 3–14

Exercises IX

Construct a formal proof of validity for each of the following valid arguments. Proofs for each of these can be constructed by following steps 2 through 4 as listed above. Any of our quantifier inferences may be required and may be used.

*1. $\forall x(Rx \supset Tx)$
$\exists xRx$
$\therefore\ \exists xTx$

2. $\forall x[(Rx \lor Tx) \supset Qx]$
$\exists xRx$
$\therefore\ \exists xQx$

3. $\forall x(\sim Mx \supset Mx)$
$\therefore\ \forall xMx$

4. $\exists xCx$
$\forall x[Cx \supset (Tx \cdot Vx)]$
$\therefore\ \exists xTx$

*5. $\forall x(Ax \supset Ux)$
$\sim Uj$
$\therefore\ \exists x\sim Ax$

6. $\forall x(Rx \supset Tx)$
$\forall x(Rx \supset \sim Tx)$
$\therefore\ \forall x\sim Rx$

7. $\forall x(Vx \equiv Nx)$
Nj
$\therefore\ \exists xVx$

8. $\forall x(Ax \supset Bx)$
$\therefore\ \forall x[(Ax \cdot Cx) \supset Bx]$

*9. $\forall x[Ax \supset (Bx \cdot Cx)]$
$\therefore\ \forall x(Ax \supset Bx)$

10. $\forall x[(Ex \cdot Cx) \supset Ox]$
$\forall x(Ex \supset Cx)$
$\therefore\ \forall x(Ex \supset Ox)$

11. $\exists x(Fx \cdot Dx)$
$\therefore\ \exists xFx$

12. $\forall x[(Bx \lor Cx) \supset Kx]$
$\forall x[(Kx \cdot Ox) \supset (Dx \cdot Nx)]$
$\therefore\ \forall x[Bx \supset (Ox \supset Nx)]$

*13. $\forall x[(Ax \lor Bx) \supset (Dx \cdot Cx)]$
$\exists x(Bx \cdot Rx)$
$\therefore\ \exists x(Dx \cdot Rx)$

14. $\forall x[(Ax \cdot Bx) \supset Cx]$
$\exists x(Ax \cdot \sim Cx)$
$\therefore\ \exists x\sim Bx$

15. $\forall x(\sim Hx \equiv \sim Ix)$
$\forall x[(\sim Ix \cdot \sim Hx) \supset Kx]$
$\exists x\sim Ix$
$\forall x(\sim Ix \equiv Qx)$
$\forall x(Qx \supset Rx)$
$\therefore\ \exists x(Kx \cdot Rx)$

16. $\forall x[Tx \supset (Rx \supset Cx)]$
$\exists x[(Rx \cdot Bx) \cdot \sim Kx]$
$\forall x[(Tx \supset Cx) \supset (Qx \supset Kx)]$
$\therefore\ \exists x(Bx \cdot \sim Qx)$

Exercises X

Symbolize each of the following arguments with the artificial language and provide a formal proof of validity. Formal proofs show that an argument is valid. There is a possibility that your symbolization might be incorrect. If so, it might represent an invalid argument. Be sure to review your symbolization if you become stuck.

*1. Nothing is both mental and material. Some thoughts are mental. Hence, there is something that is not material.

2. Whatever is material has weight and takes up space. Thoughts don't take up space. Hence, thoughts are not material.

Italy was torn by warring factions for much of the 15th century. Niccolò Machiavelli (1469–1527) thought that Italy needed a strong leader, a "prince," someone who could quell internal dissent and provide a united front against invaders. Machiavelli died in exile, but since its publication in 1532, *The Prince* has been a handbook for those aspiring to gain and hold power. All of the following problems are based on Machiavelli's ideas. Although Machiavelli had the Medici family in mind, for these exercises "the prince" merely refers to a successful leader.

3. A prince who spends the money of others can be generous. Caesar was a prince who spent the money of others and remained in power. Hence, some princes can be generous and remain in power.

4. The prince who spends his own money must raise taxes. No prince who raises taxes can remain in power. Hence, no prince who spends his own money remains in power.

*5. The prince who is not overthrown is not hated. Only the prince who has a strong army, need not fear invasion. Hence, if a prince is not to be overthrown and need not fear invasion, then he is not hated and has a strong army.

6. The prince must govern by love or fear. Those who govern by love are subject to the good will of others. A prince can remain in power if and only if he is not subject to the goodwill of others. Some princes have remained in power. Hence, some princes have remained in power and have governed by fear.

The following problem is provided as a challenge!

*7. The lion can protect himself from wolves, but cannot foresee traps. The fox can foresee traps, but cannot protect himself from wolves. Hence, if the prince is either a lion or a fox, then he cannot both foresee traps and protect himself from wolves.

Concept Reviews

1. What must be true for a universal quantification to be true? For an existential quantification to be true? Given the truth conditions for quantified statements, explain why universal instantiation does not

need restrictions for designating individual constants, but existential instantiation does.

III Multiple Quantifications

A. Symbolization

All of the statements that we have symbolized until now have used only one quantifier. Also, the entire statement has been either a singular statement or a universal statement or an existential statement. This section introduces multiple quantifications and mixed-quantity statements.

DEFINITION 7.17

A well-formed formula in predicate logic that contains only one quantifier is called a *unary quantification*.

DEFINITION 7.18

A well-formed formula in predicate logic that contains two or more quantifiers is called a *multiple quantification*.

Suppose that someone claimed,

Some politicians are corrupt, but some aren't.

It might be tempting to try and express this statement as follows:

$$\exists x[Px \cdot (Cx \cdot {\sim}Cx)]$$

But this is incorrect. The symbolization asserts that there is at least one thing in the universe such that it is a politician and it is **both** corrupt and not corrupt. In the symbolization, all occurrences of the variable x are within the scope of the same (existential) quantifier, so all of the predicates are understood to apply to the same individual. The initial English sentence likely intended to claim that some politicians are corrupt but that others—a different 'some'—are not. The different 'somes' can be expressed by using a different quantifier for each of the groups. Symbolically, we have the conjunction of two existential statements:

$$\exists x(Px \cdot Cx) \cdot \exists x(Px \cdot {\sim}Cx)$$

To avoid ambiguity in the artificial language, both the quantity and group at issue must be clearly defined for each variable. It must be clear which 'some' applies to which individuals. For this reason, the following is *not* a WFF:

$\exists x \exists x [Px \cdot (Cx \cdot \sim Cx)]$

Since both existential quantifiers and all of the variables in the quantified expression *each* use the variable x, there is no way to tell from the expression which quantifier (which 'at least one . . .') is to be applied to a given variable.

Also, it must be clear for each variable, whether it is universally or existentially quantified. The following is also *not* a WFF:

$\exists x [(Px \cdot Cx) \cdot \forall x (Rx \supset Tx)]$

Since the x in Rx and the x in Tx are within the scope of both quantifiers, it is unclear in this expression whether the x in Rx and the x in Tx is universally or existentially quantified.

With multiple quantifications, we need an additional restriction for well-formed formulas.

> **No variable within a quantified expression can be within the scope of more than one quantifier that has that variable.**

Multiple quantifications are frequently created by using our connectives to link quantified expressions. Class-action lawsuits are often based on the implicit belief that if some of the claims are legitimate, then they all are. Suppose that someone said:

If some families of Flight 255 have legitimate claims, then they all do.

Complex statements such as this are most easily symbolized in steps. In this example we have a conditional whose antecedent is an existential statement, and whose consequent is a universal statement.

First, we will express the statement by merely using the non-italicized letters for our needed predicate constants:

If some F are L, then all F are L.

The conditional can be expressed as follows:

Some F are L $\supset$ all F are L.

Finally, we should symbolize the existential and universal statements:

$\exists x (Fx \cdot Lx) \supset \forall x (Fx \supset Lx)$

i. Restricted Domains

Singular statements, existential statements, and universal statements can all be combined to produce compound statements. In combining them, however, we frequently have to take into account the fact that our quantifiers do not define particular groups of individuals.

Several years ago, the army issued a directive that required utmost clarity for all written communications. In response, a sergeant came up with a rather entertaining test of clarity. He required that all communications be comprehensible to Smitty (not his real name). Smitty had a well-earned reputation for not being able to understand much. The sergeant's implicit premiss was:

If Smitty can understand the memorandum, then anyone can.

This might *appear* to be equivalent to:

$Us \supset \forall x U x$

But this symbolization claims that if Smitty can understand the memorandum, then any individual in the universe can understand the memorandum. According to the symbolization, if Smitty can understand the memorandum, then tables, chairs, and giraffes would be able to understand the memoranadum. Smitty was slow, but he was notoriously faster than tables and chairs. (Some people claimed that when it came to giraffes, Smitty ran a dead heat.)

There are two possible solutions for such symbolization problems. One solution consists of defining the groups at issue by adding predicates. Given that the sergeant was referring to *p*ersons on *b*ase, we might use the following:

$Us \supset \forall x[(Px \cdot Bx) \supset Ux]$

Alternatively, we might side with standard conversational assumptions, and limit the universe of things to be considered. We might restrict the quantifier domains. Until now, our quantifiers have been unrestricted. There have been no restrictions on the kinds of individuals that they might pick out. Rather than add qualifying predicates, we can restrict the universe, so that only relevant individuals are represented. We can restrict the range of discourse so that it is understood that only relevant individuals are to be considered. Rather than see $\forall x$ as referring to any individual in the universe, we can see it as referring to any individual of a certain kind.

Suppose we restrict our domain of discourse to "persons on base." With this restriction, '$\forall x U x$' is equivalent to '$\forall x[(Px \cdot Bx) \supset Ux]$', if the latter is considered in an unrestricted domain.

In a restricted domain, the universal and existential quantifiers apply only to individuals in the domain.

By restricting the domain of discourse, we can often avoid expressing assumed predicates. Mark Twain once noted that

Everybody talks about the weather, but nobody does anything about it.[6]

The assumed range of discourse is persons. With this restriction, Twain's claim can be symbolized as:

$\forall x Tx \ \cdot \ \forall x {\sim} Dx$

Given the restricted domain, for any person, x, x talks about the weather, and for any person, x, x does not do anything about it.

Using restricted domains simplifies symbolizations and subsequent formal proofs. We will use restricted domains, and note the relevant individuals with 'RD:———'. For example, 'RD: persons' means that the domain for quantifiers is restricted to persons. 'RD: persons on base' means that the domain has been restricted to persons on base. And so on. If the domain is unrestricted, as it has been with our previous symbolizations, no domain will be specified.

'If Smitty can *u*nderstand the memorandum, then anyone can' can be symbolized as '$Us \supset \forall x Ux$', with the stipulation 'RD: persons on base'.

"Everybody *t*alks about the weather, but nobody *d*oes anything about it" can be expressed as '$\forall x Tx \ \cdot \ \forall x {\sim} Dx$', with the stipulation 'RD: persons'.

ii. Additional Symbolization Patterns

P and Q indicate predicates.

Any attempt to specify a listing of all possible patterns for symbolizations at this point, given the flexibility of our symbolic system, would be futile. There are a couple of problematic patterns, however, that are worth noticing.

1. If any P, then . . . . 'Any', when part of the antecedent of a multiple quantification, is ambiguous in English. Under these conditions, it usually means "some." Suppose that a dealership is having trouble diagnosing a car. The service manager might turn and say: "If anyone can *f*igure this out, Mech can." The service manager does *not* mean if everyone can figure this out . . . ." Rather, she is claiming that if *someone* can figure this out, Mech can. The statement can be symbolized as:

RD: persons $\exists x Fx \supset Fm$

When we come across a sentence of this form, we should try reading 'some' for 'any', and use either a universal or an existential quantifier, as needed, to express the correct meaning.

2. Almost all Ps are Qs. If almost all Ps are Qs, then at least one P

---

[6]This saying is often attributed to Mark Twain, but likely originated with one of his friends, Charles Dudley Warner.

must be a Q, and at least one P must not be a Q. 'Almost all Ps are Qs' is symbolized as:

$$\exists x(Px \cdot Qx) \cdot \exists x(Px \cdot \sim Qx)$$

'Almost all politicians are corrupt' is symbolized as $\exists x(Px \cdot Cx) \cdot \exists x(Px \cdot \sim Cx)$'. This symbolization does not have quite the same meaning as the English sentence, but it is as close to the same meaning as can be expressed in the artificial language. The "nearly all" meaning of 'almost', present in the English sentence, is missing in the symbolization.

3. Most Ps are Qs.   Our artificial language is incapable of expressing the "more than half" meaning of 'most'. In addition, the word 'most' in 'most Ps are Qs' is ambiguous in English. It frequently implies that some Ps are not Qs. Suppose that someone claimed:

Most doctors accept Medicaid patients.

Depending on the context, this sentence can be understood to assert either of the following:

Some doctors accept Medicaid patients

or

Some doctors accept Medicaid patients, but some do not.

When 'most Ps are Qs' merely claims that some Ps are Qs, it should be symbolized as

$$\exists x(Px \cdot Qx)$$

'Some doctors accept Medicaid patients' should be symbolized as '$\exists x(Dx \cdot Ax)$'.

When 'most Ps are Qs' claims that some Ps are Qs, but some Ps are not Qs, it should be symbolized as

$$\exists x(Px \cdot Qx) \cdot \exists x(Px \cdot \sim Qx)$$

'Some doctors accept Medicaid patients, but some do not' should be symbolized as '$\exists x(Dx \cdot Ax) \cdot \exists x(Dx \cdot \sim Ax)$'.

Sentences with 'most' should be viewed in context and then symbolized by using one of the above patterns.

4. Definitions: The P is a Q; a P is a Q; or P is Q.
Definitions can frequently be symbolized in predicate logic by using universally quantified biconditionals:

$$\forall x(Px \equiv Qx)$$

Definitions claim that the term being defined and the defining phrase *apply to exactly the same collection of objects*. 'Thiamine is vitamin B$_1$' claims that 'thiamine' and 'vitamin B$_1$' apply to the same collection of objects. For anything in the universe, if it is thiamine then it is vitamin B$_1$, *and* it is thiamine only if it is vitamin B$_1$. Our example can be symbolized as:

$\forall x(Tx \equiv Vx)$

The following is a more complex example. The *American Heritage Dictionary* defines a carpetbagger as "a Northerner who went to the South after the Civil War for political or financial advantage." For anything in the universe, it is a carpetbagger if and only if it is a Northerner who went to the South after the Civil War for political or financial advantage.

Since this example is fairly complex, we will symbolize it in steps.

$\forall x$ [x *is a carpetbagger if and only if* (x *is a Northerner who went to the South after the Civil War for* political *or* financial *advantage*)].

$\forall x$ {x *is a carpetbagger* $\equiv$ [x *is a Northerner and* (x *went to the South after the Civil War for* political *advantage or* x *went to the South after the Civil War for* financial *advantage*)]}.

Finally, we have:

$\forall x\{Cx \equiv [Nx \cdot (Px \lor Fx)]\}$

Exercises XI

Symbolize each of the following with our predicate-logic notation.

*1. If God exists, then evil doesn't. [Gx = 'x is God'; Ex = 'x is evil'.]

 2. If no one is without sin, then no one will cast the first stone.
    [Sx = 'x has sin'; Cx = 'x casts the first stone'; RD: persons.]

 3. If everything that acts out of design is directed by a being possessed of knowledge, then there is a being who designed the universe.
    [Ax = 'x acts out of design'; Dx = 'x is directed by a being possessed of knowledge'; Ux = 'x designed the universe'.]

 4. If he that is not with me is against me, then no one can be neutral.
    [Mx = 'x is with me'; Ax = 'x is against me'; Nx = 'x is neutral'; RD: persons.]

In a less religious vein:

*5. The communist is a person who believes in common ownership of the means of production. [Cx = 'x is a communist'; Bx = 'x believes in common ownership of the means of production'; RD: persons.]

 6. If anyone can't stand the heat, then someone should get out of the

kitchen. [Sx = 'x can stand the heat'; Kx = 'x should get out of the kitchen'; RD: persons in the kitchen.]

7. Some classes will proceed to a consideration of formal proofs, and some will proceed to more advanced symbolizations. [Cx = 'x is a class'; Fx = 'x will proceed to a consideration of formal proofs'; Sx = 'x will proceed to more advanced symbolizations'.]

8. An estuary is a body of water that is found where a river meets the sea. [Ex = 'x is an estuary'; Bx = 'x is a body of water'; Fx = 'x is found where a river meets the sea'.]

*9. Speech is silver, but whatever is not speech is golden. [Sx = 'x is speech'; Ix = 'x is metaphorically silver'; Gx = 'x is metaphorically golden'.]

10. If Julius Caesar came, saw, and conquered, then someone must have assassinated him. [Cx = 'x came'; Sx = 'x saw'; Qx = 'x conquered'; Jx = 'x assassinated Julius Caesar'; RD: persons.]

11. If an act is determined to be right if and only if it benefits people, then some terrible acts would be justified. [Dx = 'x is determined to be right'; Bx = 'x benefits people'; Tx = 'x is terrible'; Jx = 'x would be justified; RD: acts.]

12. If any covenant without the sword is meaningless, then most covenants are meaningless. [Cx = 'x is a covenant'; Sx = 'x has the sword'; Mx = 'x is meaningless'.]

*13. If any expressions have variables but no quantifiers, then some expressions are not WFFs. [Ex = 'x is an expression'; Vx = 'x has variables'; Qx = 'x has quantifiers'; Wx = 'x is a WFF'.]

14. Only some presidents have been treated kindly by the press. [Px = 'x is a president'; Tx = 'x has been treated kindly by the press'.]

15. A buffer is a solution that can neutralize either an acid or a base. [Ux = 'x is a buffer'; Sx = 'x is a solution'; Ax = 'x can neutralize an acid'; Bx = 'x can neutralize a base'.]

16. If an estuary is a body of water that is found where a river meets the sea, then all estuaries contain salt water. [Ex = 'x is an estuary'; Bx = 'x is a body of water'; Fx = 'x is found where a river meets the sea'; Cx = 'x contains salt water'.]

*17. If every carpetbagger went to the South for either political or financial advantage, then almost all carpetbaggers were opportunists. [Cx = 'x was a carpetbagger'; Px = 'x went to the South for political advantage'; Fx = 'x went to the South for financial advantage'; Ox = 'x was an opportunist'.]

Concept Reviews

1. Carefully review the requirements for WFFs. Which, if any, of the following are not WFFs? You should be able to give reasons for your answers!

   a. $\forall x[(Px \cdot Qx) \supset Ry]$ b. $\forall x(Px \supset Qx)$
   c. $\forall xPx \supset \exists xPx$ d. $\exists xPx \cdot Qx$
   e. $\forall x\forall y(Px \supset Qy)$ f. $Px \supset \exists xPx$

2. Using restricted domains often eliminates the need for writing some predicate constants. Review the following examples, and formulate a rule for adding domain restrictions in relation to eliminating predicate constants.

   Unrestricted:

   $$\forall x(Px \supset Tx) \cdot \forall x(Px \supset {\sim}Dx)$$

Same meaning, but RD: persons, those xs with the quality P:

   $$\forall xTx \cdot \forall x{\sim}Dx$$

   Unrestricted:

   $$\exists x(Px \cdot Tx) \cdot \exists x(Px \cdot {\sim}Dx)$$

Same meaning, but RD: persons, those xs with the quality P.

   $$\exists xTx \cdot \exists x{\sim}Dx$$

Apply your rule to numbers 2, 6, and 11 of Exercises XI and determine whether it will allow you to convert symbolizations in restricted domains to symbolizations in unrestricted domains.

B. Formal Proofs

No additional rules of inference are needed to construct formal proofs for valid arguments that contain multiple quantifications. Quantified statements and singular statements are statements, and so can be used as conditional-proof and indirect-proof assumptions. Our quantifier inferences can be used in restricted domains as they have been used in unrestricted domains. However:

> *Universal instantiation and existential instantiation must only be used on universal and existential quantifications, not on quantifiers whose scope is a portion of a line.*

The following argument is based on the Gospel of John.

If he who is without sin casts the first stone, then no one will cast the first stone.

No one is without sin.

Hence, no one will cast the first stone.

Symbolizing, we have:

RD: persons $\forall x(\sim Sx \supset Cx) \supset \forall x \sim Cx$
$\qquad\qquad\quad \forall x \sim \sim Sx$
$\qquad\qquad\quad \underline{}$
$\qquad\qquad\quad \therefore\ \forall x \sim Cx$

Suppose that we construct a formal proof for this argument.

1. $\forall x(\sim Sx \supset Cx) \supset \forall x \sim Cx$ $\diagup \forall x \sim Cx$
2. $\forall x \sim \sim Sx$
$\underline{}$

U.I. cannot be applied to premiss 1, since the scope of neither of its quantifiers is over the entire expression. Premiss 1 is not a universal quantification.

Premiss 2 is a universal quantification, and U.I can be applied to it. Rather than charge blindly forward, however, we should attempt to develop a strategy for the problem. Notice that the conclusion of the argument is the same statement as the consequent of premiss 1: '$\forall x \sim Cx$'. Quantification statements are statements, and can be used as any other statement when forming instances of our inferential forms. Perhaps we can complete the formal proof by setting up the following modus ponens inference:

$\forall x(\sim Sx \supset Cx) \supset \forall x \sim Cx$
$\forall x(\sim Sx \supset Cx)$
$\underline{}$
$\therefore\ \forall x \sim Cx$

If we are going to complete the formal proof by using this strategy, then we will have to derive '$\forall x(\sim Sx \supset Cx)$'. '$\forall x(\sim Sx \supset Cx)$' is a universal quantification. To derive it we should make '$\sim \forall x(\sim Sx \supset Cx)$' an indirect-proof assumption, and attempt to derive a contradiction. This strategy has additional appeal, since an indirect-proof assumption will provide another line that can be used in constructing the proof. Although the argument has multiple quantifications, we can see its formal proof in terms of deriving the unary quantification '$\forall x(\sim Sx \supset Cx)$'.

1. $\forall x(\sim Sx \supset Cx) \supset \forall x \sim Cx$ $\diagup \forall x \sim Cx$
2. $\forall x \sim \sim Sx$
$\underline{}$

> 3. $\sim\forall x(\sim Sx \supset Cx)$ *I.P.A.*
> 4. $\exists x\sim(\sim Sx \supset Cx)$ *Q.N. 3*
> 5. $\sim(\sim Sa \supset Ca)$ *E.I. 4*
> 6. $\sim Sa \cdot \sim Ca$ *N.C. 5*
> 7. $\sim Sa$ *Simp. 6*
> 8. $\sim\sim Sa$ *U.I. 2*
> 9. Sa *D.N. 8*
> 10. $Sa \cdot \sim Sa$ *Conj. 9, 7*

> 11. $\forall x(\sim Sx \supset Cx)$ *I.P. 3–10*
> 12. $\forall x\sim Cx$ *M.P. 1, 11*

The expression "a modest proposal" refers (usually ironically) to an innovative suggestion. The expression originated with the publication of Jonathan Swift's pamphlet, *A Modest Proposal*, published in 1729. Swift, an Anglican clergyman, was concerned with improving living conditions in eighteenth-century Ireland.

> [I suggest that the remaining infants] may, at a year old, be offered for sale to the persons of quality and fortune through the kingdom; always advising the mother to let them suck plentifully in the last month, so as to render them plump and fat for a good table. A child will make two dishes at an entertainment for friends; and when the family dines alone, the fore or hind quarter will make a reasonable dish, and seasoned with a little pepper or salt will be very good boiled on the fourth day, especially in winter. . . .

> It would increase the care and tenderness of mothers toward their children, when they were sure of a good settlement for life to the poor babes, provided in some sort by the public, to their annual profit instead of expense. We should see an honest emulation among the married women, which of them would bring the fattest child to the market. Men would become as fond of wives during the time of their pregnancy as they are now for mares in foal, their cows in calf, their sows when they are ready to farrow; nor offer to beat or kick them (as is too frequent a practice) for fear of miscarriage.[7]

A masterpiece of satire, the above passage contains a number of predication arguments in the form of "modest proposals." The following is

---

[7]Jonathan Swift, *A Modest Proposal for Preventing the Children of Poor People in Ireland from Being a Burden to Their Parents or Country, and for Making Them Beneficial to the Public*, reprinted in Sylvan Barnet and Hugo Bedau, eds., *Current Issues and Enduring Questions* (Boston: Bedford Books, 1990), 106, 109.

not a direct symbolization of Swift's statements. It merely paraphrases some of them.

If an infant is used for food, then it will feed a family for four days.

Anything that feeds a family for four days will improve Irish diets.

If an infant is used for food, then it will produce better marriages.

Hence, if some infants are used for food, then some things improve Irish diets and produce better marriages.

Symbolization:

$\forall x[(Ix \cdot Ux) \supset Fx]$

$\forall x(Fx \supset Dx)$

$\underline{\forall x[(Ix \cdot Ux) \supset Bx]}$

$\therefore \exists x(Ix \cdot Ux) \supset \exists x(Dx \cdot Bx)$

How should we attempt a formal proof of the paraphrased argument? Notice that the argument's conclusion is a *conditional* that has '$\exists x(Ix \cdot Ux)$' as its antecedent and '$\exists x(Dx \cdot Bx)$' as its consequent. The overall structure of the argument suggests that we should attempt to derive the conclusion by using conditional proof. As in all conditional proofs, our conditional-proof assumption should be the antecedent of the desired conditional. In this example, our conditional-proof assumption should be '$\exists x(Ix \cdot Ux)$'. Once we have made a conditional-proof assumption, we should attempt to derive the consequent of the conditional. In our example, we should attempt to derive '$\exists x(Dx \cdot Bx)$'.

We can adopt the following strategy:

1. $\forall x[(Ix \cdot Ux) \supset Fx]$ $\diagup \exists x(Ix \cdot Ux) \supset \exists x(Dx \cdot Bx)$

2. $\forall x(Fx \supset Dx)$

3. $\underline{\forall x[(Ix \cdot Ux) \supset Bx]}$

> *4.* $\exists x(Ix \cdot Ux)$ C.P.A.
> .
> .
> .
> $\exists x(Dx \cdot Bx)$

$\exists x(Ix \cdot Ux) \supset \exists x(Dx \cdot Bx)$ C.P.

'$\exists x(Dx \cdot Bx)$' is a unary quantification. After making the conditional-proof assumption, we should make '$\sim \exists x(Dx \cdot Bx)$' an indirect-proof assumption and attempt to derive a contradiction. We can construct the following formal proof:

1. $\forall x[(Ix \cdot Ux) \supset Fx]$ $\diagup \exists x(Ix \cdot Ux) \supset \exists x(Dx \cdot Bx)$

2. $\forall x(Fx \supset Dx)$

3. $\forall x[(Ix \cdot Ux) \supset Bx]$

> *4.* $\exists x(Ix \cdot Ux)$ C.P.A.
>
> > *5.* $\sim\exists x(Dx \cdot Bx)$ I.P.A.
> > *6.* $\forall x \sim (Dx \cdot Bx)$ Q.N. 5
> > *7.* $Ia \cdot Ua$ E.I. 4
> > *8.* $(Ia \cdot Ua) \supset Fa$ U.I. 1
> > *9.* $Fa \supset Da$ U.I. 2
> > *10.* $(Ia \cdot Ua) \supset Ba$ U.I. 3
> > *11.* Fa M.P. 8, 7
> > *12.* Ba M.P. 10, 7
> > *13.* Da M.P. 9, 11
> > *14.* $Da \cdot Ba$ Conj. 13, 12
> > *15.* $\sim(Da \cdot Ba)$ U.I. 6
> > *16.* $(Da \cdot Ba) \cdot \sim(Da \cdot Ba)$ Conj. 14, 15
>
> *17.* $\exists x(Dx \cdot Bx)$ I.P. 5–16

18. $\exists x(Ix \cdot Ux) \supset \exists x(Dx \cdot Bx)$ C.P. 4–17

Notice that if the conclusion has a horseshoe as its major connective, conditional proof can be used as in Chapter 4. Conditional and indirect proofs can be nested as in Chapter 5.

When an argument's conclusion has the dot as its major connective, the formal proof usually has two indirect proofs—one to derive each conjunct—and then is ended with conjunction. Our next example follows this pattern.

1. $\forall x(Ix \supset Ux)$ $/\exists xUx \cdot \exists xBx$

2. $\forall x(Sx \supset Bx)$

3. $\exists x(Ix \cdot Sx)$

> *4.* $\sim\exists xUx$ I.P.A.
> *5.* $\forall x \sim Ux$ Q.N. 4
> *6.* $Ia \cdot Sa$ E.I. 3
> *7.* $Ia \supset Ua$ U.I. 1
> *8.* Ia Simp. 6
> *9.* Ua M.P. 7, 8
> *10.* $\sim Ua$ U.I. 5
> *11.* $Ua \cdot \sim Ua$ Conj. 9, 10

12. ∃xUx I.P. 4–11

> 13. ~∃xBx I.P.A.
> 14. ∀x~Bx Q.N. 13
> 15. Ib · Sb E.I. 3
> 16. Sb ⊃ Bb U.I. 2
> 17. Sb Simp. 15
> 18. Bb M.P. 16, 17
> 19. ~Bb U.I. 14
> 20. Bb · ~Bb Conj. 18, 19

21. ∃xBx I.P. 13–20
22. ∃xUx · ∃xBx Conj. 12, 21

Notice that the E.I. step in line 15 uses a new individual constant, *b*. Since *a* appears previously in the problem, it would be incorrect to instantiate to *a* in line 15.

Exercises XII

Construct a formal proof of validity for each of the following valid arguments.

*1. *Mj*
   ~*Ms*
   ∴ ∃*xMx* · ∃*x*~*Mx*

2. ∃*x*(*Mx* · *Gx*)
   ∴ ∃*xMx* · ∃*xGx*

3. ∀*x*(*Ax* ⊃ *Hx*)
   Rb
   ∃*xAx*
   ∴ ∃*xHx* · ∃*xRx*

4. ∀*x*(*Mx* ⊃ *Gx*)
   ∴ ∀*xMx* ⊃ ∀*xGx*

*5. ∀*x*(*Qx* ⊃ *Tx*)
   ∀*x*(*Qx* ⊃ *Vx*)
   ∴ ∃*xQx* ⊃ ∃*x*(*Tx* · *Vx*)

6. ∃*x*(*Ix* · *Sx*)
   ∃*x*(*Cx* · *Tx*)
   ∴ ∃*xIx* · ∃*xCx*

7. ∃*xIx* ⊃ ∃*xLx*
   ∀*x*(*Lx* ⊃ *Rx*)
   ∃*xIx*
   ∴ ∃*x*(*Lx* · *Rx*)

8. ∀*x*(*Ax* ≡ *Bx*)
   ∴ ∀*x*(*Ax* ⊃ *Bx*) · ∀*x*(*Bx* ⊃ *Ax*)

*9. ∀*x*(*Ax* ⊃ *Bx*) · ∀*x*(*Bx* ⊃ *Ax*)
   ∴ ∀*x*(*Ax* ≡ *Bx*)

10. ∀*x*[(*Rx* · *Sx*) ⊃ *Tx*]
   ∃*xRx*
   ∴ ∀*xSx* ⊃ ∃*xTx*

11. $\exists x(Dx \cdot Vx)$
    $\exists xDx \supset \forall x(Ex \supset Jx)$
    $\forall x(Wx \supset Ex)$
    $\therefore \forall x(Wx \supset Jx)$

12. $\forall x[(Mx \cdot Nx) \supset Ox]$
    $\forall x(Ox \supset Px)$
    $\exists xPx \supset \forall x(Px \supset \sim Nx)$
    $\therefore \forall xMx \supset \exists x\sim Nx$

    [Hint: Derive '$\exists xPx$' after your initial-proof assumptions.]

Exercises XIII

Symbolize each of the following arguments with the artificial language and provide a formal proof.

John Stuart Mill (1806–73), one of England's most influential philosophers, published *On Liberty* in 1859. *On Liberty* is a series of arguments defending freedom of speech and freedom of expression. The following examples are all paraphrasings of Mill's ideas.

*1. If some *o*pinions are compelled to *s*ilence, then some *t*ruths should not be *e*xpressed. All *t*ruths should be *e*xpressed. Hence, no *o*pinions are compelled to *s*ilence.

 2. All statements that are *p*artially false *c*ontain a portion of the truth. No statement that *c*ontains a portion of the truth should not be *e*xpressed. Hence, if some statements are *p*artially false, then some *p*artially false statements should be *e*xpressed. RD: statements.

*3. A law is *j*ustified if and only if it *p*revents harm. Almost all laws *p*revent harm. Hence, almost all laws are *j*ustified. RD: laws.

 4. Any law is either in a *c*ivilized or *b*arbaric society. In a *c*ivilized society, a law is *j*ustified if and only if it *p*revents injury. Hence, if some laws are not in a *b*arbaric society, then there is at least one law such that if it doesn't *p*revent injury then it is not *j*ustified. RD: laws.

IV Invalidity

A. General Concepts

Chapter 3 provided a definition of validity for statement/propositional logic. The definition of 'valid' for predicate logic is similar, but includes the idea that statements in predicate logic make claims about individuals.

DEFINITION 7.19

An argument in predicate logic is *valid* if and only if, when one or more individuals are considered to exist, it is impossible for the argument to have all true premisses and a false conclusion.

DEFINITION 7.20

An argument in predicate logic is *invalid* if and only if, when one or more individuals are considered to exist, it is possible for the argument to have all true premisses and a false conclusion.

On the assumption that something exists, if the premisses of a valid argument in predicate logic are all true, then its conclusion must be true as well.[8]

Our actual universe has, if not an infinite number, at least a very large number of existing things. Our galaxy has presidents, trees, protons, and many other things. Our universe has more things than our galaxy. Clearly, we are unable to consider whether the premisses of an argument are all true and its conclusion false in relation to each thing in our actual universe. Fortunately, we do not have to.

If an argument is valid, then it is valid regardless of the number of things or kinds of things that exist. Hence, if we can show that there is a possible or imaginary universe, one with far fewer things than our own, where an argument is invalid, then we have shown that the argument is invalid. An invalid argument in predicate logic is proved so by showing that there is an imaginary universe where all of its premisses can be true and its conclusion false. Imaginary universes that are used to consider whether arguments in predicate logic are valid are called "model universes."

DEFINITION 7.21

A *model universe*, or *model,* is an imaginary universe that contains a limited number of countable things.

---

[8]If we were to assume that nothing exists, then the inference from 'all things take up space', $\forall x S x$, to 'some things take up space', $\exists x S x$, would be invalid. But this inference is surely valid. The assumption that nothing exists has odd logical consequences, and assuming that *something* exists is hardly controversial!

Rather than attempt to show that an argument is invalid in our actual universe, we will attempt to show that it is invalid in a model universe.

Model universes are specified by using statement constants to identify their members. The statement constants are separated by commas, and placed in braces.

Suppose that we wish to specify a model universe that contains only the one individual, *a*. We can do so by writing '{*a*}'. Suppose that we wish to specify a model universe that contains the two individuals, *a* and *b*. We can specify this model by writing '{*a, b*}'. A model universe that contains the three members, *a*, *b*, and *c*, can be specified by writing '{*a, b, c*}'. And so on.

Our partial-truth-table technique and truth-tree technique, which were developed in Chapter 6, can be used to determine whether arguments in monadic predicate logic are valid.

Each of the following sections assumes that you have a working knowledge of the corresponding section in Chapter 6.

B. Partial Truth Tables

First, we should notice when statements in predicate logic are true and when they are false.

i. Truth Conditions

a. Singular Statements

A singular statement is true if and only if the individual designated by the individual constant has the attributed quality or qualities.

'Canberra is the capital of Australia' is true if and only if Canberra has the quality of being the capital of Australia. For any predicate *P*,

> **Pa *is true if and only if the individual designated by* a *has the quality indicated by* P.**

b. Universal Statements

A universal statement is true if and only if the qualities it attributes are true of each and every member of the universe.

'All *a*nimals experience *p*ain', '$\forall x(Ax \supset Px)$', is true if and only if it is true of every member of the universe that, if it is an animal, then it experiences pain. Generally:

> **$\forall$x(... Px ...)' *is true if and only if* '(... Px ...)' *is true of every member*, x, *of the universe.*

Suppose that we consider whether '∀x(Ax ⊃ Px)' is true in a model universe that has only the one individual, *a*. Under these conditions, '∀x(Ax ⊃ Px)' will be true if and only if 'Aa ⊃ Pa' is true. If "everything" is just one thing, then the universal quantification will be true if and only if what it says is true of that one thing.

Now suppose that we consider our universal statement in the model universe {*a*, *b*}. That is, suppose that exactly two individuals exist, *a* and *b*. '∀x(Ax ⊃ Px)' will be true if and only if both 'Aa ⊃ Pa' and 'Ab ⊃ Pb' are true. If we assume that exactly three individuals exist, *a*, *b*, and *c*, then '∀x(Ax ⊃ Px)' is true if and only if 'Aa ⊃ Pa' and 'Ab ⊃ Pb' and 'Ac ⊃ Pc' are all true.

We have discovered a way to express truth conditions for universal statements.

In a model universe that contains *a*, *b*, *c*, ..., *n* as members, '∀x(... Px ...)' is true if and only if '[(... Pa ...) · (... Pb ...) · (... Pc ...) · ... · (... Pn ...)]' is true.

A universal quantification is equivalent to the conjunction that results from conjoining instances, for each member of the universe, of the quantified expression.

c. Existential Statements

An existential statement is true if and only if the qualities it attributes are true of at least one member of the universe.

'Some *a*nimals experience *p*ain', '∃x(Ax · Px)', is true if and only if there is at least one thing in the universe such that it is an animal and experiences pain. Generally:

'∃x(... Px ...)' *is true if and only if* '(... Px ...)' *is true of at least one member,* x, *of the universe.*

Consider '∃x(Ax · Px)' in the model universe {*a*}. Under these conditions, '∃x(Ax · Px)' will be true if and only if 'Aa · Pa' is true. The "at least one thing" must be *the* thing that exists. Again, suppose that exactly two individuals exist, *a* and *b*. '∃x(Ax · Px)' will be true if and only if either 'Aa · Pa' or 'Ab · Pb' is true. If we assume that exactly three individuals exist, *a*, *b*, and *c*, then '∃x(Ax · Px)' will be true if and only if 'Aa · Pa' or 'Ab · Pb' or 'Ac · Pc' is true. We can now express truth conditions for existential quantifications without using the existential quantifier.

> In a model universe that contains a, b, c, ..., n as members, '$\exists x(\dots Px \dots)$' is true if and only if '$[(\dots Pa \dots) \vee (\dots Pb \dots) \vee (\dots Pc \dots) \vee \dots \vee (\dots Pn \dots)]$' is true.

An existential quantification is equivalent to the disjunction that results from disjoining instances, for each member of the universe, of the quantified expression.

ii. Partial Truth Tables for Predicate Logic

For an example, we will consider the invalid argument that was first stated in Section II.C.

Some citizens of the USSR are patriotic.
Some citizens of the United States are patriotic.
Hence, some citizens of the USSR are citizens of the United States.

In symbols, we have:

$\exists x(Ux \cdot Px)$
$\underline{\exists x(Sx \cdot Px)}$
$\therefore \exists x(Ux \cdot Sx)$

First, we will consider this argument in the model universe $\{a\}$. Under these conditions, the above argument is equivalent to:

$Ua \cdot Pa$
$\underline{Sa \cdot Pa}$
$\therefore Ua \cdot Sa$

We can use the partial-truth-table method to determine whether it is possible for this argument to have all true premises and a false conclusion in a one-member model. To make the conclusion false, we must assign either Ua or Sa false. But either of these assignments will result in a false premiss. Hence, it is not possible to show that this argument is invalid by using a one-member model.

Next, we should consider the argument with respect to a two-member model, $\{a, b\}$. Under these conditions, the argument is equivalent to:

$(Ua \cdot Pa) \vee (Ub \cdot Pb)$
$\underline{(Sa \cdot Pa) \vee (Sb \cdot Pb)}$
$\therefore (Ua \cdot Sa) \vee (Ub \cdot Sb)$

Notice that since all three statements in this argument are existential quantifications, we have interpreted the instances as *disjuncts*. Can we use the partial-truth-table method to show that it is possible for the argument to have all true premisses and a false conclusion in a two-member model? Suppose we assign *Ua* and *Sb* false. The conclusion is false with these assignments. (Why?) The first premiss can be made true by assigning *Ub* true and *Pb* true. The second premiss can be made true by assigning *Sa* true and *Pa* true. Hence, it *is* possible for the argument to have all true premisses and a false conclusion in a two-member model:

Ua F	*Pb* T
Sb F	*Sa* T
Ub T	*Pa* T

Since it is impossible for a valid argument to have all true premisses and a false conclusion in *any* model universe, we have shown that the argument is invalid.

The next example contains three kinds of statements.

$$Rq$$
$$\forall x(Rx \supset Tx)$$
$$\underline{\exists x Tx}$$
$$\therefore\ \forall x Tx$$

The first premiss in this example is a singular statement. The individual *q* has some quality *R*.

When an argument has a singular statement, attempts at showing that the argument is invalid begin by assuming that the individual named by the individual constant exists in the model universe.

In this case, we will begin by assuming that some individual, *q*, exists. Is it possible to prove the argument invalid by using a one-member model, {*q*}? If we can show the possibility of all true premisses and a false conclusion in a one-member model, the problem is done. If not, then we should consider models with more members.

$$Rq$$
$$Rq \supset Tq$$
$$\underline{Tq}$$
$$\therefore Tq$$

Tq must be assigned false, so that the conclusion is false. We have, however, made the third premiss false. Hence, it is not possible to prove that this argument is invalid by using a one-member model. We should proceed to consider this argument with respect to a two-member model. Using *a* to identify the second member, we have:

$$Rq$$
$$(Rq \supset Tq) \cdot (Ra \supset Ta)$$
$$\underline{Tq \lor Ta}$$
$$\therefore Tq \cdot Ta$$

Notice that the universal quantifications, the second premiss and the conclusion, are stated as *conjunctions* of the instances. The third premiss, an existential quantification, is stated as a *disjunction* of the instances. Now our partial-truth-table method will enable us to assign truth-values so that all of the premisses are true and the conclusion is false. Rq must be true to make the first premiss true. Tq must be true to make the first conjunct of the second premiss true. But if Ra and Ta are each assigned false, the remaining premiss is true and the conclusion is false. Our final assignments are:

Rq T	Ra F
Tq T	Ta F

Since an argument is invalid if it is possible for it to have all true premisses and a false conclusion (when one or more individuals are assumed to exist), this argument has been shown invalid.

Our last example for this section has a negated quantification:

$$\forall x(Ax \supset Bx)$$
$$\forall x(Cx \supset Ax)$$
$$\therefore \sim\exists x(Ax \cdot \sim Cx)$$

If an argument contains a negated quantification, apply quantifier negation, and then proceed to use the partial-truth-table method to determine whether the argument is valid. Applying Q.N. to the conclusion we obtain:

$$\forall x(Ax \supset Bx)$$
$$\forall x(Cx \supset Ax)$$
$$\therefore \forall x\sim(Ax \cdot \sim Cx)$$

This argument can now be shown invalid by using a one-member model:

$Aa \supset Ba$	Aa T
$Ca \supset Aa$	Ca F
$\therefore \sim(Aa \cdot \sim Ca)$	Ba T

Partial-Truth-Table Procedure for Predicate Logic

1. If necessary, use quantifier negation to replace negated quantifiers.
2. Eliminate the quantifiers by forming an instance, and consider the argument's validity in a one-member model.
3. If the argument is valid in a one-member model, it should next be considered in a two-member model; and so on. If an argument is invalid[9] and has n predicates, then the largest model that might have

---

[9]And if it is of the type that we have been considering. The predicate letters must abbreviate neither logically true nor logically false properties, and the argument must contain only monadic predicates.

to be considered is 2^n. All of the invalid arguments in this text can be proved so by using models that have three or fewer members.

Exercises XIV

Use the partial-truth-table method to prove that each of the following arguments is invalid. None of these requires models that have more than three members.

*1. $\exists xFx$
   ∴ $\forall x(Gx \supset {\sim}Fx)$

2. $\forall x(Dx \supset Sx)$
   $\forall x({\sim}Sx \supset Rx)$
   ∴ $\forall x(Dx \supset {\sim}Rx)$

3. Rt
   ∴ ${\sim}\exists x(Ax \cdot {\sim}Rx)$

4. $\forall x(Cx \supset Px)$
   ∴ $\exists x(Cx \cdot Px)$

*5. $\exists x(Ax \cdot {\sim}Bx)$
   $\exists x(Rx \cdot {\sim}Bx)$
   ∴ $\exists x(Ax \cdot Rx)$

6. $\exists x(Cx \cdot Px)$
   ∴ ${\sim}\exists x(Cx \cdot {\sim}Px)$

7. $\forall x[Ax \supset (Bx \lor Cx)]$
   $\forall x(Bx \supset Rx)$
   ∴ $\forall x(Ax \supset Rx)$

8. $\exists x[Px \cdot (Hx \cdot Dx)]$
   $\exists x(Px \cdot Hx)$
   ∴ $\forall x(Px \supset Dx)$

*9. $\exists x(Ax \cdot {\sim}Bx)$
   $\exists x(Cx \cdot Bx)$
   $\exists x({\sim}Cx \cdot Dx)$
   ∴ $\exists x(Ax \cdot Dx)$

10. $\exists x(Jx \cdot Fx)$
   $\exists x(Jx \cdot {\sim}Fx)$
   ∴ $\forall x[Ox \supset (Jx \cdot Fx)]$

See Exercises XVII.A for additional problems.

iii. Multiple Quantifications

When they are part of a multiple quantification, existential and universal quantifications are expanded as in the previous section. Once the existential and universal quantifications have been expressed as disjunctions and conjunctions, we might have to add punctuation so that the connectives of the initial statement are unchanged.

Our partial-truth-table method can be applied at this point. Again we should attempt to assign truth-values so that all of the argument's premises are true and its conclusion is false.

Suppose that we interpret the following multiple quantification in a one-member model:

$\forall x(Ax \supset Bx) \supset \exists x(Fx \cdot Gx)$

In the one-member model, {*a*}, '∀*x*(*Ax* ⊃ *Bx*)' is interpreted as '*Aa* ⊃ *Ba*', and '∃*x*(*Fx* · *Gx*)' is interpreted as '*Fa* · *Ga*'. The multiple quantification is interpreted as

(*Aa* ⊃ *Ba*) ⊃ (*Fa* · *Ga*)

This statement is true, unless assignments make '(*Aa* ⊃ *Ba*)' true and '(*Fa* · *Ga*)' false.

Suppose that we consider the above statement in a two-member model, {*a*, *b*}. '∀*x*(*Ax* ⊃ *Bx*)' will be interpreted as:

(*Aa* ⊃ *Ba*) · (*Ab* ⊃ *Bb*)

'∃*x*(*Fx* · *Gx*)' will be interpreted as

(*Fa* · *Ga*) ∨ (*Fb* · *Gb*)

When we replace the universal quantification with the corresponding conjunction and the existential quantification with the corresponding disjunction, we obtain:

[(*Aa* ⊃ *Ba*) · (*Ab* ⊃ *Bb*)] ⊃ [(*Fa* · *Ga*) ∨ (*Fb* · *Gb*)]

Notice that brackets have been added so that the horseshoe remains the major connective. The statement is true unless assignments make '(*Aa* ⊃ *Ba*) · (*Ab* ⊃ *Bb*)' true and '(*Fa* · *Ga*) ∨ (*Fb* · *Gb*)' false.

Finally, suppose that we interpret the statement in the three-member model, {*a*, *b*, *c*}. '∀*x*(*Ax* ⊃ *Bx*)' is interpreted as

(*Aa* ⊃ *Ba*) · (*Ab* ⊃ *Bb*) · (*Ac* ⊃ *Bc*)[10]

'∃*x*(*Fx* · *Gx*)' is interpreted as

(*Fa* · *Ga*) ∨ (*Fb* · *Gb*) ∨ (*Fc* · *Gc*)

If we replace the universal and existential quantifications and retain the horseshoe as the major connective, we obtain:

[(*Aa* ⊃ *Ba*) · (*Ab* ⊃ *Bb*) · (*Ac* ⊃ *Bc*)] ⊃ [(*Fa* · *Ga*) ∨ (*Fb* · *Gb*) ∨ (*Fc* · *Gc*)]

The statement is true unless assignments make '[(*Aa* ⊃ *Ba*) · (*Ab* ⊃ *Bb*) · (*Ac* ⊃ *Bc*)]' true and '[(*Fa* · *Ga*) ∨ (*Fb* · *Gb*) ∨ (*Fc* · *Gc*)]' false.

---

[10]Both this conjunction and the following disjunction lack adequate punctuation to be a correct sentence in the artificial language. If desired, there are two ways that punctuation can be added so that each connected statement is clearly defined. Our equivalence inference of association shows that each way of punctuating the expression will be logically equivalent to the other, so there is no harm in assigning truth-values as the statement is written here.

Exercises XV

Use the partial-truth-table method to prove that each of the following multiple quantification arguments is invalid. None of these requires considering models that have more than two members.

1.   ∃xFx · ∃x~Fx
     ──────────────
     ∴ ∃x(Fx · ~Fx)

2.   ∀x(Cx ⊃ Ex) ⊃ ∀x(Rx ⊃ Hx)
     ──────────────────────────────
     ∴ ∃x(Cx · ~Ex) ⊃ ∃x(Rx · ~Hx)

*3. ∃x(Cx · Rx) ⊃ ∀x(Cx ⊃ Rx)
     ∃x(Hx · ~Cx)
     ──────────────
     ∴ ∃x(Hx · ~Rx)

4.   Fc
     ∃xFx ⊃ ∀xGx
     Fc ⊃ ∃xBx
     ──────────────
     ∴ ∀x(Gx ⊃ Bx)

See Exercises XIX.A, pages 306–307, for additional problems.

C. Truth Trees for Predicate Logic

Chapter 6 claimed that an argument is valid if and only if the completed truth tree for the set that consists of the argument's premises and the negation of its conclusion has only closed paths. All of our previous reduction patterns remain fully usable.

Recapitulation of Truth-Tree Reduction Patterns

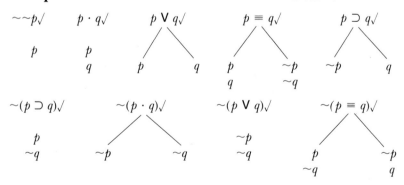

The above principles can be applied to arguments in predicate logic, but we need to add four reduction patterns for quantified expressions. Each of them corresponds to a rule of inference in predicate logic.

Where '∀x(... Px ...)' indicates a universal quantification that has the variable x, and '∃x(... Px ...)' indicates an existential quantification that has the variable x:

∀x(... Px ...)   *   ∃x(... Px ...)√
  (... Pa ...) (or b, or c, etc.)   (... Pa ...) (or b, or c, etc.); a
                                        (or b, or c, etc.) cannot appear
                                        anywhere   previously   in   the
                                        problem.

~∀x(... Px ...)√   ~∃x(... Px ...)√
∃x~(... Px ...)   ∀x~(... Px ...)

An existential quantification is true if and only if the quantified expression is true of *some* individual. As in formal proofs, there is no necessity that the 'some' that is intended by one existential quantification has to be the same 'some' that is intended by another existential quantification. Hence, truth-tree reductions of existential quantifications must use a constant that does not appear previously in the tree. Since universal quantifications apply to all individuals, universal quantifications may be reduced to *any* constant. The rules for negated quantifications are Q.N. (see section II.B).

The following example, proved valid in section II.D, shows that additional restrictions are required for truth trees to determine whether monadic predication arguments of the kind we have been considering are valid.

> *Every revolution is based on love.*
>
> *Nothing based on love is intended to be harmful.*
>
> *Hence, no revolution is intended to be harmful.*

In symbols, we have:

∀x(Rx ⊃ Bx)
∀x(Bx ⊃ ~Ix)
∴ ∀x(Rx ⊃ ~Ix)

Our previous formal proof has shown that this argument is valid. Hence, the following set must be inconsistent.

{∀x(Rx ⊃ Bx), ∀x(Bx ⊃ ~Ix), ~∀x(Rx ⊃ ~Ix)}

The completed truth tree should have only closed paths. We can create the trunk of the tree as in Chapter 6:

∀x(Rx ⊃ Bx)
∀x(Bx ⊃ ~Ix)
~∀x(Rx ⊃ ~Ix)

Next, we can reduce the negated quantification and the resulting existential quantification by using the above patterns:

∀x(Rx ⊃ Bx)
∀x(Bx ⊃ ~Ix)
~∀x(Rx ⊃ ~Ix)√
∃x~(Rx ⊃ ~Ix)√
~(Ra ⊃ ~Ia)

Predicate-logic reduction patterns are applied to all open paths below, just as they were in Chapter 6. You may have noticed, however, that the reduction pattern for universal quantifiers has an asterisk, '*', rather than the usual check mark.

Universal quantifications apply to any individual in the universe (or restricted domain). Some problems require considering a number of instances of a universal quantification in order to close their paths. A universal quantification may have to be reduced more than once. Placing an asterisk next to a statement each time that it is reduced helps us to keep track of our progress with a problem. (Existential quantifications require the existence of only one individual, and so may be checked off.) Even so, unless reductions create instances by using a minimum number of individual constants, there is no guarantee, *even if the set is inconsistent*, that all paths will close. To see this, suppose we were to continue the above problem as follows:

∀x(Rx ⊃ Bx) **
∀x(Bx ⊃ ~Ix) *
~∀x(Rx ⊃ ~Ix)√
∃x~(Rx ⊃ ~Ix)√
~(Ra ⊃ ~Ia)
Rb ⊃ Bb
Bc ⊃ ~Ic
Rd ⊃ Bd   and so on

Truth trees determine whether a set is consistent and whether an argument is valid, only if all of the following requirements are met.

Requirements for Using Truth Trees in Predicate Logic

1. Each existential quantification has been reduced and checked off on each path that it appears.
2. Each universal quantification in the tree has been reduced to an instance of each individual constant in the tree.
3. All compound statements have been reduced as required in Chapter 6.

Hence, when constructing truth trees in predicate logic, we should use the following strategies:

1. Reduce existential quantifications before reducing universal quantifications.

2. When reducing universal quantifications, choose individual constants that are in the tree. If the tree does not have any individual constants, *then* use a new one.

Now we can satisfactorily complete our example:

$$\forall x(Rx \supset Bx) \ *$$
$$\forall x(Bx \supset \sim Ix) \ *$$
$$\sim\forall x(Rx \supset \sim Ix)\sqrt{}$$
$$\exists x\sim(Rx \supset \sim Ix)\sqrt{}$$
$$\sim(Ra \supset \sim Ia)\sqrt{}$$
$$Ra$$
$$\sim\sim Ia\sqrt{}$$
$$Ia$$
$$Ba \supset \sim Ia\sqrt{}$$

$$\sim Ba \qquad\qquad \sim Ia$$
$$Ra \supset Ba\sqrt{} \qquad\qquad \mathbf{X}$$

$$\sim Ra \qquad Ba$$
$$\mathbf{X} \qquad \mathbf{X}$$

Since each path closes, the set of statements is inconsistent, and the argument is valid.

Our next example was presented in section II.C and section IV.B.

Some citizens of the USSR are patriotic.

Some citizens of the United States are patriotic.

Hence, some citizens of the USSR are citizens of the United States.

In symbols we have:

$$\exists x(Ux \cdot Px)$$
$$\underline{\exists x(Sx \cdot Px)}$$
$$\therefore \ \exists x(Ux \cdot Sx)$$

We know that this argument is valid if and only if the following set is inconsistent:

$$\{\exists x(Ux \cdot Px), \ \exists x(Sx \cdot Px), \ \sim\exists x(Ux \cdot Sx)\}$$

The trunk of our truth tree is:

$$\exists x(Ux \cdot Px)$$
$$\exists x(Sx \cdot Px)$$
$$\sim\exists x(Ux \cdot Sx)$$

The negated quantification should be reduced first so that the remaining reductions can be made and the tree can be completed:

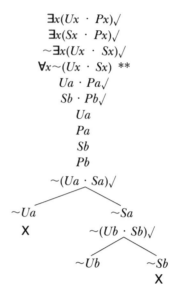

Since our three requirements for predicate-logic truth trees have been met and a path remains open, the set is consistent and the argument is invalid. The open path shows that it is possible for the argument to have all true premises and a false conclusion in the two-member model, {*a, b*}. It is invalid owing to the following possibility:

~*Ub* is true (*Ub* is false)   ~*Sa* is true (*Sa* is false)
Pb is true   *Sb* is true
Pa is true   *Ua* is true

Our next example contains a singular statement.

Cq · Rq
∃*xTx*
∴ ∃*x*(*Cx · Tx*)

We know that this is a valid argument if and only if the following set is inconsistent:

{*Cq · Rq*, ∃*xTx*, ~∃*x*(*Cx · Tx*)}

No quantifier reduction is required for singular statements. We can construct the following truth tree:

Cq · Rq√
∃*xTx*√
~∃*x*(*Cx · Tx*)√
∀*x*~(*Cx · Tx*) **
Ta
Cq
Rq

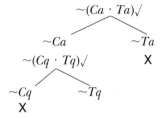

Notice that the reduction of the existential quantification introduced a new individual constant, a. Since our conditions for predicate-logic truth trees have been met and an open path remains, the last set is consistent and the argument is invalid. The open path shows that it is possible for the argument to have all true premisses and a false conclusion in the two-member model, $\{q, a\}$. It is invalid owing to the following possibility:

$\sim Tq$ is true (Tq is false) Rq is true
$\sim Ca$ is true (Ca is false) Cq is true
Ta is true

Exercises XVI

Use truth trees to determine which of the following arguments are valid. For those that are invalid, specify the model and the possibilities that prove it can have all true premisses and a false conclusion.

*1. $\forall x[(Ax \cdot Bx) \supset Cx]$
$\exists x(Ax \cdot Bx)$
$\therefore\ \exists x Cx$

2. $\exists x(Ax \cdot Bx)$
$\forall x(Bx \supset \sim Cx)$
$\therefore\ \forall x(Ax \supset \sim Cx)$

3. $\forall x[Ax \supset (Bx \lor Cx)]$
$\exists x(Ax \cdot \sim Cx)$
$\therefore\ \forall x(Ax \supset Bx)$

4. $\forall x(Ax \supset Bx)$
$\forall x(Cx \supset \sim Dx)$
$\exists x[(Ax \cdot Rx) \cdot Cx]$
$\therefore\ \exists x[(Bx \cdot \sim Dx) \cdot Rx]$

*5. $\forall x[Ax \supset (Bx \lor Cx)]$
$\forall x(Bx \supset Rx)$
$\therefore\ \forall x(Ax \supset Rx)$

6. $\exists x[Px \cdot (Hx \cdot Dx)]$
$\exists x(Px \cdot Hx)$
$\therefore\ \forall x(Px \supset Dx)$

7. $\exists x(Ax \cdot \sim Bx)$
    $\exists x(Cx \cdot Bx)$
    $\underline{\exists x(\sim Cx \cdot Dx)}$
    $\therefore \exists x(Ax \cdot Dx)$

8. $\exists x(Jx \cdot Fx)$
    $\underline{\exists x(\sim Jx \cdot Fx)}$
    $\therefore \forall x[Ox \supset (Jx \cdot Fx)]$

Exercises XVII

Symbolize each of the following arguments, and then:

A. Prove validity by constructing a formal proof, or prove invalidity by using the partial-truth-table method.

B. Use truth trees to determine which of the following arguments are valid. For those that are invalid, specify the model and list the values that show that it is possible for the argument to have all true premises and a false conclusion. *If* you have instantiated all existential quantifications *and* additional instantiations of universal quantifications cannot possibly cause additional paths to close, consider the problem finished.

*1. Any scientific *t*heory must be *c*apable of falsification. Creationism is not *c*apable of falsification. Hence, creationism is not a scientific *t*heory. [*Tx* = '*x* is a scientific theory'; *Cx* = '*x* is capable of falsification'.]

2. Creationists *b*elieve that God created species differences. *E*volutionists believe that *n*atural selection created species differences. No *c*reationists are *e*volutionists. Hence, anyone who *b*elieves that God created species differences does not believe that *n*atural selection created species differences. [*Cx* = '*x* is a creationist'; *Bx* = '*x* believes that God created species differences'; *Ex* = '*x* is an evolutionist'; *Nx* = '*x* believes that natural selection created species differences'.]

3. No *s*cientific theory has been proved either *t*rue or *f*alse. Neither *c*reationist beliefs nor *n*atural-selection beliefs have been proved either *t*rue or *f*alse. Hence, neither *c*reationist beliefs nor *n*atural-selection beliefs are *s*cientific theories. [*Sx* = '*x* is a scientific theory'; *Tx* = '*x* has been proved true'; *Fx* = '*x* has been proved false'; *Cx* = '*x* is a creationist belief'; *Nx* = '*x* is a natural-selection belief'.]

4. Any *i*ssue that cannot be proved either *t*rue or *f*alse, cannot be *d*ecided by an appeal to facts. What cannot be *d*ecided by an appeal to facts should be decided by *f*aith. Creationism versus natural selection is an *i*ssue that cannot be *d*ecided by an appeal to facts. Hence, creationism versus natural selection is an *i*ssue that should be decided by *f*aith. [*Ix* = '*x* is an issue'; *Tx* = '*x* can be proved true';

Fx = 'x can be proved false'; Dx = 'x can be decided by an appeal to facts'; Ax = 'x should be decided by faith'.]

*5. Some *c*reationists *a*ccept the Bible. Some *c*reationists believe that *n*atural selection accounts for individual differences. Hence, some *c*reationists *a*ccept the Bible and believe that *n*atural selection accounts for individual differences. [Cx = 'x is a creationist'; Ax = 'x accepts the Bible'; Nx = 'x believes that natural selection accounts for individual differences'.]

6. No *i*ssue can be *r*esolved unless it can be *s*een from more than one side. Some *i*ssues can be *s*een from more than one side. Hence, some *i*ssues can be *r*esolved. [Ix = 'x is an issue'; Rx = 'x can be resolved'; Sx = 'x can be seen from more than one side'.]

7. Some of those *i*nterviewed were *b*lack. Some of those *i*nterviewed were *J*ewish. Some of those *i*nterviewed were *w*omen. Hence, some of those *i*nterviewed were *b*lack *J*ewish *w*omen. [Ix = 'x was interviewed'; Bx = 'x is black'; Jx = 'x is Jewish'; Wx = 'x is a woman'.]

8. Only *a*nimals that can experience either *p*leasure or pa*i*n can be the *s*ubject of moral rights. Some *a*nimals cannot experience either *p*leasure or pa*i*n. Hence, some *a*nimals cannot be the *s*ubject of moral rights. [Ax = 'x is an animal'; Px = 'x can experience pleasure'; Ix = 'x can experience pain'; Sx = 'x can be the subject of moral rights'.]

*9. Individuals have a *s*oul if and only if they can use *l*anguage. Individuals have moral *r*ights if and only if they have a *s*oul. No *d*ogs use *l*anguage. Hence, no *d*ogs have moral *r*ights. [Sx = 'x has a soul'; Lx = 'x can use language'; Rx = 'x has moral rights'; Dx = 'x is a dog'.]

10. *E*arthworms and *l*obsters either have a *b*rain structure similar to that of humans or they *s*ecrete endorphins. There are *e*arthworms that do not have a *b*rain structure similar to that of humans, but that do *s*ecrete endorphins. Hence, there are *l*obsters that have a *b*rain structure similar to that of humans. [Ex = 'x is an earthworm'; Lx = 'x is a lobster'; Bx = 'x has a brain structure similar to that of humans'; Sx = 'x secretes endorphins'.]

11. *T*ractors and *c*ars can be *h*armed but do not have moral *r*ights. There are *t*ractors. Hence, some things can be *h*armed but do not have moral *r*ights. [Tx = 'x is a tractor'; Cx = 'x is a car'; Hx = 'x can be harmed'; Rx = 'x has moral rights'.]

12. No *a*nimal that is a *m*onkey or that is *b*elow monkeys on the evolutionary scale can be the subject of moral *r*ights. Hence, no *a*nimals that are *m*onkeys can be the subject of moral *r*ights. [Ax = 'x is an animal'; Mx = 'x is a monkey'; Bx = 'x is below monkeys on the evolutionary scale'; Rx = 'x can be the subject of moral rights'.]

*13. Anything that has a right to life can comprehend its life. Some humans do not wish to die. Some humans cannot comprehend their lives. Hence, some things that cannot comprehend their lives and do not wish to die do not have a right to life. [Rx = 'x has a right to life'; Cx = 'x can comprehend its life'; Hx = 'x is a human'; Wx = 'x wishes to die'.]

14. Zygotes have a right to life if and only if they are potentially persons. Whatever is the result of a lab experiment and potentially a person has a right to life, only if it will not become a detriment to society. Some results of lab experiments have been potential persons who would be a detriment to society. Hence, some zygotes do not have a right to life. [Zx = 'x is a zygote'; Rx = 'x has a right to life'; Px = 'x is potentially a person'; Lx = 'x is the result of a lab experiment'; Dx = 'x will become a detriment to society'.]

15. If a moral right is determined by a broader moral theory, then it is superfluous; whereas if it is not determined by a broader moral theory, then it is unsupported. Moral rights that apply to fetuses are not superfluous. Hence, moral rights that apply to fetuses are unsupported. [Rx = 'x is a moral right'; Dx = 'x is determined by a broader moral theory'; Ux = 'x is unsupported'; Ax = 'x applies to fetuses'.]

16. John Muir persuaded Congress to authorize Yosemite National Park. No one could persuade Congress to authorize Yosemite National Park unless he or she was an avid naturalist. Hence, at least one avid naturalist persuaded Congress to authorize Yosemite National Park. [Px = 'x persuaded Congress to authorize Yosemite National Park'; Nx = 'x is an avid naturalist'.]

*17. Some natural-rights advocates are vegetarians and oppose the destruction of natural resources. There are natural-rights advocates who are not vegetarians. All natural-rights advocates believe that nature deserves respect. All animal-rights advocates are vegetarians. Hence, some animal-rights advocates do not believe that nature deserves respect. [Nx = 'x is a natural-rights advocate'; Vx = 'x is a vegetarian'; Ox = 'x opposes the destruction of natural resources'; Rx = 'x believes that nature deserves respect'.]

18. Some rights advocates believe that trees have moral rights. Anyone who believes that trees have moral rights accepts either a direct or an indirect theory of obligation.[11] No rights advocates accept an indirect

[11]An indirect theory of obligation claims that we have obligations to other animals or things, based on how treating them affects us. Thoreau, for example, believed that cruelty is wrong, not for what it does to the animal, but for what it does to the person inflicting it. A direct theory of obligation claims that we have obligations to other animals or things, based on how our actions affect them.

theory of moral obligation. Some rights *a*dvocates believe that *s*treams have moral rights. *U*tilities that *b*uild dams do not believe that *s*treams have rights. Hence, some rights *a*dvocates do not *b*uild dams. [*Ax* = '*x* is a rights advocate'; *Tx* = '*x* believes that trees have moral rights'; *Dx* = '*x* accepts a direct theory of obligation'; *Ix* = '*x* accepts an indirect theory of obligation'; *Sx* = '*x* believes that streams have moral rights'; *Ux* = '*x* is a utility'; *Bx* = '*x* builds dams'.]

19. No *a*nimal that cannot *e*xperience sensations has moral *r*ights. Anything that is *s*elf-aware and has moral *r*ights has a right to *l*ife. Some *a*nimals are *s*elf-aware and *e*xperience sensations. Anything that is *s*elf-aware can see itself through *t*ime. Not all *a*nimals that can *e*xperience sensations can see themselves through *t*ime. Hence, not all *a*nimals have moral *r*ights. [*Ax* = '*x* is an animal; *Ex* = '*x* can experience sensations'; *Rx* = '*x* has moral rights'; *Sx* = '*x* is self-aware'; *Lx* = '*x* has a right to life'; *Tx* = '*x* can see itself through time'.]

20. Only those who go *c*amping *e*njoy nature. Anyone who *e*njoys nature either uses *p*rimitive campgrounds or goes *b*ackpacking in the woods or is *h*appy in the city. Some *e*njoy nature, but won't *l*eave their TV sets at home. If anyone *e*njoys nature and goes *c*amping, then if he or she uses *p*rimitive campgrounds, he or she *l*eaves the TV set at home. No one who goes *c*amping is *h*appy in the city. Hence, some who *e*njoy nature go *b*ackpacking in the woods. [*Cx* = '*x* goes camping'; *Ex* = '*x* enjoys nature'; *Px* = '*x* uses primitive campgrounds'; *Bx* = '*x* goes backpacking in the woods'; *Hx* = '*x* is happy in the city'; *Lx* = '*x* leaves the TV set at home'.]

D. Multiple Quantifications

Truth trees systematically unpack complex statements according to the truth-functional definitions of their connectives. The previous section showed how truth trees are used to reduce universal quantifications, existential quantifications, and their negations.

Most multiple quantifications result from combining quantified statements with one of our connectives. Since quantified statements are statements, any connectives between them have the same function as they did in the first five chapters of this book. Accordingly, connectives between quantified statements are treated exactly as in Chapter 6.

Any resulting quantifications are next reduced as in the previous section. Suppose that the following multiple quantification is part of some tree:

$$\forall x(Ax \supset Bx) \supset \exists x(Fx \cdot Gx)$$

In this case, a universal quantification and an existential quantification are connected with the horseshoe. The statement as a whole is a conditional that has '$\forall x(Ax \supset Bx)$' as its antecedent and '$\exists x(Fx \cdot Gx)$' as its consequent. When we apply our method of constructing truth trees as developed in Chapter 6, we obtain:

$$\forall x(Ax \supset Bx) \supset \exists x(Fx \cdot Gx)\sqrt{}$$

$$\sim\forall x(Ax \supset Bx) \qquad \exists x(Fx \cdot Gx)$$

We can now reduce each branch as in the previous section:

$$\forall x(Ax \supset Bx) \supset \exists x(Fx \cdot Gx)\sqrt{}$$

$\sim\forall x(Ax \supset Bx)\sqrt{}$	$\exists x(Fx \cdot Gx)\sqrt{}$
$\exists x\sim(Ax \supset Bx)\sqrt{}$	$Fb \cdot Gb\sqrt{}$
$\sim(Aa \supset Ba)\sqrt{}$	Fb
Aa	Gb
$\sim Ba$	

Exercises XVIII

Use truth trees to determine which of the following arguments are valid. For those that are invalid, specify the model and list the values that show that it is possible for the argument to have all true premises and a false conclusion. *If* you have instantiated all existential quantifications *and* additional instantiations of universal quantifications cannot possibly cause additional paths to close, consider the problem finished.

*1. $\exists x(Fx \cdot Sx)$
$\therefore \exists xFx \cdot \exists xSx$

2. $\forall xAx \lor \forall xBx$
$\therefore \forall x(Ax \lor Bx)$

3. $\exists xAx \lor \exists xBx$
$\therefore \exists x(Ax \lor Bx)$

4. $\exists xRx \supset \forall xCx$
$\therefore \forall x(Rx \supset Cx)$

*5. $\forall x(Tx \supset Hx)$
$\forall x(Lx \supset Nx)$
$\therefore \forall x(Nx \supset Tx) \supset \forall x(Lx \supset Hx)$

6. $Rt \cdot Nt$
$\exists x(Rx \cdot Nx) \supset \forall x(Rx \supset Nx)$
$\therefore \forall x(Rx \supset Nx)$

7. $\forall x(Qx \supset Tx) \supset \forall x(Zx \supset Ax)$
$\therefore \exists x(Qx \cdot Zx) \supset \exists x(Tx \cdot Ax)$

8. $\exists x(Tx \cdot Yx) \supset \forall x(Tx \supset Yx)$
$\exists x(Ax \cdot \sim Tx)$
$\therefore \exists x(Ax \cdot \sim Yx)$

Exercises XIX

The following arguments contain multiple quantifications. Symbolize each of them, and then:

A. Prove validity by constructing a formal proof, or prove invalidity by using the partial-truth-table method.

B. Use truth trees to determine which of the following arguments are valid. For those that are invalid, specify the model and list the values that show that it is possible for the argument to have all true premises and a false conclusion. *If* you have instantiated all existential quantifications *and* additional instantiations of universal quantifications cannot possibly cause additional paths to close, consider the problem finished.

*1. If some drugs have adverse reactions, then no drugs should be prescribed without careful supervision. Some monoamine oxidase inhibitors have caused death. Any drug that has caused death has adverse reactions! Hence, no drugs should be prescribed without careful supervision. [Ax = 'x has adverse reactions'; Px = 'x should be prescribed'; Cx = 'x is carefully supervised'; Mx = 'x is a monoamine oxidase inhibitor'; Dx = 'x has caused death'; RD: drugs.]

2. Icarus had artificial wings that were held together with wax. If anyone *flies* near the sun with artificial wings that are held together with wax, then someone will fall to the earth. Icarus *flew* near the sun. Hence, someone fell to the earth. [Ax = 'x has artificial wings that are held together with wax'; Fx = 'x flies near the sun'; Ex = 'x falls to the earth'; RD: beings.]

3. Whenever someone *steals*, then everyone *pays* higher prices. Smitty hasn't had to *pay* higher prices. Hence, no one has *stolen*. [Sx = 'x steals'; Px = 'x pays'; RD: people.]

4. "All our yesterdays have *lighted* fools the way to dusty death" (Shakespeare, *Macbeth*). If all of us have yesterdays, then all of us have yesterdays that have *lighted* fools the way to dusty death. [Yx = 'x is a person's yesterday'; Lx = 'x has lighted fools the way to dusty death'; RD: people.]

*5. If what's good for General Motors is good for the *country*,[12] then whatever *eliminates* foreign competition is good for the *country*. Tough trade *laws* *eliminate* foreign competition. Hence, tough trade *laws* are good for the *country*. [Gx = 'x is good for General Motors'; Cx = 'x is good for the country'; Ex = 'x eliminates foreign competition'; Lx = 'x is a tough trade law'.]

---

[12]This statement was made by Charles E. Wilson when he was president of General Motors Corporation.

8 Polyadic Predication

Our monadic symbolization methods are capable of expressing many arguments in predicate logic. Some arguments, however, require the ability to express relationships that hold between two (or more) individuals. As mentioned in Chapter 7, one politician cannot be more liberal than another unless there are at least two politicians. 'More liberal' indicates a relation between two individuals. Similarly, one cannot be against, unless one is against something. Predicates that indicate relations between two or more individuals are called "polyadic predicates."

DEFINITION 8.1

A *polyadic predicate* is a predicate which claims that a relation holds between two or more individuals.

Jonathan Swift once said, "When a true genius appears in the world, you may know him by this sign, that the dunces are all in confederacy against him."[1] Suppose that Smitty is a genius who has appeared in the world. It follows that the dunces are all in confederacy against Smitty. We are presently unable to express this argument, however, since we are unable to express that dunces and true geniuses have this relation.

Most polyadic predicates, such as 'against' and 'more liberal than', express relations that can hold between two individuals. These are called "dyadic" predicates.

Some predicates are "triadic"; they express relations that hold between three individuals. Peter Abelard (1079–1142) provides an argument with a triadic predicate. Abelard, a respected logician and theologian of the Notre

---

[1]Jonathan Swift, "Thoughts on Various Subjects, Moral and Diverting."

Dame school in Paris, "fell all on fire with love" (and lust!) for Heloïse.[2] Heloïse's uncle subsequently had Abelard castrated. Effectively denied lust, Abelard came to realize that he had been bound to Heloïse "with such a burning desire that I preferred these—pleasures—to both God and myself." His reasoning can be outlined as follows.

> *If someone continues an action knowing that God disapproves, then they must prefer the action to God's approval.*

> *If someone continues an action knowing that it will result in their downfall, then they must prefer the action to their personal well-being.*

> *I continued to see Heloïse, knowing that God disapproved and that it would result in my personal downfall.*

> *Hence, I must have preferred seeing Heloïse to having God's approval, and preferred it to my personal well-being.*

Abelard's argument has us notice that

Abelard preferred Heloïse to God's approval.

The predicate 'prefers . . . to . . .' is a three-place (triadic) predicate. There has to be *someone* who prefers, and *something* that he or she prefers to *something else*.

Although there is no limit to the number of individuals that predicates might require, this chapter focuses on dyadic and triadic predicates.

With minor additions, the sections of Chapter 7 that discuss formal proofs and invalidity can be readily applied to arguments that have polyadic predicates. The major goal of this chapter consists in expanding our symbolization methods so that portions of Chapter 7 can be applied to these arguments.

KEY TERMS

Use the glossary as necessary, and review the definitions of these terms prior to a second reading of this chapter.

Polyadic predicate	**Nonsymmetrical relation**
Transitive relation	**Totally reflexive relation**
Intransitive relation	**Reflexive relation**
Nontransitive relation	**Irreflexive relation**
Symmetrical relation	**Nonreflexive relation**
Asymmetrical relation	

---

[2]Peter Abelard, *Historia Calamitatum*. See J. T. Muckle, *The Story of Abelard's Adversities* (Toronto: Pontifical Institute of Mediaeval Studies, 1964), 26–31.

I   Symbolization

A. Individual Constants

Our predicate letters are unchanged: they are all of the capital letters, A–Z. The number of lower-case letters that are placed next to a predicate letter is decided by the number of individuals that are required for the predicate to express the relation. With monadic predicates, only one individual is required. Hence, only one lower-case letter, either an individual constant or an individual variable, is placed next to a predicate letter that abbreviates a monadic predicate. With dyadic predicates, two lower-case letters are placed next to the predicate letters, since dyadic predicates express relations that hold between two individuals. Triadic predicates have us place three lower-case letters next to their predicate letters, since they express relations that hold between three individuals. And so on.

Abelard was unsure if he desired Heloïse as an end, for her own sake, or if he desired her as a means, as a way to obtain her "pleasures." In any event, it is certain that he desired her. Using D to abbreviate the dyadic predicate 'desires',

> *'Abelard desires Heloïse' can be expressed as* Dah.

Notice that when expressing polyadic predicates, the order of the lower-case letters, individual constants in this case, is important. Using the same abbreviations,

> Dha *expresses 'Heloïse desires Abelard'.*

Although 'Abelard desires Helöse' and 'Heloïse desires Abelard' were both true, they clearly have different meanings. The difference in meaning is expressed in the artificial language by changing the order of the individual constants.

English uses both the active voice and the passive voice to express predicates. In the active voice, we can say "Abelard desires Heloïse." The equivalent meaning expressed in the passive voice is "Heloïse is desired by Abelard." In order to simplify our task of symbolizing English sentences, we will adopt the convention of using our predicate letters to abbreviate predicates that are in the active voice. Always letting our predicate letters abbreviate predicates in the active voice eliminates the bother of trying to remember whether the active or the passive voice has been abbreviated.

Accordingly, we will let D abbreviate 'desires', not 'is desired by'. If necessary, passive-voice constructions can be changed to active-voice constructions and then expressed in the artificial language.

'Abelard desires Heloïse' and 'Heloïse is desired by Abelard' are identical in meaning. Since we have decided to let the predicate letter D abbreviate 'desires', we will express both English sentences as *Dah*.

B. Quantifiers

Polyadic predicates are often quantified. Suppose we want to say "Abelard desires someone," or "someone is desired by Abelard." 'Some*one*' in English indicates that the relevant "things" are people. We can symbolize these sentences as

RD: persons
∃*xDax*

'Someone desires Abelard', or 'Abelard is desired by someone', is symbolized as '∃*xDxa*': "There is at least one person such that that person desires Abelard." The following table assumes that predicate letters abbreviate predicates that are expressed in the active voice. It summarizes dyadic-predicate symbolizations that have no more than one quantifier. The Abelard/Heloïse examples assume RD: persons. *P* indicates some dyadic predicate. 'Everyone' means "every person," and 'someone' means "at least one person."

	Active	*Passive*
Dah	Abelard desires Heloïse.	Heloïse is desired by Abelard.
Pab	*a Ps b.*	*b* is *P*ed by *a.*
∃*xDxh*	Someone desires Heloïse.	Heloïse is desired by someone.
∃*xPxa*	Something *Ps a.*	*a* is *P*ed by something.
∃*xDax*	Abelard desires someone.	Someone is desired by Abelard.
∃*xPax*	*a Ps* something.	Something is *P*ed by *a.*
∀*xDxh*	Everyone desires Heloïse.	Heloïse is desired by everyone.
∀*xPxa*	Everything *Ps a.*	*a* is *P*ed by everything.
∀*xDhx*	Heloïse desires everyone.	Everyone is desired by Heloïse.
∀*xPax*	*a Ps* everything.	Everything is *P*ed by *a.*

Multiple quantifications of dyadic predicates are also straightforward *when both quantifiers are of the same type.*

'∃*x*∃*yDxy*' is read: "There is at least one person *x* and there is at least one person *y*, such that *x* desires *y*." In more natural English, we have: "Someone desires someone."

'∃*y*∃*xDxy*' is read: "There is at least one person *y* and at least one person *x*, such that *x* desires *y*." In more natural English, we have: "Someone is desired by someone."

Obviously, the truth conditions for both of these statements are the same. One person can desire a second person if and only if the second person is desired by the first person. Similarly, one person can be desired by a second person if and only if the second person desires the first person. The above statements are logically equivalent. The order in which two existential quantifiers are applied to a dyadic predicate is irrelevant.

The order in which two universal quantifiers are applied to a dyadic predicate is also irrelevant. '$\forall x \forall y Dxy$' claims that for any person x and for any person y, x desires y. In standard English, we have: "Everyone desires everyone." '$\forall y \forall x Dxy$' claims that for any person y and for any person x, x is desired by y. In short, "Everyone is desired by everyone." These statements are also logically equivalent. The following table expresses typical multiple-quantification meanings for dyadic predicates when both quantifiers are of the same type.

	Active	*Passive*
$\forall x \forall y Dxy$	Everyone desires everyone.	Everyone is desired by everyone.
$\forall x \forall y Pxy$	Everything Ps everything.	Everything is Ped by everything.
$\exists x \exists y Dxy$	Somone desires someone.	Someone is desired by someone.
$\exists x \exists y Pxy$	Something Ps something.	Something is Ped by something.
$\forall x \forall y {\sim} Dxy$	No one desires anyone.	No one is desired by anyone.
$\forall x \forall y {\sim} Pxy$	Nothing Ps anything.	Nothing is Ped by anything.

Quantifier order is important when different types of quantifiers are used.

For some amusement and to help visualize the differences in meaning, try picturing each of the following in the setting of a singles' bar.

'$\exists x \forall y Dxy$' means that there is at least one person, x, such that for any person y, x desires y. More naturally, "There is a person who desires everyone." (Some people are desperate at closing time.)

In contrast, '$\forall y \exists x Dxy$' claims that for any person, y, there is at least one person x, such that y is desired by x. More naturally, "Every person is desired by at least one person." (Everyone is wanted.)

'∃y∀xDxy' claims that there is at least one person, y, such that for any person x, y is desired by x. More naturally, "There is someone who is desired by everyone." (People are packed five deep around that person.)

Finally, we have '∀x∃yDxy': for every person x, there is some person y, such that x desires y. More naturally, "Everyone desires at least one person." (Everyone has at least one lust object.)

> *Each of the above has a distinct meaning, both in English and in the artificial language. None of them is logically equivalent to any another.*

To summarize:

∃x∀yDxy	There is a person who desires everyone.
∃x∀yPxy	There is a thing that Ps everything.
∀y∃xDxy	Everyone is desired by at least one person.
∀y∃xPxy	Everything is Ped by at least one thing.
∃y∀xDxy	There is someone who is desired by everyone.
∃y∀xPxy	There is something such that everything Ps it.
∀x∃yDxy	Everyone desires at least one person.
∀x∃yPxy	Everything Ps at least one thing.

Notice that 'someone desires someone' is *not* '∃x∃xDxx'. Our requirements for well-formed formulas are still in effect.

> *No variable within a quantified expression can be within the scope of more than one quantifier that has that variable.*

'∃xDxx' is a well-formed formula. It claims that someone desires himself or herself. '∀xDxx' is also a well-formed formula, and it claims that each person desires himself or herself.

Triadic and higher-place predicates are symbolized by following the same guidelines as for dyadic predicates.

'*Abelard* preferred *Heloïse* to *God's approval*', using obvious abbreviations, can be expressed as '*Pahg*'.

'Abelard preferred something to something else' is symbolized as '∃x∃yPaxy'.

Polyadic predicates are often used with our previous connectives and monadic predicates. Universal quantifications with polyadic predicates typically have the horseshoe as the major connective. The antecedent defines the group at issue, and the consequent asserts that a predicate (monadic, dyadic, etc.) applies to all of its members.

Suppose that we wish to symbolize "Everyone prefers something to something else." 'Everyone' means "every person," but we have no reason to believe that the "things" that we preferred to other things are people. Hence, we should *not* restrict our domain to persons. We can use E for the quality of being a person.

Sentences that contain polyadic predicates are best translated by introducing one artificial-language symbol at a time. Following a step-by-step approach helps to determine where to place any necessary parentheses, brackets, and braces.

1. Since the sentence claims that all *persons* prefer something more than something else, we can begin as follows:

   For anything in the universe, if it is a person then it prefers something to something else.

   $\forall x \ (Ex \supset x$ *prefers something to something else*$).$

2. Next, we have the claim that there is something that they prefer to something else.

   $\forall x \ (Ex \supset \exists y$ *such that* x *prefers* y *to something else*$).$

3. There must be a 'something else', z, and x prefers y to z.

   $\forall x \ (Ex \supset \exists y \exists z$ *such that* x *prefers* y *to* z*$).$

   If we let 'Pxyz' abbreviate 'x prefers y to z', we can finish our translation:

   $\forall x \ (Ex \supset \exists y \exists z Pxyz)$

C. Steps for Symbolizing by Paraphrasing

Step 1 Express the meaning of the sentence to be symbolized in standard English. If the sentence reasonably has more than one meaning, write out the meanings in standard English.

Step 2 Restate the paraphrase, using 'someone', 'everyone', 'something', and 'everything'. When reasonable, use the English equivalents for the connectives of Chapter 2: 'if . . . then . . .', 'and', 'or', and 'not'.

Step 3 Symbolize the paraphrased meaning by gradually introducing artificial-language symbols.

In describing Nazarath's reaction to his teaching, Jesus said:

A prophet is not without honor, save in his own country.

Step 1 'A prophet is not without honor' means "a prophet has honor." 'Save' means "unless." Hence,

A prophet has honor, unless he is in his own country.

Step 2   Taking the statement to be about all prophets, we have:

If anyone is a prophet, then he has honor, unless there is a country that is his country and he is in his country.

Now we can complete our translation by introducing our artificial-language symbols in a step-by-step fashion.

Step 3   Since the statement makes a claim about all prophets, we have:

∀x (Px ⊃ x has honor, unless x is in x's own country).

∀x [Px ⊃ (x has honor V x is in x's own country)].

x has honor unless there is a y, and x's country is y, and x is in y:

∀x [Px ⊃ (x has the honor V there is a y and x's country is y and x is in y)].

∀x [Px ⊃ (Hx V there is a y and x's country is y and x is in y)].

∀x {Px ⊃ [Hx V ∃y (x's country is y and x is in y)]}.

Suppose that we let Cxy abbreviate x's country is y, and let Ixy abbreviate 'x is in y'. We obtain:

∀x{Px ⊃ [Hx V ∃y(Cxy · Ixy)]}

Suppose that we try to symbolize the statement:

Some prophets have honor when they are in their own country.

Step 1

There is at least one prophet who has honor if he is in his own country.

Step 2   The statement is about prophets who are in their own countries.

There is at least one prophet such that if anything is his country and he is in it, then he has honor.

Step 3

∃x [x is a prophet and ∀y (if x's country is y and x is in y, then x has honor)].

∃x [Px · ∀y (x's country is y and x is in y) ⊃ x has honor].

∃x {Px · ∀y [(x's country is y · x is in y) ⊃ x has honor]}.

∃x {Px · ∀y [(Cxy · x is in y) ⊃ x has honor]}.

∃x {Px · ∀y [(Cxy · Ixy) ⊃ x has honor]}.

∃x{Px · ∀y[(Cxy · Ixy) ⊃ Hx]}

John Keats, a 19th-century English poet, originated the following saying in the poem "Endymion":

A thing of beauty is a joy forever.

This example shows that English phrases are often ambiguous. It also shows how time can frequently be represented with polyadic predicates.

Keats's logical subject is obviously "things of beauty." Beyond this, it is unclear exactly what is meant. There are several translations that might be used for Keats's claim. The following provides a fairly literal translation.

Step 1   Keats's statement is about all things of beauty.

Step 2

> *If anything is a thing of beauty, then it is a joy at all times.*

Step 3

> $\forall x$ ($Bx \supset x$ is a joy at all times).

Suppose that we decide to let Tx abbreviate 'x is a time'. We can express 'x is a joy at all times' as:

> $\forall y$ (*if y is a time, then x is a joy at y*).

"For anything in the universe, if it is a time, then x is a joy at that time." We can now continue our step-by-step approach:

> $\forall x$ [$Bx \supset \forall y$ ($Ty \supset x$ is a joy at y)].
>
> $\forall x[Bx \supset \forall y(Ty \supset Jxy)]$

The above provides a reasonable translation of Keats's statement. A bit of reflection, however, shows that a more sophisticated translation is also possible. Something cannot be a thing of beauty unless it is a thing of beauty to *someone*. It is a "joy forever" to this person. Paraphrasing these ideas, we have the following.

Step 1

> *If anyone finds anything to be a thing of beauty, then that thing always brings that person joy.*

Step 2

> *If any person x finds beauty in any object y, then at any time y brings that person joy.*

Step 3

> $\forall x$ {*if x is a person, then* $\forall y$ [*if x finds beauty in y, then* (*at all times x finds joy in y*)]}.
>
> $\forall x$ {*x is a person* $\supset \forall y$ [*x finds beauty in y* $\supset$ (*at all times x finds joy in y*)]}.
>
> $\forall x$ {*x is a person* $\supset \forall y$ [*x finds beauty in y* $\supset \forall z$ (*Tz* $\supset$ *x finds joy in y at z*)]}.
>
> $\forall x$ {$Px \supset \forall y$ [$Bxy \supset \forall z$ ($Tz \supset x$ *finds joy in y at z*)]}.
>
> $\forall x\{Px \supset \forall y[Bxy \supset \forall z(Tz \supset Jxyz)]\}$

D. Additional Individual Variables

All of our symbolizations have been accomplished by using only the individual variables x, y, and z. Many symbolizations can be accomplished with only these three individual variables. If additional variables are needed, we will use subscripts to create them: x_1, y_1, z_1; x_2, y_2, z_2; and so on. Corresponding universal and existential quantifiers can also be created: $\exists x_1$, $\exists y_1$, $\exists z_1$, and so on.

Exercises I

Paraphrase, and then symbolize each of the following statements.

*1. St. Paul's Cathedral is located in London. [Lxy = 'x is located in y'.]

2. Tennessee is between Michigan and Florida. [$Bxyz$ = 'x is between y and z'.]

3. "The reports of my death are greatly exaggerated" (Mark Twain). [Rxy = 'x is a report of y'; Ex = 'x is greatly exaggerated'.]

4. "Man is the measure of all things" (Protagoras). [Px = 'x is a person'; Mxy = 'x is the measure of y'.]

*5. 'Venereal' is derived from 'Venus'. [Dxy = 'y is derived from x'.]

6. For every number, there is a greater number. [Nx = 'x is a number'; Gxy = 'x is greater than y'.]

7. RD: people; Uxy = 'x understands y'.
   a. Heloïse understands Abelard.
   b. Everyone understands Abelard.
   c. Heloïse understands everyone.
   d. No one understands anyone.
   e. Someone understands everyone.
   f. There is someone who is understood by everyone.

8. Use the following dictionary, and translate each of the following into standard English.
   Mx = 'x is a man'; Wx = 'x is a woman'; Uxy = 'x understands y'.
   a. $\exists x \exists y[(Wx \cdot My) \cdot Uxy]$
   b. $\exists x \exists y[(Wx \cdot My) \cdot \sim Uyx]$
   c. $\exists x \exists y[(Wx \cdot Wy) \cdot \sim Uxy]$
   d. $\forall x \forall y[(Wx \cdot My) \supset \sim Uxy]$
   e. $\forall x[Wx \supset \exists y(My \cdot Uxy)]$
   f. $\forall x[Wx \supset \exists y(My \cdot \sim Uyx)]$
   g. $\exists x[Mx \cdot \forall y(Wy \supset Uxy)]$
   h. $\exists x[Mx \cdot \forall y(Wy \supset Uyx)]$

*9. Px = 'x is a person'; Gxy = 'x got y'; Wx = 'x wanted y'.
   a. Everyone got everything that they wanted.

      b. No one got anything that they wanted.

      c. Some people got some things that they wanted.

      d. Not everyone got everything that they wanted.

      e. Some people got nothing that they wanted.

10. An invertebrate is an animal without a backbone. [Ix = 'x is an invertebrate'; Ax = 'x is an animal'; Wxy = 'x is without y'; Bx = 'x has a backbone'.]

11. Celibacy doesn't get it. [Cx = 'x is celibate'; Sxy = 'x has sex with y'.]

12. Abelard felt Heloïse tremble if he touched her. [Fxy = 'x feels y tremble'; Txy = 'x touches y'.]

*13. The one who names the game is the one who wins it. [Nxy = 'x names y'; Gx = 'x is a game'; Wxy = 'x wins y'.]

14. Nobody knows the trouble I've seen. [Px = 'x is a person'; Kxy = 'x knows y'; Tx = 'x is trouble'; Sxy = 'x has seen y'.]

15. Most people always remember some experiences. [Px = 'x is a person'; Tx = 'x is a time'; $Rxyz$ = 'x remembers y at z'; Ex = 'x is an experience'.]

16. Someone gave a war and nobody came to it. [Px = 'x is a person'; Gxy = 'x gave y'; Wx = 'x is a war'; Cxy = 'x came to y'.]

Each of the following has more than one interpretation. Be sure to paraphrase a likely meaning before attempting a symbolization.

*17. There is no personality trait more helpful in assisting learning than a sense of humor. [Px = 'x is a personality trait'; Sx = 'x is a sense of humor'; Lx = 'x assists learning'; Hxy = 'x is more helpful than y'.]

18. "Nothing is more important for the well-being of a nation than putting milk in the mouths of its infants" (Winston Churchill). For your symbolization, shorten this to: "Nothing is more important than putting milk in the mouths of infants." [Ixy = 'x is more important than y'; Mx = 'x is milk'; $Pxyz$ = 'x puts y in z'; Ix = 'x is the mouth of an infant'.]

19. "Those who cannot remember the past are condemned to repeat it" (George Santayana). [Px = 'x is a person'; Rxy = 'x remembers y'; Ex = 'x is an event'; Yx = 'x is in the past'; Cxy = 'x is condemned to repeat y'.]

20. Anyone can be educated if there is enough time and someone has the patience to teach them. [Px = 'x is a person'; Ex = 'x can be educated'; Tx = 'x is enough time'; Axy = 'x has the patience to teach y'.]

Concept Reviews

1. In Chapter 2, 'Abelard desires Heloïse' would have been expressed as *D*. In Chapter 7, it would have been expressed as *Da*. In this chapter, it is expressed as *Dah*. Symbolize the following argument as in each of the three mentioned chapters.

   RD: persons

   Abelard desired Heloïse.

   Hence, someone desired someone.

   The next section develops formal proofs. We will be able to prove that the above argument is valid. "Prove" that it is invalid with the symbolization methods of Chapters 2 and 7.

2. "Tetradic" predicates express relations that require four individuals. Try to think of a statement with a tetradic predicate. How, given the guidelines of this chapter, should your statement be represented?

3. Explain the difference in meaning that is intended by the following sentences:

   Everyone desired someone.

   There was a person that everyone desired.

4. The following expression is *not* a WFF. Why not?

   $\forall x \exists y [Rxy \supset \exists x Vxy]$

II Formal Proofs

A. Application of Available Inference Rules

Chapter 7's inference rules are adequate for arguments that have polyadic predicates. For example:

Abelard desired Heloïse.

Hence, someone desired Heloïse.

We can readily symbolize this argument and provide a formal proof:

1. *Dah* $/\exists x Dxh$

   2. $\sim\!\exists x Dxh$ *I.P.A.*
   3. $\forall x \sim\! Dxh$ *Q.N. 2*
   4. $\sim\! Dah$ *U.I. 3*
   5. *Dah* · $\sim\! Dah$ *Conj. 1, 4*

6. $\exists x Dxh$ *I.P. 2–5*

The introduction to this chapter claimed that the following (slightly abbreviated here) is a valid argument:

When a true genius appears in the world, the dunces are all in confederacy against him.

Smitty is a genius who has appeared in the world.

Hence, the dunces are all in confederacy against Smitty.

We can symbolize this argument and prove that it is valid.

Tx = 'x is a true genius'; Ax = 'x appears in the world'; Dx = 'x is a dunce'; Cxy = 'x is in confederacy against y'

1. $\forall x[(Tx \cdot Ax) \supset \forall y(Dy \supset Cyx)]$ $/\forall x(Dx \supset Cxs)$
2. $Ts \cdot As$

---

3. $\sim\forall x(Dx \supset Cxs)$ I.P.A.
4. $\exists x\sim(Dx \supset Cxs)$ Q.N. 3
5. $(Ts \cdot As) \supset \forall y(Dy \supset Cys)$ U.I. 1
6. $\forall y(Dy \supset Cys)$ M.P. 5, 2
7. $\sim(Da \supset Cas)$ E.I. 4
8. $Da \supset Cas$ U.I. 6
9. $(Da \supset Cas) \cdot \sim(Da \supset Cas)$ Conj. 8, 7

---

10. $\forall x(Dx \supset Cxs)$ I.P. 3–9

The universal instantiation step taken on line 5 is legitimate, since line 1 is a universal quantification. To review: A well-formed formula (WFF) is a universal quantification if and only if it begins with a universal quantifier whose scope is the entire remainder of the WFF (Definition 7.15); and a WFF is an existential quantification if and only if it begins with an existential quantifier whose scope is the entire remainder of the WFF (Definition 7.16).

Line 1 begins with a universal quantifier whose scope is the entire remainder of the WFF. Notice that U.I. cannot be applied to line 5, since it does not begin with a universal quantifier and is not a universal quantification. Line 4 is an existential quantification. Line 7, in applying E.I., instantiates to a constant that does not appear previously in the problem.

'$\forall x\exists yDxy$' is a universal quantification. '$\exists x\forall yDxy$' is an existential quantification. '$\forall x\exists yDxy \supset \exists x\forall yDxy$' is neither a universal nor an existential quantification.

B. Revised Forms of U.I., E.I., and Q.N.

Formal proofs frequently have lines with adjacent quantifiers, all of which have to be instantiated. We will simplify formal proofs by allowing more than one instantiation *of the same kind* to take place in a given step. Lines in formal proofs frequently begin with the negation of a quantifier. The negated quantifier is often adjacent to other quantifiers. We will also simplify formal proofs by allowing more than one application of quantifier negation to take place in a given step. Consider the following argument and formal proof:

Everyone desired everyone.
Hence, everyone was desired by everyone.

We can *at present* provide the following symbolization and formal proof:

RD: persons

1. $\forall x \forall y Dxy$ $/\forall y \forall x Dxy$

> 2. $\sim \forall y \forall x Dxy$ I.P.A.
> 3. $\exists y \sim \forall x Dxy$ Q.N. 2
> 4. $\exists y \exists x \sim Dxy$ Q.N. 3
> 5. $\exists x \sim Dxa$ E.I. 4
> 6. $\sim Dba$ E.I. 5
> 7. $\forall y Dby$ U.I. 1
> 8. Dba U.I. 7
> 9. $Dba \cdot \sim Dba$ Conj. 8, 6

10. $\forall y \forall x Dxy$ I.P. 2–9

Universal instantiation and existential instantiation can be restated to allow more than one application in deriving a line.

UNIVERSAL INSTANTIATION (U.I.)

Where '$(\ldots Pxyz \ldots)$' indicates some expression that has the variables $x, y, z \ldots$, from '$\forall x \forall y \forall z (\ldots Pxyz \ldots)$' we may infer '$(\ldots Ptuv \ldots)$', where $t, u, v \ldots$ indicate any individual constants, so long as all occurrences of $x, y, z \ldots$ are uniformly replaced.

EXISTENTIAL INSTANTIATION (E.I.)

Where '(. . . $Pxyz$ . . .)' indicates some expression that has the variables x, y, z . . . , from '$\exists x \exists y \exists z$(. . . $Pxyz$ . . .)' we may infer '(. . . $Ptuv$ . . .) where t, u, v . . . indicate different individual constants, so long as all occurrences of x, y, z . . . are uniformly replaced, each variable is replaced with a different constant, and none of the constants appears anywhere previously in the problem.

The above revised forms of U.I. and E.I. permit exactly the same inferences as are presently allowed, but they allow multiple applications in deriving a given line.

Quantifier negation can also be modified to allow multiple applications.

QUANTIFIER NEGATION (Q.N.)

If a quantification begins with a tilde and a string consisting only of quantifiers, the tilde may be placed after the last quantifier, and each quantifier may be switched to the other quantifier.

For example, '$\sim \exists x \forall y \forall z Axyz$' is equivalent to '$\forall x \exists y \exists z \sim Axyz$'. The tilde at the beginning of the expression has been moved to the right of the string of quantifiers, and each quantifier has been switched. '$\sim \forall x \forall y \exists z Axyz$' is equivalent to '$\exists x \exists y \forall z \sim Axyz$'.

The number of applications of an inference should be indicated as part of the justification. The following is an alternative formal proof for our previous example.

1. $\forall x \forall y Dxy$ $\diagup \forall y \forall x Dxy$

> *2.* $\sim \forall y \forall x Dxy$ *I.P.A.*
> *3.* $\exists y \exists x \sim Dxy$ *(2)Q.N. 2*
> *4.* $\sim Dba$ *(2)E.I. 3*
> *5.* Dba *(2)U.I. 1*
> *6.* $Dba \cdot \sim Dba$ *Conj. 5, 4*

7. $\forall y \forall x Dxy$ *I.P. 2–6*

Notice that each of the applications of E.I. on line 4 instantiates to a different individual constant. Had the instantiations been carried out in two moves, one of the constants would have been in the problem prior to the second application of E.I. Our revised version of E.I. requires that each variable be replaced with a unique individual constant. Taking two moves in one step does not change our requirements for valid inferences.

C. Dyadic Relations

i. Transitivity

Some kinds of dyadic relations are of particular interest. Imagine the following conversation between two racquetball players about a third player:

Dave: What kind of a game am I going to have against Sam?

Bill: Well, I can beat him and you can beat me, so I don't think you'll have much of a match.

As stated,[3] Bill's argument is invalid. We can symbolize it as follows:

RD: racquetball players; Bxy = 'x *can beat* y'

1. *Bbs · Bdb*   /*Bds*

With merely this information, it is impossible to begin a formal proof. Bill's argument is based on the additional premiss that 'being able to beat' is a "transitive" relation.

DEFINITION 8.2

A dyadic relation is *transitive* if and only if, whenever (1) one individual, x, has the relation to a second individual, y, and (2) the second individual, y, has the relation to a third individual, z, then the first individual, x, has the relation to the third individual, z.

R is a transitive relation if and only if

$$\forall x \forall y \forall z[(Rxy \cdot Ryz) \supset Rxz]$$

Bill's argument assumes that for 'being able to beat', the following is true:

$$\forall x \forall y \forall z[(Bxy \cdot Byz) \supset Bxz]$$

---

[3]Bill's argument is an enthymeme, an incompletely stated argument. Enthymemes were discussed in Chapter 1.

This claims that if one individual can beat a second individual, and the second individual can beat a third individual, then the first individual can beat the third individual. By adding Bill's assumption that 'being able to beat' is transitive, we can quickly prove that his argument is valid:

1. $Bbs \cdot Bdb$ /Bds
2. $\forall x \forall y \forall z[(Bxy \cdot Byz) \supset Bxz]$
3. $Bdb \cdot Bbs$ Comm. 1
4. $(Bdb \cdot Bbs) \supset Bds$ (3)U.I. 2
5. Bds M.P. 4, 3

Bill's argument is valid, which is not the same thing as claiming that it is sound. His assumption is at least debatable.

'Being south of' is a transitive relation. If Tennessee is south of Michigan and Florida is south of Tennessee, then Florida must be south of Michigan.

Some relations are "intransitive."

DEFINITION 8.3

A dyadic relation is *intransitive* if and only if, whenever (1) one individual, x, has the relation to a second individual, y, and (2) the second individual, y, has the relation to a third individual, z, then the first individual, x, does not have the relation to the third individual, z.

R is an intransitive relation if and only if

$\forall x \forall y \forall z[(Rxy \cdot Ryz) \supset \sim Rxz]$

'Weighs exactly twice as much' is an example of an intransitive relation. If Alexander weighs exactly twice as much as Elizabeth, and Elizabeth weighs exactly twice as much as Nancy, Alexander cannot weigh exactly twice as much as Nancy. In symbols

$(Wae \cdot Wen) \supset \sim Wan$

DEFINITION 8.4

A dyadic relation is *nontransitive* if and only if it is neither transitive nor intransitive.

'Hates' is an example of a nontransitive relation. If Nancy hates Alexander and Alexander hates Elizabeth, we have no basis for knowing whether or not Nancy hates Elizabeth. Bill's earlier argument *assumes* that 'being able to beat' is a transitive relation. But, it is more likely a nontransitive relation.

ii. Symmetry

Most states have legislation that prevents one spouse from being forced to testify against the other spouse. Such legislation can be symbolized as follows.

Mxy = '*x is married to* y'; Fxy = '*x can be forced to testify against* y'
$\forall x \forall y (Mxy \supset \sim Fxy)$

In this context, the following is a reasonable argument:

Sam is married to Martha.
Hence, she can't be forced to testify against him.

We can symbolize it as follows:

1. $\forall x \forall y (Mxy \supset \sim Fxy)$ $\diagup \sim Fms$
2. Msm

It is impossible to complete the formal proof. This argument (correctly) assumes that 'being married to' is what is called a "symmetrical" relation.

DEFINITION 8.5

A dyadic relation is *symmetrical* if and only if, whenever one individual has the relation to a second individual, then the second individual has the relation to the first individual.

R is a symmetrical relation if and only if

$\forall x \forall y (Rxy \supset Ryx)$

If Sam is married to Martha, then Martha must be married to Sam. Since she is married to him, she cannot be forced to testify against him. By adding the claim that 'being married to' is a symmetrical relation, we can complete the symbolization and provide the following formal proof.

1. $\forall x \forall y (Mxy \supset \sim Fxy)$ $\diagup \sim Fms$
2. Msm
3. $\forall x \forall y (Mxy \supset Myx)$
4. $Msm \supset Mms$ (2)$U.I.$ 3

5. $Mms \supset \sim Fms$ (2)U.I. 1
6. Mms M.P. 4, 2
7. $\sim Fms$ M.P. 5, 6

Some relations are called "asymmetrical."

DEFINITION 8.6

A dyadic relation is *asymmetrical* if and only if, whenever one individual has the relation to a second individual, then the second individual does not have the relation to the first individual.

R is an asymmetrical relation if and only if

$\forall x \forall y (Rxy \supset \sim Ryx)$

'Is older than' is an asymmetrical relation. If Dave is older than Bill, Bill cannot be older than Dave:

$Odb \supset \sim Obd$

DEFINITION 8.7

A dyadic relation is *nonsymmetrical* if and only if it is neither symmetrical nor asymmetrical.

'Hates' is an example of a nonsymmetrical relation. If one person hates another, we cannot infer whether or not the second person hates the first.

iii. Reflexivity

DEFINITION 8.8

A dyadic relation is *totally reflexive* if and only if everything has the relation to itself.[4]

---

[4]There is a lack of agreement among logicians on what to call these relations. Some logicians prefer to call our totally reflexive relations "reflexive," and to call our reflexive relations "partially reflexive."

R is a totally reflexive relation if and only if

$\forall x Rxx$

Without assuming a restricted domain, few relations are *totally* reflexive. Few relations can be meaningfully predicated of *everything*, and fewer yet are such that everything has the relation to itself. 'Is identical to' is an example of a totally reflexive relation. Everything is identical to itself: '$\forall x Ixx$'.

Merely reflexive relations are much more common than totally reflexive ones.

DEFINITION 8.9

A dyadic relation is *reflexive* if and only if everything that takes part in the relation has the relation to itself.

'Is the same age' is a reflexive relation. If one thing is the same age as anything else, or anything else is the same age as it, then it is the same age as itself. If Methuselah was the same age as anything, or anything was the same age as Methuselah, then Methuselah was the same age as himself.[5] In symbols:

$\forall x[(Sxm \lor Smx) \supset Smm]$

R is a reflexive relation if and only if

$\forall x \forall y[(Rxy \lor Ryx) \supset Rxx]$

DEFINITION 8.10

A dyadic relation is *irreflexive* if and only if nothing has the relation to itself.

R is an irreflexive relation if and only if

$\forall x \sim Rxx$

Many relations are irreflexive. Nothing is literally married to itself. Nothing is next to itself. Nothing is more talented than itself.

---

[5]Methuselah was the grandfather of Noah. According to the Book of Genesis, he lived 969 years and then died.

DEFINITION 8.11

A dyadic relation is *nonreflexive* if and only if it is neither reflexive nor irreflexive.

Many relations are nonreflexive. Some things hate themselves, and some do not. Some things have seen themselves on TV, and some have not.

D. Triadic Predicates

Most arguments that contain polyadic predicates have only dyadic predicates. Occasionally, an argument will require applying our quantifier inferences to triadic and higher-order predicates.

Abelard came to see himself as the ultimate sinner. To arrive at this conclusion, he assumed that 'one thing is more important than another' is transitive. God was more important to Abelard than he himself was. Satan, from his actions, was more important to Abelard than God was. Hence, Abelard realized Satan was more important to Abelard than he himself was, and more important to him than God was. There is some scriptural support for believing that self-indulgent acts are forgivable sins. There is no scriptural support for believing that the pursuit of Satan himself is a forgivable sin. Abelard had come to value sin itself.

His argument:

$Ixyz$ = '*x is more important for y than z*'

1. $Igaa$ $/Isaa \cdot Isag$
2. $Isag$
3. $\forall x \forall y \forall z \forall x_1 [(Ixyz \cdot Izyx_1) \supset Ixyx_1]$

4. $(Isag \cdot Igaa) \supset Isaa$ (4)U.I. 3
5. $Isag \cdot Igaa$ Conj. 1, 2
6. $Isaa$ M.P. 4, 5
7. $Isaa \cdot Isag$ Conj. 6, 2

Exercises II

Provide a formal proof for each of the following valid arguments.

*1. Hab
     $\therefore\ \ \exists x \exists y Hxy$

2. Hab
   $\exists x Hxb \supset Hbb$
   $\therefore Hbb$

3. Aab
    $\exists xAxb \supset \forall xAxb$
    $\therefore Abb$

*5. $\exists x\forall yAxy$
    $\therefore \ \forall x\exists yAyx$

7. $\forall x\forall y(Axy \supset Axa)$
    $\forall x(Bx \supset Axb)$
    $\therefore \ \forall x(Bx \supset Axa)$

*9 $\forall x\forall y[(Ax \cdot Byx) \supset Cy]$
    Aa
    $\therefore \ \forall x(Bxa \supset Cx)$

4. $\exists xAxa$
    $\forall x(Axa \supset Bx)$
    $\sim Ba$
    $\therefore \ \exists xBx \cdot \exists x\sim Bx$

6. $\forall x(Axa \supset \sim Aax)$
    $\therefore \sim Aaa$

8. $\forall x(\exists yAxy \supset \forall yAyx)$
    $\exists x\exists yAxy$
    $\therefore \ \exists y\forall xAxy$

10. $\forall x(Rax \supset Qcxa)$
    $\therefore \ \forall x(Rax \supset \exists y\exists zQyxz)$

Exercises III

Symbolize, and provide a formal proof for each of the following valid arguments.

*1. The bigger they are, the harder they fall. Nixon was bigger than most. Hence, he fell harder than most. [RD: persons; $Bxy = $ 'x is bigger than y'; $Hxy = $ 'x falls harder than y'.]

2. Everyone in Mudville is unhappy.[6] No one who has read *The Power of Positive Thinking* is unhappy. Hence, no one in Mudville has read *The Power of Positive Thinking*. [$Px = $ 'x is a person'; $Ixy = $ 'x is in y'; $Ux = $ 'x is unhappy'; $Rxy = $ 'x has read y'.]

3. Don Juan pursued every woman he knew. There were women that Don Juan knew. Hence, there were women that Don Juan pursued. [$Pxy = $ 'x pursues y'; $Kxy = $ 'x knows y'; $Wx = $ 'x is a woman'.]

4. A "Don Juan" pursues every woman he knows. Don Juan was a "Don Juan" who knew [the woman] Lady Elvire. Hence, Don Juan pursued Lady Elvire. [$Dx = $ 'x is a "Don Juan" '; $Pxy = $ 'x pursues y'; $Wx = $ 'x is a woman'; $Kxy = $ 'x knows y'.]

*5. If anyone finds anything, then they've looked for it. Hence, if anyone finds El Dorado, then they've looked for it.[7] [$Px = $ 'x is a person'; $Fxy = $ 'x finds y'; $Lxy = $ 'x has looked for y'.]

---

[6]From Ernest Thayer's poem, "Casey at Bat": "There is no joy in Mudville, mighty Casey has struck out."
[7]El Dorado was a legendary king of Manoa, a city located somewhere on the Amazon. El Dorado was reputed to be so wealthy that he covered himself with gold dust every evening. Sir Walter Raleigh led two unsuccessful expeditions to discover Manoa. The supposed territory has come to be called "El Dorado."

6. The brontosaurus was a herbivore. Hence, any tooth of a brontosaurus is a tooth of a herbivore. [Bx = 'x is a brontosaurus'; Hx = 'x is a herbivore'; Txy = 'x is a tooth of y'.]

7. Any event is meaningful only if there is an event that is understood to precede it. One event is the cause of another if and only if it is understood to precede the other. Hence, any meaningful event is understood to have a cause. [RD: events; Mx = 'x is meaningful'; Uxy = 'x is understood to precede y'; Cxy = 'x is the cause of y'.]

8. All women hate the Marquis de Sade. All chauvinists hate anyone who hates him. Hence, all chauvinists hate all women. [Wx = 'x is a woman'; Hxy = 'x hates y'; Cx = 'x is a chauvinist'.]

*9. I certainly think that it is better to be impetuous than cautious, for fortune is a woman, and it is necessary, if you wish to master her, to conquer her by force; and it can be seen that she lets herself be overcome by the bold rather than by those who proceed coldly. And therefore, like a woman, she is always a friend to the young, because they are less cautious, fiercer, and master her with greater audacity.[8]

In the above passage, Machiavelli reveals himself as sexist by modern standards. Some of his claims about women are clearly false, though some of his claims about politics are clearly true. Symbolize and provide a formal proof for the following argument.

Younger men are more audacious than older men. More audacious men master women more easily. Women favor those who master them more easily. Hence, women favor younger men. [Mx = 'x is a man'; Yxy = 'x is younger than y'; Axy = 'x is more audacious than y'; Wx = 'x is a woman'; $Sxyz$ = 'x masters y more easily than z'; $Fxyz$ = 'x favors y more than z'.]

10. There is a tide in the affairs of men
    Which, taken at the flood, leads on to fortune;
    Omitted, all the voyage of their life
    Is bound in shallows and in miseries.
    On such a full sea are we now afloat,
    And we must take the current when it serves,
    Or lose our ventures.[9]

After making the above speech, Brutus loses the battle when his "soldiers [fall] to spoil." He then commits suicide. Symbolize and provide a formal proof of the following.

All men have a tide, which produces their fortune if and only if they take it at the flood. Brutus was a man, but nothing produced fortune for him. Hence, there was a tide which Brutus didn't take at the flood. [Mx =

---

[8]Niccolo Machiavelli, *The Prince*, in *The Prince and Discourses*, trans. Luigi Ricci, revised by E. R. P. Vincent (New York: Modern Library, 1950), 94.
[9]William Shakespeare, *Julius Caesar*, act 4, scene 3, lines 217–23.

'x is a man'; Txy = 'x is a tide for y'; Fxy = 'x takes y at the flood'; Pxy = 'x produces fortune for y'.]

Exercises IV

Symbolize each of the following. Add the indicated relation as an additional premiss, and provide a formal proof for the resulting argument.

*1. Any horse looks faster than any fence. Hence, no fence looks faster than any horse. ['Looks faster' is asymmetric. Hx = 'x is a horse'; Lxy = 'x looks faster than y'; Fx = 'x is a fence'.]

2. A horse is able to outrun any fence. Hence, no fence is a horse. ['Being able to outrun' is irreflexive. Hx = 'x is a horse'; Oxy = 'x can outrun y'; Fx = 'x is a fence'.]

3. Guest: Mr. Churchill, you are drunk.

   Churchill: And you, my good man, are a fool. But I shall be sober in the morning.

Churchill obviously accepted the guest's comparison, and suggested additional ones. The guest will be a fool forever. Symbolize and prove that the following argument is valid.

A fool is better than a drunk. A statesman is better than a fool. There are fools. Hence, a statesman is better than a drunk. ['Is better than' is transitive. Fx = 'x is a fool'; Bxy = 'x is better than y'; Dx = 'x is a drunk'; Sx = 'x is a statesman'.]

Concept Reviews

Relations have a number of interesting logical properties. In addition to reviewing some of the relations from the previous section, we will examine some connections between them.

1. Any totally reflexive relation is reflexive. Suppose that R is a totally reflexive relation. A formal proof can be used to show that R is a reflexive relation. Prove that the following argument is valid.

   $\forall x Rxx$
   $\therefore \ \forall x \forall y [(Rxy \lor Ryx) \supset Rxx]$

2. Any asymmetrical relation is irreflexive. Suppose that R is an asymmetrical relation. Assume '$\forall x \forall y (Rxy \supset \sim Ryx)$' as a premiss. Provide a formal proof that derives '$\forall x \sim Rxx$'.

3. Any intransitive relation is irreflexive. Suppose that R is an intransitive relation. Provide a formal proof which shows that R is an irreflexive relation.

4. If a relation is irreflexive and transitive, then it is asymmetrical. Assume that R is an irreflexive relation, and assume that R is a transitive relation. Provide a formal proof which shows that R is an asymmetrical relation.

Challenging:

5. Although not all symmetrical and transitive relations are *totally reflexive*, any symmetrical and transitive relation is reflexive. Assume that R is a symmetrical relation. Assume that R is a transitive relation. Provide a formal proof which shows that R is a reflexive relation.

III Invalidity

Partial truth tables and truth trees can be used to determine whether *most* arguments that are stated with polyadic predicates are valid. It has been proved, however, that there can be no single, general decision procedure that applies to all such arguments.[10] Each of the following sections shows how to apply our previous concepts to arguments with polyadic predicates. Each also indicates limitations on our methods.

A. Partial Truth Tables

Our partial truth table procedures, requirements, and guidelines remain in effect as they were developed in Chapter 7. If an argument that is expressed with polyadic predicates appears to be valid in a one-member model, then it should be considered with respect to a two-member model.

---

[10]Alonzo Church first verified this claim in "A Note on the Entscheidunsproblem," *Journal of Symbolic Logic* 1 (1936): 40–41 and 101–2. A more accessible presentation of Church's ideas in relation to the partial-truth-table method can be found in S. C. Kleene, *Introduction to Meta-Mathematics* (New York: Van Nostrand, 1952). A more accessible presentation of Church's ideas in relation to the method of constructing truth trees can be found in Richard Jeffrey, *Formal Logic: Its Scope and Limits* (New York: McGraw-Hill, 1981), chapter 6.

If it appears to be valid in a two-member model, then it should be considered with respect to a three-member model. And so on. We will continue to express existential quantifications as a series of *disjuncts*, and universal quantifications as a series of *conjuncts*.

When interpreting expressions with polyadic predicates, however, quantifiers are expanded for the members of a model universe *by expanding one quantifier at a time*.

Consider the following argument:

Everyone is desired by at least one person.

Hence, there is a person who desires everyone.

We can symbolize this argument as:

RD: persons
$$\forall x \exists y Dyx$$
$$\therefore \quad \exists x \forall y Dxy$$

A bit of reflection tells us that this argument *should* be invalid. Imagine that there are three people: a, b, and c. Suppose that a desires b, b desires c, and c desires a. Under these conditions, everyone is desired by at least one person, but there is no one who desires everyone. We can imagine a situation that shows that it is possible for the argument to have a true premiss and a false conclusion. How can we show that the argument is invalid by constructing a partial truth table?

In a one-member model, $\{a\}$, the argument is equivalent to:

$$\frac{Daa}{\therefore \ Daa}$$

The argument cannot have all true premises and a false conclusion in a one-member model, since any assignment of truth-values that makes the conclusion false will make the premiss false. Suppose that we consider the argument in a two-member model, $\{a, b\}$. '$\forall x \exists y Dyx$' is a universal quantification. We will begin by considering the significance of the universal quantifier in a two-member model. Each member of the model must be desired by at least one person:

$$\exists y Dya \ \cdot \ \exists y Dyb$$

Our "at least one person" must be either a or b. '$\exists y Dya$' is expanded as '$Daa \lor Dba$'. '$\exists y Dyb$' is expanded as '$Dab \lor Dbb$'. We can now express the argument's premiss as:

$$(Daa \lor Dba) \cdot (Dab \lor Dbb)$$

Suppose that we apply the above process to the argument's conclusion:

'$\exists x \forall y Dxy$' is expressed as '$\forall y Day \lor \forall y Dby$'.

'$\forall yDay$' is expressed as '$Daa \cdot Dab$', and '$\forall yDby$' is expressed as '$Dba \cdot Dbb$'. In a two-member model, the conclusion is equivalent to

$$(Daa \cdot Dab) \lor (Dba \cdot Dbb)$$

Can we show that the argument is invalid in a two-member model?

$$(Daa \lor Dba) \cdot (Dab \lor Dbb)$$
$$\therefore (Daa \cdot Dab) \lor (Dba \cdot Dbb)$$

The following assignments show that the argument can have all true premises and a false conclusion in a two-member model.

Daa false

Dba true

Dbb false

Dab true

We have shown that the argument is invalid!

Next we will use our partial-truth-table method to show that Pooh's argument, as expressed at the beginning of Chapter 7, is invalid.

"That's funny," thought Pooh. "I said 'Ow!' without really oo'ing."

"Help!" said a small, high voice.

"That's me again," thought Pooh. "I've had an Accident, and fallen down a well, and my voice has gone all squeaky and works before I'm ready for it, because I've done something to myself inside, Bother!"

Paraphrasing, we have:

Any time that I'm injured, I hear "Ow!"

I hear "ow!" now.

Hence, I'm injured now.

Suppose that we let Tx abbreviate 'x is a time', let Hxy abbreviate 'x hears "ow!" at y', and let Ixy abbreviate 'x is injured at y'. Pooh's argument can be symbolized as:

$$\forall x[(Tx \cdot Ipx) \supset Hpx]$$
$$Hpn$$
$$\therefore Ipn$$

We will begin by considering the argument in the model universe that consists of those members that are specified by the argument's individual constants, $\{p, n\}$.

$[(Tp \cdot Ipp) \supset Hpp] \cdot [(Tn \cdot Ipn) \supset Hpn]$

$\underline{Hpn}$

$\therefore Ipn$

A number of truth-value assignments, including the following, show that the argument is invalid when considered in this two-member model:

Ipn false

Hpn true

Tp false

Although more steps are required, quantified triadic and higher-order predicates are expanded by using the same process. Suppose that we interpret '$\exists y \forall x \forall z Rxyz$' in the two-member model, $\{a, b\}$. The existential quantification must be true for either a or b:

$\forall x \forall z Rxaz \quad \lor \quad \forall x \forall z Rxbz$

Each of the above disjuncts must be true for each member of the model:

$(\forall z Raaz \cdot \forall z Rbaz) \lor (\forall z Rabz \cdot \forall z Rbbz)$

Each of the above conjuncts must be true for each member of the model:

$[(Raaa \cdot Raab) \cdot (Rbaa \cdot Rbab)] \lor [(Raba \cdot Rabb) \cdot (Rbba \cdot Rbbb)]$

Although partial truth tables can be used to determine that many invalid arguments are invalid, there are arguments that cannot be determined to be either valid or invalid by this method, since an *infinite* universe would be required to make all of their premises true. The following is such an argument.

> *Every number is greater than some number.*
>
> *'Greater than' is a transitive relation. (If one number is greater than a second number and the second number is greater than a third number, then the first number is greater than the third number.)*
>
> *'Greater than' is irreflexive. (No number is greater than itself.)*
>
> *Hence, some number is greater than any number.*

Suppose that we symbolize this argument as follows:

RD: numbers

$\forall x \exists y Gxy$

$\forall x \forall y \forall z [(Gxy \cdot Gyz) \supset Gxz]$

$\underline{\forall x \sim Gxx}$

$\therefore \quad \exists x \forall y Gxy$

No finite model is capable of proving that this argument is invalid. None of the following arguments requires considering infinite models!

Exercises V

Use the partial-truth-table method and prove that each of the following arguments is invalid.

*1. Dah
$\overline{\therefore \ \forall xDax}$

2. $\sim Tab$
$\overline{\therefore \ \ \forall x\forall y\sim Txy}$

*3. $\forall x\exists yDyx$
$\overline{\therefore \ \ \exists x\forall yDxy}$

4. $\forall x\exists yDxy$
$\overline{\therefore \ \ \exists y\forall xDxy}$

*5. $\forall x[Qx \ \supset \ \exists yAxy]$
$\overline{\therefore \ \exists x\forall y(Qx \ \supset \ Axy)}$

6. $\forall x\exists yAxy$
$\exists x\exists y\sim Axy$
$\overline{\therefore \ \ \exists x\forall yAxy}$

7. $\forall x\forall y[(Rx \ \cdot \ Bx) \supset \ \sim Nxy]$
$\overline{\therefore \ \ \forall x[Bx \ \supset \ \forall y\sim Nxy]}$

8. $\forall x\{[Ox \ \cdot \exists y(Ay \ \cdot Zxy] \supset \exists z(Qz \ \cdot Zxz)\}$
$\overline{\therefore \ \ \forall x(Ax \ \supset \ Qx)}$

*9. $\exists x\exists y(Caxy \ \cdot \ Cbxy)$
$\exists x(Cacx \ \lor \ Cbcx)$
$\overline{\therefore \ \ \exists x(Cacx \ \cdot \ Cbcx)}$

10. $\forall x\forall y(Axy \ \supset \ Txy)$
$\exists x(Ax \ \cdot \ \exists yTyx)$
$\overline{\therefore \ \ \forall x\forall y[Axy \ \supset \ (Txy \ \cdot \ Tyx)]}$

See Exercises VI.A for additional problems.

B. Truth Trees

Our truth-tree procedures, requirements, and guidelines remain in effect as they were developed in the last chapter. It is convenient to be able to combine multiple applications of U.I., E.I., and Q.N. when constructing formal proofs. Similarly, it is convenient to be able to combine multiple applications of them when constructing truth trees. Accordingly, we will restate our quantification-reduction patterns so that multiple applications are allowed.

Where '$(\ldots Pxyz \ldots)$' indicates some expression that has the variables $x, y, z \ldots$,

$$\forall x\forall y\forall z(\ldots Pxyz \ldots) \quad *$$
$$(\ldots Ptuv \ldots)$$

where t, u, v, ... indicate any individual constants, so long as all occurrences of x, y, z ... are uniformly replaced.

$$\exists x \exists y \exists z(\dots Pxyz \dots) \quad \checkmark$$
$$(\dots Ptuv \dots)$$

where t, u, v ... indicate different individual constants, so long as all occurrences of x, y, z ... are uniformly replaced. Each variable must be replaced with a unique constant and none of the constants can appear anywhere previously in the tree.

If a WFF begins with a tilde and a string only of quantifiers, it may be checked off. The WFF that results from placing the tilde after the last quantifier and switching each quantifier to the other quantifier is added to the tree.

We know, from number 5 in the last set of concept reviews, that any symmetrical and transitive relation is reflexive. Is every symmetrical and transitive relation *totally* reflexive? We can construct the following truth tree to find out:

$$\forall x \forall y(Rxy \supset Ryx) \; *$$
$$\forall x \forall y \forall z[(Rxy \cdot Ryz) \supset Rxz] \; *$$
$$\sim\!\forall x Rxx \quad \checkmark$$
$$\exists x \sim\! Rxx \quad \checkmark$$
$$\sim\! Raa$$
$$Raa \supset Raa \quad \checkmark$$

```
                    ~Raa                      Raa
        (Raa · Raa) ⊃ Raa  √                   X
                /    \
        ~(Raa · Raa) √     Raa
            /    \          X
        ~Raa      ~Raa
```

Even though we could continue to introduce new constants, doing so would be pointless. Every existential quantification has been checked off. Every universal quantification has been instantiated to each constant on the tree. A one-member model with Raa assigned false shows that the argument is invalid. Not every symmetrical and transitive relation must be *totally* reflexive.

The following example has both monadic and dyadic predicates.

$\forall x(Hx \supset Cx)$
$\therefore \forall x[\exists y(Hy \lor Rxy) \supset \exists y(Cy \lor Rxy)]$

We can use the following truth tree to determine whether it is valid.

$$\forall x(Hx \supset Cx) \;*$$
$$\sim\forall x[\exists y(Hy \lor Rxy) \supset \exists y(Cy \lor Rxy)] \;\surd$$
$$\exists x\sim[\exists y(Hy \lor Rxy) \supset \exists y(Cy \lor Rxy)] \;\surd$$
$$\sim[\exists y(Hy \lor Ray) \supset \exists y(Cy \lor Ray)]\surd$$
$$\exists y(Hy \lor Ray) \;\surd$$
$$\sim\exists y(Cy \lor Ray)] \;\surd$$
$$\forall y\sim(Cy \lor Ray) \;*$$
$$Hb \lor Rab \;\surd$$

```
                    Hb                Rab
            ~(Cb V Rab) √      ~(Cb V Rab) √
                ~Cb                ~Cb
               ~Rab               ~Rab
             Hb ⊃ Cb √              X

          ~Hb        Cb
           X          X
```

All paths close. Hence, as in Chapters 6 and 7, the corresponding set of statements is inconsistent and the argument is valid.

For a final example, suppose someone inferred that "There is a number that is greater than any number" from the fact that "For any number, there is some number that is greater." Is this person's argument valid? We can symbolize the argument, set up a truth tree, and begin as follows.

RD: numbers; Gxy = 'x is greater than y'
$\forall x\exists yGyx$
$\therefore \;\; \exists y\forall xGyx$

$$\forall x\exists yGyx \;\;**$$
$$\sim\exists y\forall xGyx \;\;\surd$$
$$\forall y\exists x\sim Gyx \;\;**$$
$$\exists yGya \;\;\surd$$
$$Gba$$
$$\exists x\sim Gbx \;\;\surd$$
$$\sim Gbc$$
$$\exists yGyc \;\;\surd$$
$$Gdc$$
$$\exists x\sim Gdx \;\;\surd$$

Reviewing our tree shows that we are in an infinitely repeating pattern. We have to introduce a new constant with each reduction of an existential quantification, and then reduce a universal quantification to *that* constant. Next, we have to introduce a new constant for the resulting existential quantification, and so on.

Problems that require infinite trees, such as the above example, show why the truth-tree method is not a no decision procedure for arguments in polyadic predicate logic. Some trees have paths that never close and that never exhaust the need for additional constants.

There is no recipe for determining which trees will be nonterminating. Often, however, we can sense that introducing a new constant will merely make the introduction of another constant necessary.

Exercises VI

Symbolize each of the following arguments, and then:

A. Prove validity by constructing a formal proof, or prove invalidity by using the partial-truth-table method.

B. Use truth trees to determine which of the following arguments are valid. For those that are invalid, specify the model and list the values that show that it is possible for the argument to have all true premises and a false conclusion. If you encounter an argument that requires a tree of infinite length, consider the argument to be undetermined.

*1. Freud was a person and cocaine didn't ruin his life. Hence, cocaine doesn't ruin anyone's life. [Px = 'x is a person'; Cx = 'x is cocaine'; Rxy = 'x ruins the life of y'.]

2. God helps those people who help themselves. Hence, God helps some people. [Hxy = 'x helps y'; Px = 'x is a person'.]

3. God helps those who help themselves. Some people help themselves. Hence, God helps some people. [As number 2.]

4. Guns don't hurt people, but some people do. Something should be illegal if and only if it hurts people. Hence, some people should be illegal. [Gx = 'x is a gun'; Hxy = 'x hurts y'; Px = 'x is a person'; Ix = 'x should be illegal'.]

*5. Electromagnetic waves and light waves move at the same speed. Hence, anything is an electromagnetic wave if and only if it is a light wave. [Ex = 'x is an electromagnetic wave'; Lx = 'x is a light wave'; Sxy = 'x moves at the same speed as y'.]

6. If God foreknows an event, then it will happen. If God causes an event, then it will happen. Hence, if God foreknows an event, then He causes it. [Fxy = 'x foreknows y'; Ex = 'x is an event'; Hx = 'x happens'; Cxy = 'x causes y'.]

7. Most purchases are not determined by using reason. Hence, most purchases are not determined by anything at all. [Px = 'x is a purchase'; Dxy = 'x determines y'; Rx = 'x is a case of using reason'.]

8. If anything is a subject of morality, then it must be something over which people have control. People have control only over intentions. Hence, only intentions are the subject of morality. [Sx = 'x is a subject of morality'; Px = 'x is a person'; Cxy = 'x has control over y'; Ix = 'x is an intention'.]

*9. Just as a stray horse is better than a stone which is not astray, since the stone does not have its own motion or perception, so the creature who sins with his free will is more excellent than the creature who does not sin because he has no free will. I would praise, as well, wine which was good in itself, and yet I would censure a man who got drunk on that very wine. I would still prefer the drunken man whom I just censured to the wine I praised.[11]

Symbolize and determine whether the following argument is valid.

Every person has a free will. No wine has a free will. Anything with a free will is superior to anything without a free will. Hence, any person is superior to any wine. [Px = 'x is a person'; Fx = 'x has free will'; Hxy = 'x has y'; Wx = 'x is wine'; Sxy = 'x is superior to y'.]

10. If anyone is guilty of murder, then they've killed a person. No fetus is a person. Hence, no one who kills a fetus is guilty of murder. [Mx = 'x is guilty of murder'; Px = 'x is a person'; Kxy = 'x has killed y'; Fx = 'x is a fetus'.]

---

[11]Saint Augustine, *On Free Choice of the Will*, trans. Anna S. Benjamin and L. H. Hackstaff (Indianapolis: Bobbs-Merrill, 1964), 98–99.

9 Theorems and Introductory Metalogic

I Constructing Formal Proofs to Derive Theorems

We are presently able to construct formal proofs and prove that truth-functional arguments are valid. This section points out how our formal proof techniques can also be used to derive truth-functional tautologies and truth-functional self-contradictions. In order to expand the applications of our formal-proof system, we will first look at how different kinds of statements are related to valid and invalid arguments.

A. Relationships between Statements and Arguments

Our Chapter 3 characterization of statement forms and valid argument forms enables us to show how different kinds of statements are related to valid and invalid arguments. To review: A truth-functional statement form is tautologous if and only if it is true on every line of its truth table. (Definition

3.6.) A truth-functional statement form is self-contradictory if and only if it is false on every line of its truth table. (Definition 3.7.)

A truth-functional argument form is valid if and only if no line of its truth table has all true premises and a false conclusion. A truth-functional argument form is invalid if and only if its truth table has one or more lines with all true premises and a false conclusion.

Our definitions of the dot and the horseshoe enable us to show how different kinds of statements are related to valid and invalid arguments. First, we should notice that conjunctions, as expressed by the dot, are true when, and only when, both conjuncts are true. Suppose that we create a conjunction by conjoining two premises of an argument or an argument form. The resulting statement or statement form is true when, and only when, both of the premises are true. For example:

$$(p \supset q) \cdot p^1$$

is true only in cases when the premises—

$$p \supset q$$
$$\underline{p }$$

—are true. If an argument form has more than two premises, a conjunction that is formed by making each of the premises a conjunct is true when, and only when, each of the conjuncts is true. We might have to add parentheses (and brackets and braces) so that each conjunct is clearly defined, but we know (by association) that alternative groupings have equivalent truth-values.

A statement of the form

$$P_1 \cdot P_2 \cdot P_3 \cdot \ldots$$

is true if and only if the premises of an argument that has the form

$$P_1$$
$$P_2$$
$$P_3$$
$$\cdot$$
$$\cdot$$
$$\cdot$$
$$\underline{\therefore C}$$

are all true.

We also know that a statement that has the horseshoe as its major connective is true unless its antecedent is true and its consequent is false. If

---

[1]Since we know that '$p \cdot q$' is logically equivalent to '$q \cdot p$', it does not matter in what order the conjuncts are conjoined.

we create a conditional that has the conjunction of an argument form's premises as its antecedent and the conclusion of the argument form as its consequent, then the conditional will be true unless the premises of the argument form are all true and the conclusion of the argument form is false. The conditional will be true except when the argument form is invalid. Hence:

> **An argument form is valid if and only if a conditional that has the conjunction of the argument form's premises as its antecedent and the argument form's conclusion as its consequent is tautologous.**

The following examples show the above relationship of argument forms to statement forms.

Example 1 (Modus Ponens)

Argument form:

$$p \supset q$$
$$\underline{p}$$
$$\therefore q$$

Statement form:

$$[(p \supset q) \cdot p] \supset q$$

Truth table:

p	$\supset$	q	p	q
T	T	T	T	T
T	F	F	T	F
F	T	T	F	T
F	T	F	F	F

Valid; there is no line with all true premises and a false conclusion.

Truth table:

$[(p$	$\supset$	$q)$	$\cdot$	$p]$	$\supset$	q
T	T	T	T	T	T	T
T	F	F	F	T	T	F
F	T	T	F	F	T	T
F	T	F	F	F	T	F

Tautologous; there is no line where the antecedent is true and the consequent is false.

Example 2

Argument form:

$$p \supset (q \supset r)$$
$$p$$
$$\underline{\sim q}$$
$$\therefore \sim r$$

Statement form:

$$\left\{ \{[p \supset (q \supset r)] \cdot p\} \cdot \sim q \right\} \supset \sim r$$

Truth table:

p	$\supset$	$(q$	$\supset$	$r)$	p	$\sim q$	$\sim r$
T	T	T	T	T	T	F	F
T	F	T	F	F	T	F	T

T	T	F	T	T	T	T	F
T	T	F	T	F	T	T	T
F	T	T	T	T	F	F	F
F	T	T	F	F	F	F	T
F	T	F	T	T	F	T	F
F	T	F	T	F	F	T	T

Invalid; the third line has all true premisses and a false conclusion.

Truth table:

$$\big\{\{[p \ \supset \ (q \supset r)] \ \cdot \ p\} \ \cdot \ \sim q\big\} \supset \sim r$$

T	T	T T T	T T	F F	T F
T	F	T F F	F T	F F	T T

T	T	F T T	T T	T T	F F
T	T	F T F	T T	T T	T T
F	T	T T T	F F	F F	T F
F	T	T F F	F F	F F	T T
F	T	F T T	F F	F T	T F
F	T	F T F	F F	F T	T T

Not a tautology; the third line has a true antecedent and a false consequent.

Notice that the same truth-values, those on line three, show that the argument form is invalid and that the statement form is not a tautology.

Valid argument forms and self-contradictory statement forms are also related. An argument form is valid if and only if no line of its truth table has all true premisses and a false conclusion. Negating a statement produces a statement of opposite truth-value. If we negate the conclusion of an argument, the truth table for the resulting statement will have truth-values that are opposite to those of the original argument's conclusion.

Hence, if there is no line of the truth table of an argument form with all true premisses and a false conclusion, there will be no line of the truth table that has all true premisses and the negation of the conclusion true. Similarly, if there is a line with all true premisses and a false conclusion, there must be a line with all true premisses and the negation of the conclusion true. Hence, since a conjunction is true if and only if each of its conjuncts is true:

An argument form is valid if and only if the statement formed by conjoining its premisses with the negation of its conclusion is a self-contradictory statement form.

Example 3

Argument form:

$p \supset q$
$\underline{p}$
$\therefore q$

Statement form:

$[(p \supset q) \cdot p] \cdot \sim q$

EXERCISES I   **345**

Truth table:

$p \supset q$	p	q
T T T	T	T
T F F	T	F
F T T	F	T
F T F	F	F

Valid; there is no line with all true premisses and a false conclusion.

Truth table:

$[(p \supset q)$	$\cdot$	$p]$	$\cdot \sim q$
T T T	T T	F F	
T F F	F T	F T	
F T T	F F	F F	
F T F	F F	F T	

Self-contradictory; there is no line in which every conjunct is true.

Example 4

Argument form:

$p \supset (q \supset r)$
p
$\sim q$
_____
$\therefore \sim r$

Statement form:

$\left\{ \{[p \supset (q \supset r)] \cdot p\} \cdot \sim q \right\} \cdot r$

Truth table:

$p \supset (q \supset r)$	p	$\sim q$	$\sim r$
T T T T T	T	F	F
T F T F F	T	F	T
T T F T T	T	T	F
T T F T F	T	T	T
F T T T T	F	F	F
F T T F F	F	F	T
F T F T T	F	T	F
F T F T F	F	T	T

Invalid; the third line has all true premisses and a false conclusion.

Truth table:

$\left\{ \{[p \supset (q \supset r)] \cdot p\} \cdot \sim q \right\} \cdot r$
T T T T T T T T F F F T
T F T F F F T F F F F F
T T F T T T T T T T T T
T T F T F T T T T T F F
F T T T T F F F F F T
F T T F F F F F F F F
F T F T T F F F T F T
F T F T F F F F T F F

Not self-contradictory; the third line has all true conjuncts.

Exercises I

Write out the statement forms that must be tautologous if and only if the following argument forms are valid.

*1. $p \lor q$
     p
     _____
     $\therefore \sim q$

2. $p \lor q$
    $\sim p$
    _____
    $\therefore q$

3. $p \supset q$
    $\sim p$
    _____
    $\therefore q$

4. $p \supset q$
   $q \lor \sim p$
   $\therefore p$

*5. $\sim(p \cdot q)$
    p
    $\therefore \sim q$

6. $p \supset q$
   $\sim q \lor r$
   $\sim r \supset p$
   $\therefore \sim p$

7. $\sim p \supset (p \lor q)$
   $\sim q \lor \sim p$
   $\therefore r \lor \sim p$

8. $p \supset (q \lor r)$
   $\sim q \cdot \sim r$
   $\therefore \sim p$

*9. $p \supset q$
    $r \supset q$
    q
    $\therefore p \lor r$

10. $(p \supset q) \cdot (r \supset s)$
    $p \lor r$
    $\therefore q \lor s$

Exercises II

Use the argument forms in Exercises I above, and write out the statement forms that must be self-contradictory if and only if the argument forms are valid.

B. Tautologies

Chapters 4 and 5 developed a system of "natural deduction." It is natural in the sense that it takes premises and constructs arguments. The system presents reasoning in much the same way as it takes place in life. For obvious reasons, the system is deductive. Saying "the system of Chapters 4 and 5" is awkward. The system for constructing formal proofs that we developed in Chapters 4 and 5 will be called "ND."

Since ND is capable of proving that arguments are valid, it stands to reason that it should be possible to use ND and prove that statements are either tautologous or self-contradictory. Since logically true statements are based on form rather than factual information, however, we need a way to generate statements without assuming any factual information.

Individual statements are proved tautologous in ND by constructing formal proofs for the statements as conclusions of "arguments" that *lack premises*. The "premises" of these "arguments" are introduced either as conditional-proof assumptions or as indirect-proof assumptions. Conditional and indirect proofs for statements must follow all of the rules and restrictions of Chapters 4 and 5. Statements that are derived by using only the deductive system and no premises are called "theorems."

> DEFINITION 9.1
>
> A *theorem* of ND is any statement that can be derived in ND without using any premisses.

Formal proofs which derive theorems that have the horseshoe as their major connective are typically started with a conditional-proof assumption. Formal proofs which derive theorems that do not have the horseshoe as their major connective are typically started with an indirect-proof assumption.

Suppose, for example, that we wish to establish that '$\sim A \supset (A \supset B)$' is a theorem of ND. We will attempt to prove the validity of an "argument" whose conclusion is '$\sim A \supset (A \supset B)$'. As in Chapter 4 when we had an argument with a conditional as its *conclusion*, we will use conditional proof. Our conditional-proof assumption is:

  1. $\sim A$ C.P.A.

We need to derive '$A \supset B$'. Since '$A \supset B$' is also a conditional, we begin a second conditional proof that has A as its assumption:

  1. $\sim A$ C.P.A.
  2. A C.P.A.

Next, we derive B. Ending the conditional proofs will establish that '$\sim A \supset (A \supset B)$' is a theorem.

> 1. $\sim A$ C.P.A.
>
> > 2. A C.P.A.
> > 3. $\sim A \lor B$ Add. 1
> > 4. $A \supset B$ W.E. 3
> > 5. B M.P. 4, 2
>
> 6. $A \supset B$ C.P. 2–5

7. $\sim A \supset (A \supset B)$ C.P. 1–6

Hence, '$\sim A \supset (A \supset B)$' is a theorem of ND.

Suppose that we attempt to derive '$A \lor \sim A$' as a theorem. Since the major connective in this case is not a horseshoe, we will begin this proof with an indirect-proof assumption. We will make our assumption the negation of the statement that we intend to derive:

    1. ~(A V ~A) I.P.A.

As in Chapter 5, deriving an instance of '$p \cdot \sim p$' will enable us to end the indirect proof.

> *1. ~(A V ~A) I.P.A.*
> *2. ~A · ~~A D.M. 1*
> *3. ~A · A D.N. 2*
> *4. A · ~A Comm. 3*

  5. A V ~A I.P. 1–4

Hence, 'A V $\sim A$' is also a theorem of ND.

    The next example is a bit more complex. Suppose we wish to show that the following statement is a theorem:

    $(A \supset B) \supset [(A \lor C) \supset (B \lor C)]$

The major connective is a horseshoe. We will begin with a conditional-proof assumption that is the statement's antecedent:

    1. A ⊃ B C.P.A.

We need to derive another conditional:

    $(A \lor C) \supset (B \lor C)$

Hence, we will make 'A V C' a conditional-proof assumption:

    1. A ⊃ B C.P.A.
      2. A V C C.P.A.

Now we have to derive 'B V C'. Not seeing any obvious way to do this, and noting that 'B V C' is not a conditional, we can make an indirect-proof assumption and complete the formal proof as follows:

> *1. A ⊃ B C.P.A.*
>> *2. A V C C.P.A.*
>>> *3. ~(B V C) I.P.A.*
>>> *4. ~B · ~ C D.M. 3*
>>> *5. C V A Comm. 2*
>>> *6. ~~C V A D.N. 5*
>>> *7. ~C ⊃ A W.E. 6*
>>> *8. ~C Simp. 4*

9. *A M.P. 7, 8*
10. *B M.P. 1, 9*
11. *~B Simp. 4*
12. *B · ~B Conj. 10, 11*

13. *B V C I.P. 3–12*

14. *(A V C) ⊃ (B V C) C.P. 2–13*

15. *(A ⊃ B) ⊃ [(A V C) ⊃ (B V C)] C.P. 1–14*

Hence, '(A ⊃ B) ⊃ [(A V C) ⊃ (B V C)]' is a theorem.

Since all of our inferences, including conditional proof and indirect proof, are truth preserving:

All theorems of the system ND are tautologies.

Our justification of indirect proofs claimed that all indirect proofs can be seen as incomplete conditional proofs. Hence, if we show that all statements that are derived solely from conditional-proof assumptions are necessarily true, we will have shown that any derived statement, since it must be based on either a conditional-proof assumption or an indirect-proof assumption, is necessarily true.

"ARGUMENT" A	ARGUMENT B
$\therefore p \supset q$	p
	$\therefore q$

'$p \supset q$' is tautologous if and only and argument B is valid. If we are able to provide a formal proof for an "argument" such as A without using any initial premises, then we must be able to provide a formal proof for an argument such as B. If we are able to provide a formal proof for an argument such as B, then it must be impossible for B to have all true premises and a false conclusion. If it is impossible for B to have all true premises and a false conclusion, then '$p \supset q$' must be a tautology. Hence, if we are able to derive some statement '$p \supset q$' without using any initial premises, then '$p \supset q$' must be a tautology.

C. Self-Contradictions

A statement and its negation have opposite truth values. The negation of any tautology must be a self-contradiction, and conversely. Hence, we can show that a statement is self-contradictory by showing that its negation is tautologous. Suppose we wish to show that '$A \equiv \sim A$' is self-contradictory.

We can do this by showing that '$\sim(A \equiv \sim A)$' is a theorem (and hence a tautology). Since the desired statement is not a conditional, we will begin our formal proof with an indirect-proof assumption:

1. $A \equiv \sim A$ *I.P.A.*
2. $(A \supset \sim A) \cdot (\sim A \supset A)$ *M.E. 1*
3. $\sim A \supset A$ *Simp. 2*
4. $A \supset \sim A$ *Simp. 2*
5. $\sim A \vee \sim A$ *W.E. 4*
6. $\sim A$ *Du. 5*
7. A *M.P. 3, 6*
8. $A \cdot \sim A$ *Conj. 7, 6*

9. $\sim(A \equiv A)$ *I.P. 1–8*

Exercises III

Construct a formal proof to show that each of the following is a theorem. Use either conditional- or indirect-proof assumptions, as needed, to begin the proofs.

*1. $A \supset A$

2. $A \equiv A$

3. $(A \vee A) \supset A$

4. $(A \cdot B) \supset A$

*5. $A \supset (B \supset A)$

6. $[(A \vee B) \cdot (A \vee C)] \supset [A \vee (B \cdot C)]$

7. $A \supset [B \supset (A \cdot B)]$

8. $[A \supset (A \cdot B)] \equiv (A \supset B)$

*9. $[A \supset B) \cdot (B \supset C)] \supset (A \supset C)$

10. $A \vee [(A \vee B) \supset B]$

11. $(A \supset B) \supset (\sim B \supset \sim A)$

12. $A \supset [(A \cdot B) \equiv B]$

*13. $[(A \vee B) \vee C] \vee (C \supset \sim C)$

14. $(A \equiv B) \supset [(A \supset C) \supset (B \supset C)]$

15. $\sim(A \equiv B) \equiv (\sim A \equiv B)$

Exercises IV

Construct a formal proof to show that each of the following is a self-contradiction.

*1. $(A \vee B) \cdot (\sim A \cdot \sim B)$

2. $(A \cdot B) \equiv (A \supset \sim B)$

3. $[A \cdot \sim(A \vee B)] \vee [(A \cdot B) \cdot \sim A]$

4. $\sim(A \supset B) \cdot \sim(A \supset \sim B)$

*5. $[A \supset (B \supset C)] \cdot \sim[B \supset (A \supset C)]$

II Introduction to Metalogic

The prefix 'meta-' appears in numerous words. 'Meta-', which comes to us from the ancient Greek, means "beyond" or "above." Metalogic looks beyond or above logic.

DEFINITION 9.2

Metalogic is the critical examination of systems of logic.

Metalogic reasons about logical systems. Previously pages of this text have presented an approach to logic. We have discussed different kinds of statements and connectives. We are accustomed to constructing formal proofs for theorems and valid arguments by using the system called "ND." Metalogic takes a critical look at approaches, at *systems* of connectives and methods for constructing formal proofs. Our present goal is to examine the system of propositional logic that has been presented in this text.

A. System Soundness and Consistency

It is most important for a deductive system to be sound and consistent.

DEFINITION 9.3

A deductive system is *sound* if and only if it only allows formal proofs to be constructed for valid arguments.

Notice that 'sound' has a different meaning when applied to systems than when applied to arguments. A sound argument, as defined in Chapter 1, is deductively valid and has all true premisses.

DEFINITION 9.4

A deductive system is *consistent* if and only if two contradictory statements—statements that are instances of both p and $\sim p$—cannot be derived as theorems.

A system that allowed "proofs" to be constructed for invalid arguments would be worthless. In such a system, completing a proof would tell us nothing about the validity of the "proved" argument.

A system that allowed "proofs" of contradictions would also be worthless. Any statement can be made an indirect-proof assumption. If our system allowed us to derive instances of '$p \cdot \sim p$' as theorems, *any* indirect proof could always be ended, since '$p \cdot \sim p$' can always be derived from p and $\sim p$ by using conjunction. Hence, *any* statement whatsoever could be "proved" if our system allowed us to derive instances of '$p \cdot \sim p$'.

Theorems are statements that are derived by using a deductive system. Statements that make claims about deductive systems are called "metatheorems."

DEFINITION 9.5

A *metatheorem* is a derived statement about a deductive system.

We know that ND is sound, since we know that all applications of its inferences are truth preserving. Chapters 4 and 5 justified each of our inferences in terms of preserving truth. No applications of ND's inferences permit us to derive false statements from true statements. Since no argument that can be proved by using ND can have all true premises and a false conclusion, ND is sound.

METATHEOREM 1

ND is a sound deductive system.

We know from section I of this chapter that only tautologies are theorems of ND. Since any instance of '$p \cdot \sim p$' is self-contradictory and not a tautology, we know that no instance of '$p \cdot \sim p$' is derivable as a theorem of ND. But if instances of p and $\sim p$ were derivable in ND, then, by using conjunction, an instance of '$p \cdot \sim p$' *would* be derivable in ND. Hence, instances of both p and $\sim p$ are not derivable in ND. ND is a consistent deductive system.

METATHEOREM 2

ND is a consistent deductive system.

B. System Completeness

In addition to being sound and consistent, a deductive system should also be complete for both arguments and statements.

A system of propositional logic is deductively complete for arguments if and only if it is capable of providing a formal proof for every valid propositional argument. (Definition 5.3.)

DEFINITION 9.6

A system of propositional logic is *deductively complete* for statements if and only if all truth-functional tautologies are theorems of the system.

We will prove that ND is deductively complete for both arguments and statements. First, we will show that ND is deductively complete for arguments if and only if ND is deductively complete for statements. Next, we will show that ND *is* deductively complete for statements. The completeness of ND for arguments follows from its completeness for statements.

i. Completeness for Arguments and Statements

If ND is deductively complete for arguments, then ND is deductively complete for statements.

Proof

Our proof takes the form of a reductio ad absurdum. We will show that it is *impossible* for ND to be deductively complete for arguments and not be deductively complete for statements.

1. Assume that ND is deductively complete for arguments, but is not deductively complete for statements. If ND is not deductively complete for statements, then there must be some tautology, T, that is not a theorem of ND.

2. Any argument whose conclusion is a tautology is valid, since if it is impossible for an argument's conclusion to be false, then it is impossible for all of its premises to be true and its conclusion false. (If there is no line of a truth table such that the conclusion is false, then there is no line of a truth table such that all of the premises are true and the conclusion false.) Hence, the following argument must be valid:

$$\frac{A \supset A}{\therefore T}$$

3. Since the above argument is valid and, by assumption, ND is deductively complete for arguments, the above argument must be provable in ND. But if there is a proof of the above argument in ND, then there must be a proof, by making '$A \supset A$' a conditional-proof assumption, of the following statement in ND:

$(A \supset A) \supset T$

4. '$A \supset A$' is a theorem of ND (see number 1, Exercises III of this chapter). By using modus ponens with '$A \supset A$' and the statement in step 3 above, there is a formal proof of T and T *is* a theorem of ND. Hence:

If ND is deductively complete for arguments, then ND is deductively complete for statements.

Now we will show that:

If ND is deductively complete for statements, then ND is deductively complete for arguments.

Proof

Assume that ND is deductively complete for statements and that some argument whose premises are $P_1, P_2, P_3 \ldots$ and whose conclusion is some statement C, is valid:

P_1
P_2
P_3
.
.
.
$\overline{\therefore C}$

Then a conditional of the following form must be tautologous, and hence, by assumption, derivable in ND:

$[(P_1 \cdot P_2) \cdot P_3 \cdot \ldots] \supset C$

There *must* be a formal proof for the valid argument in ND. The reason for this is that the argument's premises can always be conjoined in a formal proof to derive the antecedent of the above conditional. Since the conditional is derivable, C is derivable by using modus ponens with the conditional and the conjunction that results from conjoining the argument's premises.

Hence:

> **If ND is deductively complete for statements, then ND is deductively complete for arguments.**

Metatheorem 3 follows from the two previous proofs.

METATHEOREM 3

ND is deductively complete for arguments if and only if ND is deductively complete for statements.

---

ii. Completeness for Statements

In order to show that ND is deductively complete for statements, we have to show that *all* truth-functional tautologies are theorems of ND. In order to do this, we need a way to determine when statements are in what is called "conjunctive normal form."

a. Conjunctive Normal Form

DEFINITION 9.7

A statement is in *conjunctive normal form* if and only if (1) its only connectives are the $\sim$, $\vee$, and $\cdot$, and (2) any negation symbols, $\sim$, are applied only to statement constants, and (3) the wedge, $\vee$, never has a disjunct of the form '$p \cdot q$'.

Some statements that are in conjunctive normal form contain only disjuncts, each of which is a statement constant or a negated statement constant. '$(A \vee B) \vee \sim C$' is in conjunctive normal form. It contains only disjuncts, each of which is a statement constant or a negated statement constant.

Some statements that are in conjunctive normal form consist of a series of conjuncts, such that each conjunct is a statement constant or the negation of a statement constant. '$A \cdot B$', '$\sim A \cdot B$', and '$\sim A \cdot \sim B$' are in conjunctive normal form. Each of them consists of a series of conjuncts, such that each conjunct is either a statement constant or the negation of a statement constant.

Some statements that are in conjunctive normal form consist of a series of conjuncts, such that each conjunct is a statement constant, or is the negation of a statement constant, or is a series that contains only disjuncts, each of which is a statement constant or the negation of a statement constant. '$(A \lor B) \cdot (C \lor D)$' is in conjunctive normal form. It consists of the series of conjuncts: '$(A \lor B)$' and '$(C \lor D)$'. Each conjunct is a series that contains only disjuncts, each of which is a statement constant.

'$(\sim A \lor B) \cdot (C \lor \sim D)$' is also in conjunctive normal form. It consists of the series of conjuncts: '$(\sim A \lor B)$' and '$(C \lor \sim D)$'. Each conjunct is a series that contains only disjuncts, each of which is a statement constant or the negation of a statement constant.

'$[(\sim A \lor B) \lor (\sim C \lor D)] \cdot \{(E \lor C) \cdot [C \lor (D \lor E)]\}$' is in conjunctive normal form. It consists of the series of conjuncts: '$[(\sim A \lor B) \lor (\sim C \lor D)]$', '$(E \lor C)$', and '$[C \lor (D \lor E)]$'. Each conjunct is a series that contains only disjuncts, each of which is a statement constant or the negation of a statement constant.

Since it contains the horseshoe, '$A \supset (B \lor C)$' is *not* in conjunctive normal form. '$\sim(A \lor B) \cdot C$' is *not* in conjunctive normal form, since one conjunct is the negation of the compound statement '$(A \lor B)$'. '$A \lor (B \cdot C)$' is *not* in conjunctive normal form, since it is not a series of conjuncts.

To get a better feel for conjunctive normal form as it is used in the coming completeness proof, we will temporarily ignore all punctuation in strings of conjuncts and strings of disjuncts. Temporarily, '$A \lor B \lor C \lor D \lor \ldots$' and '$A \cdot B \cdot C \cdot D \cdot \ldots$' will be acceptable expressions. Instead of '$[(A \lor \sim B) \lor (C \lor D)] \cdot E$', we will write '$(A \lor \sim B \lor C \lor D) \cdot E$'. Instead of '$[(\sim A \lor B) \lor (\sim C \lor D)] \cdot \{(E \lor C) \cdot [C \lor (D \lor E)]\}$', we will write '$(\sim A \lor B \lor \sim C \lor D) \cdot (E \lor C) \cdot (C \lor D \lor E)$'.

b. Tautologies That Are in Conjunctive Normal Form   Until now, we have used p, q, r, and so on, for our statement variables. But a series of conjuncts can have any number of members. In order more clearly to indicate strings of conjuncts and disjuncts, we will subscript p to indicate our statement variables. Our new statement variables are p_1, p_2, p_3, and so on.

Our completeness proof requires us to focus on tautologies. A series of conjuncts is true if and only if *each* conjunct is true. '$p_1 \cdot p_2 \cdot \ldots \cdot p_n$' is true if and only if each conjunct is true.

Also:

A series of conjuncts is tautologous if and only if each conjunct is tautologous.

Imagine that there are truth-value assignments such that some statement, p_1, is false. The conjunction of p_1 with any other statement will be false, and that statement conjoined with any other statement will be false, and . . . . Hence, '$p_1 \cdot p_2 \cdot \ldots \cdot p_n$' is a tautology if and only if *each* of p_1, p_2, through p_n is a tautology.

Neither statement constants nor negated statement constants are tautologies. Hence:

> *If a series that contains only disjuncts is tautologous, it must contain both a statement constant and the negation of that statement constant. Otherwise, there will be a truth-value assignment such that each disjunct, and hence the disjunction, is false.*

Suppose we let PCNF indicate that P is a statement in conjunctive normal form. It follows that:

> *If PCNF is tautologous and consists of the conjunction '$p_1 \cdot p_2 \cdot \ldots \cdot p_n$, each p must be tautologous. Each p must be a series of disjuncts that includes both a statement constant and its negation.*

'$A \lor \sim A$' is in conjunctive normal form and is a tautology, since it includes both a statement constant, A, and its negation.

'$(A \lor \sim A) \cdot (\sim B \lor B) \cdot (C \lor B \lor \sim C)$' is in conjunctive normal form and is tautologous, since each conjunct includes both a statement constant and its negation. Similarly, '$(\sim A \lor \sim B \lor A) \cdot (\sim A \lor \sim B \lor B)$' is in conjunctive normal form and is tautologous. '$(\sim A \lor \sim B \lor A)$' includes the statement constant A and its negation. '$(\sim A \lor \sim B \lor B)$' includes the statement constant B and its negation.

'$(A \lor \sim B) \cdot (\sim B \lor B)$' is in conjunctive normal form, but it is not a tautology, since its first conjunct, '$(A \lor \sim B)$', does not contain both a statement constant and its negation.

'$(\sim A \lor \sim B \lor A) \cdot (\sim A \lor \sim B \lor C)$' is in conjunctive normal form, but it is not a tautology. Its second conjunct, '$(\sim A \lor \sim B \lor C)$', does not contain a statement constant and its negation.

Exercises V

Each of the following statements is in conjunctive normal form. Determine which are tautologies, *without constructing truth tables*.

*1. $C \lor \sim B \lor B$

2. $(A \lor \sim A) \cdot (A \lor \sim B)$

*3. $(\sim A \lor \sim B \lor A \lor C) \cdot (A \lor \sim B \lor A)$

4. $\sim A \lor B \lor \sim A \lor \sim B$

*5. $(C \lor B \lor \sim C) \cdot (A \lor \sim A) \cdot (\sim B \lor B)$

6. $(C \lor B \lor \sim C \lor A \lor \sim A) \cdot (\sim B \lor C \lor \sim B \lor D) \cdot (D \lor \sim D)$

c. The Proof   Our completeness proof for ND will be presented in three stages. The following is an outline of the overall strategy behind the proof.

First, we show that for *any* statement P_1, there is a statement in conjunctive normal form, $P_2\text{CNF}$ such that '$P_1 \supset P_2\text{CNF}$' and '$P_2\text{CNF} \supset P_1$' are both theorems of ND. This result will be called "metatheorem 4." Intuitively, this first step allows us to show that if a statement is a theorem of ND, then an equivalent statement in conjunctive normal form is also a theorem of ND, and conversely.

Suppose that P_1 is a theorem of ND. Then metatheorem 4 states that there is a P_2 which is in conjunctive normal form, such that '$P_1 \supset P_2$' is a theorem of ND. By modus ponens, if '$P_1 \supset P_2$' and P_1 are theorems of ND, then P_2 is a theorem of ND. Similarly, if P_2 is in conjunctive normal form and '$P_2 \supset P_1$' and P_2 are theorems of ND, then P_1 is a theorem of ND.

Second, every tautology that is in conjunctive normal form is a theorem of ND. This result will be called "metatheorem 5."

Third, every tautology is a theorem of ND. This result will be called "metatheorem 6."

If a tautology is in conjunctive normal form, then, by the second step above, it is a theorem of ND. If any tautology P_1 is not in conjunctive normal form, then there is an equivalent tautology, $P_2\text{CNF}$, that is in conjunctive normal form. The equivalent tautology in conjunctive normal form is a theorem of ND, since all tautologies in conjunctive normal form are theorems of ND. Since the conjunctive-normal-form tautology, $P_2\text{CNF}$, and '$P_2\text{CNF} \supset P_1$' (by the first step above) are theorems of ND, P_1 is a theorem of ND.

Since the following proof frequently requires us to claim that a given statement is a theorem of ND, we will introduce a new symbol, '⊢', called the "turnstile," to express 'is a theorem of'. 'ND⊢ *p*' is read: "*p* is a theorem of ND."

METATHEOREM 4

Let $P_1\text{CNF}$ indicate that P_1 is a statement in conjunctive normal form. For any statement P_2, there is a statement P_1, such that $P_1\text{CNF}$; and such that both '$P_1 \supset P_2$' and '$P_2 \supset P_1$' are theorems of ND.

Proof

1. Suppose that P_2 is *already* in conjunctive normal form (CNF). In this case the result follows immediately, since for *any* statement P_2, '$P_2 \supset P_2$' is a theorem of ND. The reason for this is that any

statement P_2 can be made a conditional-proof assumption. Ending the conditional proof will result in the derivation of '$P_2 \supset P_2$'.

> *1. P_2 C.P.A.*

2. $P_2 \supset P_2$ C.P. 1

Hence, ND⊢ $P_2 \supset P_2$.

2. Suppose, however, that P_2 is a statement that is not in CNF. Let us make P_2 a conditional-proof assumption. We will now show how to derive, from the assumption of P_2, a statement P_1, such that P_1CNF. Since our conditional proof can be ended at this point, we will have shown that '$P_2 \supset P_1$CNF' is derivable. There are four cases to consider.

    a. P_2 might fail to be in CNF by not consisting of only disjuncts and/or conjuncts. P_2 might contain the '$\supset$' connective and/or the '$\equiv$' connective.

        All occurrences of the '$\equiv$' can be eliminated by applications of material equivalence. All occurrences of the '$\supset$' can be eliminated by applications of wedge equivalence. Thus, from P_2 we can derive a statement without the '$\supset$' connective and/or the '$\equiv$' connective.

        For example, suppose that P_2 is '$(A \supset B) \equiv (\sim B \supset \sim A)$'.

1. $(A \supset B) \equiv (\sim B \supset \sim A)$ C.P.A.

2. $[(A \supset B) \supset (\sim B \supset \sim A)] \cdot [(\sim B \supset \sim A) \supset (A \supset B)]$ M.E. 1

3. $[\sim(\sim A \lor B) \lor (\sim\sim B \lor \sim A)] \cdot [\sim(\sim\sim B \lor \sim A) \lor (\sim A \lor B)]$ W.E. applied on all horseshoes

Notice that line 3 has only the connectives that are allowed for statements that are in conjunctive normal form.

    b. P_2, or the result of (a) above, might fail to be in CNF by having more than one tilde applied to a statement. Pairs of tildes can always be eliminated in a formal proof by applying double negation. Thus, from P_2 we can derive a statement that does not have more than one tilde applied to any statement.

        For example:

1. $(A \supset B) \equiv (\sim B \supset \sim A)$ C.P.A.

2. $[(A \supset B) \supset (\sim B \supset \sim A)] \cdot [(\sim B \supset \sim A) \supset (A \supset B)]$ M.E. 1

3. $[\sim(\sim A \lor B) \lor (\sim\sim B \lor \sim A)] \cdot [\sim(\sim\sim B \lor \sim A) \lor (\sim A \lor B)]$ W.E. applied on all horseshoes

4. $[\sim(\sim A \lor B) \lor (B \lor \sim A)] \cdot [\sim(B \lor \sim A) \lor (\sim A \lor B)]$ D.N. 3

c. P_2, or the result of (a) and (b) above, might have tildes that are applied to either conjunctions or disjunctions, rather than to statement constants. De Morgan's laws and double negation can always be applied so that the result has tildes that *are* only applied to statement constants. All statements of the form '$\sim(p_1 \cdot p_2)$' can be replaced with statements of the form '$\sim p_1 \lor \sim p_2$'. All statements of the form '$\sim(p_1 \lor p_2)$' can be replaced with statements of the form '$\sim p_1 \cdot \sim p_2$'. Thus, from P_2 we can derive a statement that does not have tildes applied to either conjunctions or disjunctions.

For example:

1. $(A \supset B) \equiv (\sim B \supset \sim A)$ C.P.A.
2. $[(A \supset B) \supset (\sim B \supset \sim A)] \cdot [(\sim B \supset \sim A) \supset (A \supset B)]$ M.E. 1
3. $[\sim(\sim A \lor B) \lor (\sim\sim B \lor \sim A)] \cdot [\sim(\sim\sim B \lor \sim A) \lor (\sim A \lor B)]$ W.E. applied on 2
4. $[\sim(\sim A \lor B) \lor (B \lor \sim A)] \cdot [\sim(B \lor \sim A) \lor (\sim A \lor B)]$ D.N. 3
5. $[(A \cdot \sim B) \lor (B \lor \sim A)] \cdot [(\sim B \cdot A) \lor (\sim A \lor B)]$ D.M. and D.N. applied on 4

d. P_2, or the result of (a), (b), (c) above, might fail to be in CNF by not consisting of a series of *conjuncts*. In this case, the statement must have one or both of the following forms: '$p_1 \lor (p_2 \cdot p_3)$' or '$(p_1 \cdot p_2) \lor p_3$'.

By applying commutation, all occurrences of '$(p_1 \cdot p_2) \lor p_3$' can be replaced with '$p_3 \lor (p_1 \cdot p_2)$'.

By applying distribution, all occurrences of '$p_1 \lor (p_2 \cdot p_3)$' can be replaced with '$(p_1 \lor p_2) \cdot (p_1 \lor p_3)$', which is in CNF. Thus, from P_2 we can derive a statement that does consist of a series of conjuncts.

For example:

1. $(A \supset B) \equiv (\sim B \supset \sim A)$ C.P.A.
2. $[(A \supset B) \supset (\sim B \supset \sim A)] \cdot [(\sim B \supset \sim A) \supset (A \supset B)]$ M.E. 1
3. $[\sim(\sim A \lor B) \lor (\sim\sim B \lor \sim A)] \cdot [\sim(\sim\sim B \lor \sim A) \lor (\sim A \lor B)]$ W.E. applied on 2
4. $[\sim(\sim A \lor B) \lor (B \lor \sim A)] \cdot [\sim(B \lor \sim A) \lor (\sim A \lor B)]$ D.N. 3
5. $[(A \cdot \sim B) \lor (B \lor \sim A)] \cdot [(\sim B \cdot A) \lor (\sim A \lor B)]$ D.M. and D.N. applied on 4
6. $\{[B \lor \sim A) \lor A] \cdot [(B \lor \sim A) \lor \sim B]\} \cdot \{[(\sim A \lor B) \lor \sim B] \cdot [(\sim A \lor B) \lor A]\}$ Comm. and Dist. applied on 5

Notice that line 6 is in conjunctive normal form.

As in the last example, by repeatedly applying the procedures (a), (b), (c), and (d) we will eventually derive a statement P_1 that is in conjunctive normal form from the statement P_2. By ending the conditional proof that we started with the assumption of P_2, we can derive '$P_2 \supset P_1\text{CNF}$'.

3. Hence, if $P_1\text{CNF}$ indicates that P_1 is a statement in conjunctive normal form, then for any statement P_2, there is a statement P_1 such that $P_1\text{CNF}$ and ND⊢ $P_2 \supset P_1$.

For example:

---

1. $(A \supset B) \equiv (\sim B \supset \sim A)$ *C.P.A.*

2. $[(A \supset B) \supset (\sim B \supset \sim A)] \cdot [(\sim B \supset \sim A) \supset (A \supset B)]$ *M.E. 1*

3. $[\sim(\sim A \lor B) \lor (\sim\sim B \lor \sim A] \cdot [\sim(\sim\sim B \lor \sim A) \lor (\sim A \lor B)]$ *W.E. applied on 2*

4. $[\sim(\sim A \lor B) \lor (B \lor \sim A)] \cdot [\sim(B \lor \sim A) \lor (\sim A \lor B)]$ *D.N. 3*

5. $[(A \cdot \sim B) \lor (B \lor \sim A)] \cdot [(\sim B \cdot A) \lor (\sim A \lor B)]$ *D.M. and D.N. applied on 4*

6. $\{[B \lor \sim A) \lor A] \cdot [(B \lor \sim A) \lor \sim B]\} \cdot \{[(\sim A \lor B) \lor \sim B] \cdot [(\sim A \lor B) \lor A]\}$ *Comm. and Dist. applied on 5*

---

7. $[(A \supset B) \equiv (\sim B \supset \sim A)] \supset \big\{\{[B \lor \sim A) \lor A] \cdot [(B \lor \sim A) \lor \sim B]\} \cdot \{[(\sim A \lor B) \lor \sim B] \cdot [(\sim A \lor B) \lor A]\}\big\}$ *C.P. 1–6*

It is crucial to notice that (a) through (d) above are all carried out by applying our equivalence inferential forms. Since our equivalence inferential forms can be applied in both directions, we could have made P_1 our conditional-proof assumption and derived the statement P_2. Hence, ND⊢ $P_2 \supset P_1$. Metatheorem 4 has been proved!

Now we will show that *all* CNF tautologies are theorems of ND. This result, metatheorem 5, will be established by showing that each conjunct (of the series of conjuncts) of any CNF tautology must be a theorem of ND. The conjunction—the CNF tautology—is derivable by successive applications of conjunction.

METATHEOREM 5

Every $P_1\text{CNF}$ tautology is a theorem of ND.

Proof

Since $P_1\text{CNF}$ is a tautology that is in CNF, we know that P_1 is a series of disjuncts that include a statement constant and its negation, or P_1 consists of the conjunction '$p_1 \cdot p_2 \cdot \ldots \cdot p_n$', of which each p is a series of disjuncts that include both a statement constant and its negation.

1. Any statement of the form '$p \lor {\sim}p$' is a theorem of ND. For any statement p:

   > *1. p C.P.A.*

   2. $p \supset p$ C.P. 1
   3. ${\sim}p \lor p$ W.E. 2
   4. $p \lor {\sim}p$ Comm. 3

   Hence, '$A \lor {\sim}A$', '$B \lor {\sim}B$', '$C \lor {\sim}C$', and so on, are all theorems of ND. All disjunctions of a statement constant and its negation are theorems of ND.

2. Addition enables us to add *any* statement to a statement that is the disjunction of a statement constant and its negation. That is, for any statement q and any statement constant p, we can use addition and derive '$(p \lor {\sim}p) \lor q$' as a theorem of ND.

3. We can always let q be the remaining *disjuncts* of any conjunct, p_1, or p_2, or $\ldots p_n$, of the conjunction '$p_1 \cdot p_2 \cdot \ldots \cdot p_n$'. Hence, bearing in mind that we repeatedly apply commutation and association, we know that any series of disjuncts that can make up any conjunct of $P_1\text{CNF}$ is a theorem of ND. Of course, the series of disjuncts that is derived as above might not be in the same order, and might not have the same punctuation, as is required for one of $P_1\text{CNF}$'s conjuncts. Successive applications of commutation and association will, however, allow us to derive any required order and punctuation.

4. Any conjunction of $P_1\text{CNF}$'s conjuncts, and hence any $P_1\text{CNF}$, can be derived by using conjunction with the statements that are derived in step 3.

   For example, '$(B \lor {\sim}A) \lor A$' is one of the conjuncts of the $P_1\text{CNF}$ in the example for metatheorem 4. It can be derived as follows:

   1. $A \lor {\sim}A$ theorem of ND
   2. $(A \lor {\sim}A) \lor B$ Add. 1
   3. $A \lor ({\sim}A \lor B)$ Assoc. 2
   4. $({\sim}A \lor B) \lor A$ Comm. 3
   5. $(B \lor {\sim}A) \lor A$ Comm. 4

The other conjuncts can be derived in a similar fashion. Conjoining them will derive P_1CNF.

Metatheorem 5 has been established for ND. Metatheorem 6 claims that ND is deductively complete for *all* truth-functional tautologies.

METATHEOREM 6

Any truth-functional tautology, P_1, is a theorem of ND.

Proof

Suppose that P_1 is a tautology. P_1 is either in conjunctive normal form or it is not. If P_1CNF, then metatheorem 5 gives the result. If P_1 is not in conjunctive normal form, then, by metatheorem 4, there is a statement P_2 such that P_2CNF and ND⊢ $P_2 \supset P_1$ and ND⊢ $P_1 \supset P_2$. It is obvious that P_1 and P_2 are logically equivalent and that P_1 is a tautology if and only if P_2 is a tautology. Hence, P_2CNF is a tautology. From metatheorem 5, we know that P_2CNF is a theorem of ND. Since ND⊢ $P_2 \supset P_1$, we can derive, by using modus ponens, that ND⊢ P_1. Hence, *any* truth-functional tautology P_1 is a theorem of ND.

Exercises VI

Metatheorems 4, 5, and 6 can be seen as outlining a method for deriving *any* tautology in ND. First, apply the steps outlined in the proof of metatheorem 4 to each of the following statements, and derive a logically equivalent statement in CNF. Next, apply the steps outlined in the proof of metatheorem 5 to derive each of your CNF statements as theorems of ND.

*1. $A \supset (B \supset A)$

2. $\sim\!A \supset (A \supset B)$

3. $[(A \cdot B) \supset C] \supset [A \supset (B \supset C)]$

4. $(A \supset B) \supset [(A \cdot C) \supset B]$

*5. $(A \cdot B) \supset [(A \equiv B) \vee C]$

Concept Reviews

1. Review metatheorems 3 and 6, and derive metatheorem 7.

METATHEOREM 7

ND is deductively complete for truth-functional arguments.

---

2. Can a deductive system be complete without being sound? Use the definitions to explain and justify your answer.
3. Can a deductive system be sound without being complete? Use the definitions to explain and justify your answer.

C. ND's Failings

Formal systems possess aesthetic qualities. Some systems are more elegant than others, not in terms of the appearance of their horseshoes, but in terms of the simplicity of their rules and in the way that they can be used to generate proofs. ND, from an aesthetic standpoint, is too complex. It contains more rules than are needed. Everything else being equal, systems that are developed from "independent" inferential forms are aesthetically better.

DEFINITION 9.8

An inferential form is *independent* of a group of other inferential forms if and only if it cannot be derived from them.

DEFINITION 9.9

An inferential form is *dependent* on a group of inferential forms if and only if it can be derived from them.

When a system contains only independent inferences, each of them is essential. Removing *any* of them will reduce the system's ability to prove arguments. Not all of the inferences in ND are independent. Indirect proof and the valid inferential forms of Chapter 5 were *developed* as dependent inferences. Their justifications show that any argument that might be proved with them could have been proved without them.

We could, of course, eliminate inferences from ND until we arrived at a system that remained complete and was entirely made up of independent inferences. The resulting system would, however, feel awkward.

Proving independence is a different sort of process from proving dependence. As we have seen, dependence can be established by showing that an inference can be established as a derived rule. Independence proofs require showing that an inference can*not* be derived from a set of inferences.

Independence proofs, as well as numerous other issues in metalogic, are usually treated in more advanced logic texts.

An Alternative Account of Statements and Propositions

Our Chapter 1 account of statements and propositions is adequate for an introduction to logic, but it oversimplifies some important philosophical issues. The word "sentence" is ambiguous in ordinary English. One meaning refers to a series of ink marks on paper. The previous group of ink marks can be called a sentence. With this meaning, sentences also consist of chalk marks on a board or the sounds that we hear. This meaning of 'sentence' refers to what is actually before us. Logicians call the "what is actually seen or heard" meaning of 'sentence' a "sentence token."

Arguments do *not* consist of sentence tokens. The same statement (or proposition) can appear more than once in an argument, and the same statement (or proposition) can be used to fill a number of circle or square locations in creating an argument. But the same group of *ink marks* can never appear more than once. Each group of ink marks (or chalk marks, or sounds) is unique. We cannot put the same ink marks in more than one place any more than we can put a car in more than one place!

Another ordinary English meaning of 'sentence' roughly characterizes a sentence as a "repeatable unit of language." With this meaning, two people can write, read, and verbalize the same sentence. The following two groups of ink marks express the same sentence.

Hitler committed suicide.
Hitler committed suicide.

Logicians call the "repeatable unit of language" meaning of 'sentence' a "sentence type." Some logicians claim that arguments consist of sentence types, but there are problems with this approach. Consider the following examples.

EXAMPLE 1

If Germany lost World War II, then Hitler committed suicide.
It is false that Hitler committed suicide.
Hence, it is false that Germany lost World War II.

EXAMPLE 2

If Germany lost World War II, then Hitler killed himself.
It is false that Hitler killed himself.
Hence, it is false that Germany lost World War II.

Examples 1 and 2 above have different words, and so they have different sentence types. If we define 'statement' as "sentence type," then examples 1 and 2 present *different arguments*. Even so, there is a point in saying that they express the same ideas. If we consider the two above examples to express different arguments, then we need a way to notice similarities between them.

Another approach considers examples 1 and 2 as two expressions of *the same argument*. A statement or proposition is what is attached to, or is conveyed by, a declarative sentence. Provided that sentences in different languages can convey the same information, the same argument can even be expressed in different languages. The following two sentences could be used to express part of the same argument. In Spanish:

Las puertas estan cerradas con las llaves adentro.

In English:

The keys are locked inside the car.

This last meaning of 'statement' or 'proposition' can be defined as follows.

DEFINITION A.1

A *statement* (or *proposition*) is what is claimed to be so by a declarative sentence.

But what is it that is "claimed to be so" by declarative sentences? Is it reasonable to ask what is "claimed to be so" in general terms, or can we only ask what "is claimed to be so" for particular sentences? We have hardly solved the philosophical controversy!

Although logicians disagree on how statements are related to language, and exactly what a statement is, they do agree that statements are either true or false. They also agree that arguments consist of statements. Although the areas of disagreement are significant, the areas of agreement are sufficient to develop logic in this introductory textbook.[1]

---

[1]For additional readings on this subject, as well as some additional discussion, see "Propositions, Judgments, Sentences, and Statements," in *The Encyclopedia of Philosophy*, ed. Paul Edwards (New York: Macmillan, 1967), 494–504.

Justification of Conditional Proof

I Formal Proofs That Have One Conditional Proof

With conditional proof we have a *procedure* to justify, rather than a valid argument form. Our justification should show that conditional proof can only be used to prove valid arguments. We should show that all permissible applications of conditional proof preserve truth.

Since our justification of conditional proof must apply to all of its possible applications, it is important that our justification should not depend on whether an initial argument has a particular number of premises. We will assume that conditional proof is applied when an argument has the premises $P_1, P_2, \ldots, P_n$.

Compare the following two arguments:

ARGUMENT A	ARGUMENT B
P_1	P_1
P_2	P_2
.	.
.	.
.	.
P_n	P_n
$\therefore A \supset B$	A
	$\therefore B$

Since our conditional-proof procedure adds a desired antecedent as a usable premise and then derives the consequent, it has the effect of converting an argument such as argument A to an argument such as argument B. The B-type argument is next proved valid. Ending the conditional proof has us conclude that the A-type argument is valid.

Notice that exactly the same conditions determine whether arguments of type A and type B are invalid. Arguments such as A and B are invalid if and only if there is a line of a truth table such that $P_1, P_2 \ldots, P_n$ and A are all true, and B is false.

> *The argument that is proved valid after making a conditional-proof assumption is valid if and only if the argument with the conclusion that is derived by using conditional proof is valid.*

If we can prove that an argument such as B is valid, we know that an argument such as A must be valid as well. Our conditional-proof procedure merely provides a mechanism that enables us to switch between two arguments that are valid under exactly the same conditions.

II   Formal Proofs with Multiple Applications of Conditional Proof

The above justification of conditional proof can readily be applied to formal proofs that have a series of independent conditional proofs. If each application of conditional proof preserves truth, then a series of independent applications must preserve truth. But how can we justify using nested conditional proofs—conditional proofs that are contained one within another?

Consider the following three arguments:

ARGUMENT C	ARGUMENT D	ARGUMENT E
P_1	P_1	P_1
P_2	P_2	P_2
.	.	.
.	.	.
.	.	.
P_n	P_n	P_n
$\therefore A \supset (B \supset C)$	A	A
	$\therefore B \supset C$	B
		$\therefore C$

Our justification of conditional proof for formal proofs that have one conditional proof shows us that an argument such as C is valid if and only if an argument such as D is valid. (Imagine that we had used '$B \supset C$' instead of B in arguments A and B above.) By the same reasoning as in section I, an argument such as D is valid if and only if an argument such as E is valid. Arguments C, D, and E must all be valid or must all be invalid. Hence, an argument such as C is valid if and only if an argument such as E is valid.

Formal proofs that have one conditional proof entirely contained within another conditional proof can be seen as switching from an argument such as C to an argument such as E. The E-type argument is next proved valid. When both conditional proofs are ended, our conditional-proof procedure has us conclude that the C-type argument is valid.

Since identical conditions determine whether arguments such as C and E are valid, we are justified in concluding that an argument such as C is valid once we have proved that an argument such as E is valid.

Admittedly, one conditional proof can be contained within another conditional proof that is contained within another conditional proof, and so on. Even so, our conditional-proof method can always be seen as providing a means to construct a formal proof for an argument that can be proved valid without using conditional proof. The argument that is proved with conditional proof is valid if and only if the one that can be proved without it is valid. Hence, conditional proof is an acceptable formal proof procedure.

Concept Reviews

1. Suppose that nested conditional proofs are used to provide a formal proof for the following argument:

P_1
P_2
.
.
.
P_n
$\therefore A \supset [B \supset (C \supset D)]$

What truth-values must be possible for P_1, P_2, ... P_n, and A, B, C, and D, if and only if the above argument is invalid? What argument is proved valid after making the required conditional-proof assumptions? Show that the argument above is valid if and only if the argument that is proved after making the conditional-proof assumptions is valid.

2. Our justification for conditional proof applies to conditional proofs that are independent of one another, and that are nested one within another. Is it necessary to justify conditional proofs that are partially contained within one another? Why?

APPENDIX C

Glossary of All Defined Terms

Antecedent statement The statement that follows 'if' in a conditional of the form 'if p then q' is called the *antecedent* statement.

Argument An *argument* consists of a group of statements, such that one of them is considered to be the conclusion. The conclusion is the statement intended to follow from the other statements that are presented as reasons (or premisses) for it.

Argument form An *argument form* is a group of statement forms, such that one of them is presented as following from the others.

Asymmetrical relations A dyadic relation is *asymmetrical* if and only if, whenever one individual has the relation to a second individual, then the second individual does not have the relation to the first individual.

Charity, completed with An enthymeme has been *completed with charity* if and only if (1) the completion makes the resulting argument deductively valid and (2) the argument's premisses are liable to be accepted.

Closed truth tree path A truth tree path is *closed* if and only if it contains, including the statement forms in the tree's trunk, a statement form and the negation of the same statement form.

Completed with charity See *charity, completed with*.

Complete for arguments, deductive system A system of propositional logic is *deductively complete* for arguments if and only if it is capable of providing a formal proof for every valid propositional argument.

Complete for statements, deductive system A system of propositional logic is *deductively complete* for statements if and only if all truth-functional tautologies are theorems of the system.

Compound statement A *compound statement* is any statement that has a statement as a part.

Conjunctive normal form A statement is in *conjunctive normal form* if and only if (1) its only connectives are the $\sim$, $\vee$, and $\cdot$, and (2) any negation symbols, $\sim$, are applied only to statement constants, and (3) the wedge, $\vee$, never has a disjunct of the form '$p \cdot q$'.

Conjuncts The statements that are combined with 'and' to form a conjunction are called *conjuncts*.

Connective The horseshoe, dot, wedge, tilde, and triple bar are *connectives*.

Consequent statement The statement that follows 'then' in a conditional of the form 'if p then q' is called the *consequent* statement.

Consistent deductive system A deductive system is *consistent* if and only if two contradictory statements—statements that are instances of both p and $\sim p$—cannot be derived as theorems.

Consistent set of statement forms A set of statement forms is *consistent* if and only if it is possible for all of its members to be true.

Constant See *statement constant, predicate constant, individual constant*.

Contingent statement A truth-functional statement is *contingent* if and only if it is a parallel-instance of a contingent statement form.

Contingent statement form A truth-functional statement form is *contingent* if and only if it is true on at least one line of its truth table and false on at least one line of its truth table.

Contradictory statements Two statements are *contradictories* (of one another) when the truth of one statement guarantees the falsity of the other, and the falsity of one statement guarantees the truth of the other.

Contrary statements Two statements are *contraries* (of one another) when the truth of one statement guarantees the falsity of the other, but the falsity of one statement does not guarantee the truth of the other.

Deductively invalid argument An argument is *deductively invalid* if and only if its underlying form or structure does *not* guarantee that if its premises are all true, then so is its conclusion.

Deductively invalid argument form An argument form is *deductively invalid* if and only if it is possible for it to have all true premises and a false conclusion.

Deductively valid argument An argument is *deductively valid* if and only if its underlying form or structure guarantees that if its premises are all true, then so is its conclusion.

Deductively valid argument form An argument form is *deductively valid* if and only if it is impossible for it to have all true premises and a false conclusion.

Dependent inferential form An inferential form is *dependent* on a group of inferential forms if and only if it can be derived from them.

Derived inference rule A *derived inference rule* in a deductive system that has a set of rules that are regarded as basic is an inference rule that is justified by showing that all of its derivations can be accomplished with the set of basic inference rules.

Derived statement A statement has been *derived* in a formal proof from previous statements if and only if it is an instance of an inferential form's conclusion, and previous statements are instances of the inferential form's premises.

Disjuncts The statements that are combined with 'or' to form a disjunction are called *disjuncts*.

Enthymeme   An *enthymeme* is an incompletely stated argument.

Equivalence   See *material equivalence, logical equivalence*.

Equivalence inferential form   A logical equivalence is an *equivalence inferential form* if and only if it is one of the following:

De Morgan's law (D.M.)

$\sim(p \cdot q) :: \sim p \lor \sim q$

$\sim(p \lor q) :: \sim p \cdot \sim q$

Double negation (D.N.)

$p :: \sim\sim p$

Wedge equivalence (W.E.)

$p \supset q :: \sim p \lor q$

Commutation (Comm.)

$p \cdot q :: q \cdot p$

$p \lor q :: q \lor p$

Association (Assoc.)

$p \cdot (q \cdot r) :: (p \cdot q) \cdot r$

$p \lor (q \lor r) :: (p \lor q) \lor r$

Duplication (Du.)

$p :: p \lor p$

$p :: p \cdot p$

Material equivalence (M.E.)

$p \equiv q :: (p \supset q) \cdot (q \supset p)$

Distribution (Dist.)

$p \lor (q \cdot r) :: (p \lor q) \cdot (p \lor r)$

$p \cdot (q \lor r) :: (p \cdot q) \lor (p \cdot r)$

Exclusive 'or' statement   An *exclusive 'or' statement* expresses a disjunction of two statements in that it claims that one or the other of them is true. In addition, it denies (excludes the possibility) that both statements are true.

Existential import   A statement has *existential import* if and only if it claims that things of a given kind exist.

Existential quantification   A well-formed formula (WFF) is an *existential quantification* if and only if it begins with an existential quantifier whose scope is the entire remainder of the WFF.

Existential quantifier $\exists x$, $\exists y$, and $\exists z$ are *existential quantifiers*. They abbreviate "there is at least one individual in the universe, call it x (or y, or z), ..."

Existential statement   An *existential statement* affirms or denies a predicate of some individuals of a certain kind.

Forced assignment of variables   When we apply the partial-truth-table method, a variable has a *forced assignment* if and only if it must be specified true or it must be specified false so that the conclusion will be false or so that a premiss will be true.

Form   See *argument form, statement form.*

Formal proof   A *formal proof* for a given argument consists of statements that have been derived either from the argument's premises or from previously derived statements (or both), such that the last derived statement is the argument's conclusion.

General statement   A *general statement* makes a claim about members of a group (rather than about a particular individual).

Inclusive 'or' statement   An *inclusive 'or' statement* merely expresses a disjunction of the two component statements. It claims that one or the other statement (disjunct) is true. While not expressly saying so, it leaves open (that is, it includes) the possibility that both disjuncts might be true.

Inconsistent set of statement forms   A set of statement forms is *inconsistent* if and only if it is impossible for all of its members to be true.

Independent inferential form   An inferential form is *independent* of a group of other inferential forms if and only if it cannot be derived from them.

Individual   An *individual* is any particular thing that can be discussed in an argument.

Individual constant   An *individual constant* is any lower-case letter, from a to w, used to identify a particular individual.

Individual variable   The lower-case letters x, y, and z, called *individual variables*, are placeholders for individual constants.

Inductively strong (or weak) argument   An argument is *inductively strong* (or weak) in direct proportion to the likelihood of its conclusion being true on the assumption that its premises are true.

Inferential form   See *valid inferential form, equivalence inferential form.*

Instance of an argument form   An argument is an *instance of an argument form* if and only if the argument can be produced from the form by replacing the variables with statements. The same statement must replace a given variable throughout.

Instance of a statement form   A statement is an *instance of a statement form* if and only if the statement can be produced from the form by replacing the variables with statements. The same statement must replace a given variable throughout.

Intransitive relation   A dyadic relation is *intransitive* if and only if, whenever (1) one individual, x, has the relation to a second individual, y, and (2) the second individual, y, has the relation to a third individual, z, then the first individual, x, does not have the relation to the third individual, z.

Invalid argument form   See *deductively invalid argument form.*

Invalid argument in predicate logic   An argument in predicate logic is *invalid* if and only if, when one or more individuals are considered to exist, it is possible for the argument to have all true premises and a false conclusion.

Invalid argument in propositional logic   See *deductively invalid argument*.

Irreflexive relation   A dyadic relation is *irreflexive* if and only if nothing has the relation to itself.

Logic   *Logic* is the study of what makes arguments either good or bad. Logicians consider whether an argument's premises correctly support its conclusion.

Logical equivalence   Two statements are *logically equivalent* if and only if they must have the same truth-value, owing to their respective forms. Two statements are logically equivalent if and only if the assertion that they are materially equivalent is a tautology.

Major connective   The *major connective* is the connective that determines whether the statement, considered as a whole, is a negation, a disjunction, a conjunction, a conditional, or a biconditional.

Material equivalence   Two statements are *materially equivalent* if and only if they both have the same truth-value.

Member of a set   An object within a set is called a *member* (or element) of the set.

Metalogic   *Metalogic* is the critical examination of systems of logic.

Metatheorem   A *metatheorem* is a derived statement about a deductive system.

Model universe (or model)   A *model universe*, or *model*, is an imaginary universe that contains a limited number of countable things.

Monadic predicate   A *monadic predicate* is a predicate which is used to claim that an individual has a particular quality.

Multiple quantification   A well-formed formula in predicate logic that contains two or more quantifiers is called a *multiple quantification*.

Nonreflexive relation   A dyadic relation is *nonreflexive* if and only if it is neither reflexive nor irreflexive.

Nonsymmetrical relation   A dyadic relation is *nonsymmetrical* if and only if it is neither symmetrical nor asymmetrical.

Nontransitive relation   A dyadic relation is *nontransitive* if and only if it is neither transitive nor intransitive.

Open truth-tree path   A truth-tree path is *open* if and only if it is not closed.

Parallel-instance of an argument form   An argument is a *parallel-instance of an argument form* if and only if (1) the argument is an instance of the argument form, and (2) a unique simple statement is used for each variable.

Parallel-instance of a statement form   A statement is a *parallel-instance of a statement form* if and only if (1) the statement is an instance of the statement form, and (2) a unique simple statement is used for each variable.

Polyadic predicate   A *polyadic predicate* is a predicate which claims that a relation holds between two or more individuals.

Predicate   A *predicate* is an expression that is used to attribute a quality to an individual.

Predicate constant   A *predicate constant* is any capital letter, from A to Z, used to identify a particular predicate.

Proposition   See *statement*.

Quantification   See *unary quantification, multiple quantification, universal quantification, existential quantification*.

Reflexive relation   A dyadic relation is *reflexive* if and only if everything that takes part in the relation has the relation to itself.

Scope of a quantifier   The *scope of a quantifier* consists of the entire expression, as defined by parentheses, brackets, or braces, that directly follows it.

Self-contradiction   A truth-functional statement is a *self-contradiction* if and only if its form is self-contradictory.

Self-contradictory statement form   A truth-functional statement form is *self-contradictory* if and only if it is false on every line of its truth table.

Set   A *set* is a clearly defined collection of objects.

Simple statement   A *simple statement* is any statement that does not have a statement as a part.

Singular statement   A *singular statement* asserts or denies that an individual has a particular quality.

Sound argument   An argument is *sound* if and only if it is both deductively valid and has all true premises.

Sound deductive system   A deductive system is *sound* if and only if it only allows formal proofs to be constructed for valid arguments.

Statement   A *statement* (or *proposition*) is what is claimed to be so by a declarative sentence.

Statement constant   A *statement* (or *propositional*) *constant* is any capital letter, from A to Z, that is used to stand for a particular statement (or proposition).

Statement form   A *statement form* is any properly constructed artificial-language expression that contains statement variables but no statement constants.

Statement variable   A *statement variable* is any lower-case letter, from p to z, that is used as a placeholder for statements.

Symmetrical relation   A dyadic relation is *symmetrical* if and only if, whenever one individual has the relation to a second individual, then the second individual has the relation to the first individual.

Tautologous statement form   A truth-functional statement form is *tautologous* if and only if it is true on every line of its truth table.

Tautology   A truth-functional statement is a *tautology* if and only if its form is tautologous.

Theorem of ND   A *theorem* of ND is any statement that can be derived in ND without using any premises.

Totally reflexive relation   A dyadic relation is *totally reflexive* if and only if everything has the relation to itself.

Transitive relation   A dyadic relation is *transitive* if and only if, whenever (1) one individual, *x*, has the relation to a second individual, *y*, and (2) the second individual, *y*, has the relation to a third individual *z*, then the first individual, *x*, has the relation to the third individual, *z*.

Truth-functional connective   A *connective* is *truth-functional* if and only if it is used to express truth-functionally compound statements.

Truth-functional statement   A compound statement is *truth-functional* if and only if its truth-value is determined by the truth-values of statements that it has as parts.

Truth table   A *truth table* provides a complete listing of possible truth-values for statements that can be seen as occupying the "places" (variables) of a statement form, and indicates the truth-value of each possibility.

Truth-value   The *truth-value* of a truth statement is T. The *truth-value* of a false statement is F.

Unary quantification   A well-formed formula in predicate logic that contains only one quantifier is called a *unary quantification*.

Universal quantification   A well-formed formula (WFF) is a *universal quantification* if and only if it begins with a universal quantifier whose scope is the entire remainder of the WFF.

Universal quantifier $\forall x$, $\forall y$, and $\forall z$ are *universal quantifiers*. They abbreviate "for any individual in the universe, call it *x* (or *y*, or *z*), ..."

Universal statement   A *universal statement* affirms or denies a predicate of all individuals of a certain kind.

Valid argument form   See *deductively valid argument form*.

Valid argument in predicate logic   An argument in predicate logic argument is *valid* if and only if, when one or more individuals are considered to exist, it is impossible for the argument to have all true premises and a false conclusion.

Valid argument in propositional logic   See *deductively valid argument*.

Valid inferential form   A *valid inferential form* is a valid argument form that may be used to derive statements from previous lines. The following are the four valid inferential forms of Chapter 4:

MODUS PONENS (M.P.)   SIMPLIFICATION (SIMP.)

$p \supset q$ $\underline{p \cdot q}$ $\underline{p \cdot q}$
$\underline{p}$ $\therefore p$ $\therefore q$
$\therefore q$

CONJUNCTION (CONJ.)   ADDITION (ADD.)

p $\underline{p}$
$\underline{q}$ $\therefore p \vee q$
$\therefore p \cdot q$

Variable   See *individual variable, statement variable*.

Answers for All Concept Reviews

CHAPTER 1

Page 13

1. As defined in logic, an argument must have at least an attempt at reasoning. If the two people are giving reasons in support of conclusions, there is an argument. If they are merely being abusive, there is no argument.

2. Yes! Whether an argument is deductively valid depends on the sort of connection that is present from the premises to the conclusion, *not* on whether the conclusion is true or false.

3. Since its premises are true and the conclusion follows with certainty, the conclusion of the deductively valid argument must be accepted as true. The conclusion of the inductively weak argument is weakly supported. Its conclusion might well be false.

4. a. Russell has experienced Huxley talking about "A" subjects one day and "H" subjects on another. He has inferred, but not experienced, that Huxley read one volume of the *Encyclopedia Britannica* one day, and a different volume on the other day.
    b. Additional premises that would strengthen Russell's inference include:
        (i) Huxley owns a copy of the *Encyclopedia Britannica*.
        (ii) Other conversations featured various other letters of the alphabet.
        (iii) Russell is aware of the conversational content and the information provided in the *Encyclopedia Britannica*.
        (iv) Huxley admitted that he chose topics from the *Encyclopedia Britannica*.

    Additional premises that would weaken the inference include the opposites of (i)–(iv) above. In addition, Huxley's dislike for Russell was equal to Russell's dislike for him. Perhaps Huxley mentioned that he was choosing topics from letters of the alphabet to see if Russell was clever enough to notice.

5. As long as you consistently place content in the circle and square locations, your example can be about anything whatsoever. One example:

If you've completed this concept review question, then you've completed the first set of concept reviews.

You've completed this concept review question.

Hence, you've completed the first set of concept reviews.

All arguments of this form are deductively valid.

Page 26

1. Completions become better insofar as they better express the speaker's reasoning, and insofar as they increase the likelihood that the speaker's position will be accepted.

2. It will be desirable when the point of reviewing the argument is to discover truth. People frequently have more insight in recognizing conclusions than they have in presenting their ideas in a logical fashion. Any occasion where the point of looking at an argument is either self-interest or self-preservation will be an occasion where creating a stronger expression of an opposing position is not desirable.

3. One woman's husband was particularly demanding about what she should pack for his lunch. She tried a variety of foods, everything from steak to tuna. One day, out of anger, she decided to make his sandwiches out of canned dog food. He loved them!

   The local grocer, knowing that she didn't have a dog, asked her one day why she was purchasing dog food. After swearing him to secrecy, she told the truth. He was aghast, and cautioned her that dog food might not provide a balanced diet for her husband.

   This went on for some time, until the grocer noticed that she was no longer buying dog food. She had to confess that her husband had passed away. The grocer again pointed out that the dog food had likely not provided a balanced diet, and that she might be responsible for her husband's death. She admitted that she was responsible, but not in that way. It turns out that her husband had been licking himself in the driveway when she ran over him with the van.

   This example of reasoning can be completed by using pattern II, and deriving the conclusion that the husband, in addition to enjoying dog food, had other doglike qualities.

CHAPTER 2

Page 36

1. Capital letters, such as *P* and *Q*, are statement constants. They represent particular statements. Hence, 'if *P*, then *Q*' will identify a particular statement as expressed in English. Lower-case letters, such as *p* and *q*, are statement variables. They function as a place holders. Hence, 'if *p*, then *q*' indicates the general form or pattern of conditionals rather than expressing a specific statement.

2. The statement that follows 'if' is called the antecedent. The statement that follows 'then' (in a standard conditional) is called the consequent. The antecedent statement is always expressed at the left of the

horseshoe, while the consequent statement is always expressed at the right of the horseshoe.

3. $p \supset q$.

It is false that q.

Hence, it is false that p.

Page 42

1. Your examples can have any subject matter. An example of a pure conjunction:

We have an enormous number of lawyers and they charge astronomical fees.

Conjunction with sequence:

The package had been tampered with, but I decided to keep it.

Nonconjunctive usage:

Sean and Alex play an exciting game of racquetball.

Page 61

1. If we imagine that Biology 397 does not exist, then the statements are contraries.

2. As an inclusive 'or' statement, it allows for the possibility that you will stay up all night and still pass the exam. If it is viewed as an exclusive 'or' statement, you will either stay up all night or pass the exam, *but not both*. (Perhaps you need some rest to pass exams.)

3.   a. The wedge.
     b. The horseshoe.
     c. The horseshoe.
     d. The dot.

4. There are five possibilities:

$(B \cdot T) \vee (R \supset L)$

$B \cdot [(T \vee R) \supset L]$

$B \cdot [T \vee (R \supset L)]$

$[B \cdot (T \vee R)] \supset L$

$[(B \cdot T) \vee R] \supset L$

5. A simple statement. The sentence merely makes one claim about relative proportions of people and sheep in Australia.

6. There are a number of ways to compare them. Most importantly, however, natural languages have evolved, whereas artificial languages have been planned to accomplish a specific purpose. Our artificial language in logic has been planned to express correctly validity and relationships between statements.

7. The antecedent statement is always represented at the left-hand side of the horseshoe. The consequent statement is always represented at the right-hand side of the horseshoe.

8. Conjuncts.

9. When 'and' fails to express a conjunction of two statements, it typically

expresses a relationship. Some figures of speech also contain the word 'and' and fail to express a conjunction of two statements.

10. The expression lacks adequate punctuation. It is impossible to determine how the statements are to be connected.

CHAPTER 3

Page 73

1. It is impossible for both contraries to be true. Hence, if we know that one statement is true, the other statement must be false.

2.

p	$\vee$	q	
T	F	T	(Both disjuncts are true.)
T	T	F	
F	T	T	
F	F	F	(Neither disjunct is true.)

3. Yes, the suggested table does meet our definition of a truth table, since it lists all truth-value possibilities and indicates a truth-value of the horseshoe for each of them. Yes, the suggested table could be used to define the horseshoe. As with the table previously given to define the horseshoe, the horseshoe in the suggested table is only false when the antecedent statement is true and the consequent statement is false.

4.   a. The statement would be false if Benjamin Franklin did not invent the lightning rod.

   b. The statement would be false if only five women have won the Nobel Prize, but scientists have not discriminated against women.

   c. The statement would be false either if prominent Republicans did not attend the Princess Grace Foundation meetings, or if prominent Republicans were not treated to fresh carnation petals in the toilet bowls.

   d. The statement would be false if the state does not reduce their tax assessment and the Schmidt family does not turn their land over for use as a prison farm.

Page 81

1. '$p \supset q \vee r$' lacks adequate punctuation and so is not a statement form.

2. '$A \supset (p \cdot B)$' is not a statement form. Statement forms must have variables, and must not have any statement constants.

3. A statement form with three variables (that is, with three different kinds of locations) requires eight lines to express all of the truth-value possibilities. A correct truth table could have more than eight lines, but it would have needless duplications.

4. $2^6 = 64$ lines.

Page 86

1. Since a truth table expresses *all* truth-value possibilities, the statement must be represented by the form's truth table. When a form is tautologous, every possibility is determined to be true. Hence, the

statement, being one of the represented possibilities, must be true.

2. Your example can, of course, have any subject matter. For example: *Either the two Koreas will be united or North Korea will remain a communist country, but the two Koreas will not be united and North Korea will not remain a communist country.*

The form is self-contradictory. Hence, the above statement must be false. Situations in the world have no bearing on the statement's truth-value, since it is determined false by its form.

3. The conjunction of contraries will not be a self-contradictory statement as determined by a truth table. Even so, it will not be possible for both conjuncts to be true. Hence, it will not be possible for the conjunction of them to be true.

Page 95

1. Truth tables express all truth-value possibilities for statements that might take an argument form's locations. If the form is valid, its truth table lacks any possibility (line) of statements taking its locations so that the resulting argument has all true premises and a false conclusion. It must be *impossible* for an argument that has a valid form to have all true premises and a false conclusion.

2. Invalid arguments can have any combination whatsoever: all true premises and a true conclusion, all true premises and a false conclusion, not all true premises and a true conclusion, or not all true premises and a false conclusion. In case this seems strange, remember that invalid arguments lack a relationship from their premises to their conclusions that makes them valid. In the absence of a relationship that makes the argument valid, any combination is possible.

CHAPTER 4

Page 105

1. Yes. *A* replaces *p*. *B* replaces *q*. *A* replaces *r*.

2. No. All of the variables present in the form must be replaced when creating an instance. The connectives in the form are never replaced in forming an instance. An instance can be more compound than the form, but it can never be less compound than the form.

3. No. One statement can replace two different variables in creating an instance, but not in creating a parallel-instance.

4. No. In creating a parallel-instance, compound statements cannot be used to replace the variables.

5. $(p \supset q) \lor (r \cdot {\sim}s)$

6. No. A parallel-instance is a particular kind of instance. If an argument fails to meet the requirements for being an instance, it cannot meet the requirements for being a parallel-instance.

Page 110

1. A negated statement, considered as a whole, must be either true or false. Since any true or false statement is represented by the truth table, a

negated statement that might be used to replace a variable will be expressed by the form's truth table.

2. Yes. Any instance of a valid form must be a valid argument. A parallel-instance is a particular kind of instance.

3. The form that has the argument as a parallel-instance must be valid. The form that has the argument as a parallel-instance must have at least the same connectives (perhaps more) as the form that merely has the argument as an instance. At most, the truth table for the form that has the argument as a parallel-instance might repeat these values. Repeating the values of a valid form cannot provide a line that proves invalidity.

4. Valid. *Any* instance of a valid argument form is a valid argument. The fact that an argument is merely an instance of an invalid form gives you absolutely no information about the argument's validity.

Page 128

1. In using the form to derive a line (conclusion), it is impossible to derive a false line (conclusion) from true premises.

2. No. The premises of the initial argument are taken as givens for a formal proof. They are never established as true. Since the initial premises of an argument are never proved true in a formal proof, the initial argument is not proved sound.

3. You would be trying an absolutely impossible task! Since our inferences preserve truth and the inference from the premises to the conclusion of an invalid argument does not, you will *never* be able to provide a formal proof for an invalid argument.

4. There are times when we have to replace an inferential form's variables with compound statements in order to create instances. Unless you can already see how to apply an inferential form, you cannot know how to begin labeling statements with *p*s and *q*s.

5. 'A · B'. If 'A · B' does not appear in the problem, then A and B should also be listed as new goals.

6. 'A ∨ B' and C. If 'A ∨ B' does not appear in the problem, then A should also be listed as a new goal.

7. When deriving a line, our valid inferential forms always work on major connectives. The major connective of the line that contains our goals statement will have to be unpacked by our valid inferential forms in order to derive the goals statement.

8. See number 7 above. Our goals statement's major connective will have to be derived by using our valid inferential forms.

Page 141

1. The line that has been derived, even if it is the conclusion of the initial argument, was only derived on the basis of the conditional-proof assumption. Truth need not be preserved from the premises of the initial argument to some line *within* a conditional proof.

2. Unless the conditional proof for the major (horseshoe) connective is

started first, the conditional proofs will partially overlap when they are ended. Conditional proofs that partially overlap need not preserve truth.

3. This problem will require three conditional-proof assumptions: *A*, *B*, and *C*. *D* should be derived prior to closing off the conditional proofs. The problem will have the following box pattern.

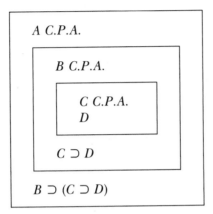

A ⊃ [*B* ⊃ (*C* ⊃ *D*)]

CHAPTER 5

Page 148

1. As developed in Chapter 2, the dot expresses pure conjunction. Since it does not indicate order, reversing the order of the conjuncts produces an equivalent expression.

2. Material equivalence merely claims that the statements have the same truth-value. Logical equivalence claims that two statements *must* have the same truth-value owing to their forms. Claiming material equivalence for two statements merely claims that the biconditional of them is a true contingent statement. Claiming logical equivalence for two statements claims that the biconditional of them is a tautology.

3. Yes. Being tautologous, each form must be true for any assignment of truth-values. Since both are true for any assignment of truth-values, both must always have the same truth-value, and are logically equivalent.

Page 176

1. A statement that results from the application of an equivalence inferential form *must* have the same truth-value as the initial statement. The statement that replaces a portion of a line must have the same truth-value as the part that it is replacing. All of the statements we are considering are truth-functional; the truth-value of the compound results from the truth-values of its parts. If we do not change the truth-values of the parts, we cannot change the truth-value of the whole.

2. The inferential forms of Chapter 4 are valid argument forms, not logical equivalences. They preserve truth, but they do not rule out inferences

from false premises to a true conclusion. Replacing a false statement with a true statement in part of a line could result in "deriving" a statement that is false as a whole from one that was true as a whole. Suppose that *A* is a false statement and *B* is a true statement. Using addition to derive '*A* ∨ *B*' from *A* derives a true statement from a false one. Suppose that *C* is false, and that we replace *A* with '*A* ∨ *B*' in '*A* ⊃ *C*'. '*A* ⊃ *C*' is true, whereas '(*A* ∨ *B*) ⊃ *C*' is false. Replacing *A* with '*A* ∨ *B*' in part of the statement would result in an invalid inference.

3. See number 2 above. Inferential forms can derive true statements from false statements. If their direction were reversed, they would enable us to infer false statements from true ones.

4. Contrary statements cannot both be true, but both might be false. Indirect proofs that used contraries as suggested in the question need not preserve truth. Showing that one of them is false—that it leads to contradiction—does *not* show that the other must be true. Suppose we derive a contradiction based on the assumption that the universe is decreasing in size. It would be an invalid inference to conclude the contrary—that it must be increasing in size—since it might be remaining the same size.

Page 178

1. Indirect proofs have been justified as abbreviated conditional proofs. Suppose that a formal proof has indirect proofs that are contained within one another. The formal proof could have been constructed by using complete conditional proofs that are contained within one another. Since the formal proof that has the nonabbreviated conditional proofs preserves truth, the formal proof that uses indirect proofs contained within one another must also preserve truth.

Page 186

1.   a. The following steps can always be taken:

1. p ⊃ q assumption
2. q ⊃ r assumption

> *3. p C.P.A.*
> *4. q M.P. 1, 3*
> *5. r M.P. 2, 4*

6. p ⊃ r C.P. 3–5

   b. The following steps can always be taken:

1. (p ⊃ q) · (r ⊃ s)
2. p ∨ r

> 3. ~q C.P.A.
> 4. p ⊃ q Simp. 1
> 5. ~p M.T. 4, 3
> 6. r D.S. 2, 5
> 7. r ⊃ s Simp. 1
> 8. s M.P. 7, 6

9. ~q ⊃ s C.P. 3–8
10. ~~q V s W.E. 9
11. q V s D.N. 10

2. No. Derived inference rules can shorten the length of formal proofs, but they cannot increase the number of provable arguments. Any argument that can be proved valid with a derived rule can be proved valid without it by merely making the steps used to derive the rule a part of the formal proof.

3. The following steps can always be taken:

1. ~(p · q) assumption
2. p
   _____
3. ~p V ~q D.M. 1
4. p ⊃ ~q W.E. 3
5. ~q M.P. 4, 2

4. There are valid truth-functional arguments for which our deductive system, without conditional and indirect proof, cannot provide a formal proof. For a frustrating experience at trying the impossible, you might try to establish the following as a derived rule *without* using either conditional or indirect proof:

p ⊃ q
_____
∴ p ⊃ (p · q)

Conditional proof cannot be established in our deductive system as a derived rule.

CHAPTER 6

Page 199

1. No line of a complete truth table can show that an argument form is valid. Rather, the lack of a line that proves invalidity shows that an argument form is valid. Pointing out a line of the complete truth table cannot show that it lacks some other line.

2. The complete truth table for the form has more than one line with all true premisses and a false conclusion. One line has the unassigned variable true and another line has the unassigned variable false.

3. Partial truth tables show that there is a line of the complete truth table such that the form is invalid. A particular argument might be an example of a different line of truth table from a line that proves that its form is invalid. The argument is invalid since it has an invalid form.

Page 216

1. No! When a set of statements is inconsistent, it is *impossible* for all of them to be true. A set of statements can have one or more false statements, and yet a truth table might show that there is a *possibility* of all of them being true.

   Yes! If a collection of statements are all true, then it must be possible for all of them to be true.

2. Disjuncts would merely become part of the tree, since both disjuncts must be false for a disjunction of them to be false. Conjunctions would now have to be split into paths, since a conjunction is false if *either* conjunct is false.

3. The completed tree will determine whether it is possible for all of the statements to be false. Reversing all of our reduction patterns, an inconsistent set will have at least one open path, and a consistent set will have all closed paths.

CHAPTER 7

Page 232

1. The quality of beginning with an attack on Fort Sumter.
4. The quality of beginning in 1861. The quality of ending in 1865.
7. The quality of being determined to secede from the Union. The quality of being determined to change the Union.
10. The quality of signing the Emancipation Proclamation. The quality of winning at Gettysburg. The quality of winning the Civil War.

Page 244

1. No. Predicate constants must have an individual constant or an individual variable placed on the right side. Statement constants do not.
2. The antecedent is a disjunction when the statement is about all of the members of two or more groups. The antecedent is a conjunction when two or more qualities are used to define members of the group.
3. Both kinds of variables are placeholders in the sense that neither picks out a particular thing. They are placeholders for different kinds of things, however.
4. If there is only one individual of a certain kind, then claiming that all individuals of that kind have a quality will have the same truth conditions as claiming that the individual named by the constant has that quality.

Page 258

1. Yes. If there are no complaints, then the universal statement is true and the existential statement is false.

2. The existential statement will be true if there are complaints and some of them are handled promptly, but some are not handled promptly. The argument from an existential statement to the corresponding universal statement is generally not valid.

3. The symbolization given here does not claim that there are complaints. There is some thing, such that *if* it is a complaint, *then* . . . .

4. 'Real' indicates a kind of vegetarian, not a kind of individual. 'Dill pickles' indicates a kind of food that is eaten, not a kind of individual. The English sentence is about individuals who eat dill pickles, and should be symbolized as '$\forall x(Ex \supset Vx)$'.

Page 273

1. A universal quantification is true if and only if it is true of each thing in the universe. An existential quantification is true if and only if it is true of at least one thing in the universe. Existential instantiation needs the restriction to avoid the assumption that a particular thing, which may or may not have the quality, is the "at least one thing" that has the quality.

Page 281

1. a. No. y is not within the scope of a quantifier that has that variable.
   b. Yes.
   c. Yes.
   d. No. x in 'Qx' is not within the scope of the quantifier.
   e. Yes.
   f. No. x in 'Px' is not within the scope of the quantifier.

2. Predicate letters are not needed to specify qualities that designate membership in the restricted domain. In an unrestricted domain, numbers 2, 6, and 11 can be symbolized as follows.
   2. $\forall x(Px \supset Sx) \supset \forall x(Px \supset \sim Cx)$
   6. $\exists x[(Px \cdot Ix) \cdot \sim Sx] \supset \exists x[(Px \cdot Ix) \cdot Kx]$
   11. $\forall x[Ax \supset (Dx \equiv Bx)] \supset \exists x[Ax \cdot (Tx \cdot Jx)]$

CHAPTER 8

Page 319

1. a. $\dfrac{D}{\therefore S}$

   D T; S F

   b. $\dfrac{Da}{\therefore (\exists x)Sx}$

   Da T; Sa F

   c. RD: *persons*

   $\dfrac{Dha}{\therefore \exists x \exists y Dxy}$

2. Example: The United States purchased the Louisiana Territory from France while Jefferson was in office. *Pulfj.*

3. Each person desired some person or other. There was at least one person such that everyone desired that person.
4. The *x* in *Vxy* is within the scope of more than one quantifier that has this variable.

Page 331

1. *1.* <u>∀xRxx</u>   /∀x∀y[(Rxy ∨ Ryx) ⊃ Rxx]

> 2. ~∀x∀y[(Rxy ∨ Ryx) ⊃ Rxx] I.P.A.
> 3. ∃x∃y~[(Rxy ∨ Ryx) ⊃ Rxx] (2)Q.N. 2
> 4. ~[(Rab ∨ Rba) ⊃ Raa] (2)E.I. 3
> 5. (Rab ∨ Rba) · ~Raa N.C. 4
> 6. ~Raa Simp. 5
> 7. Raa U.I. 1
> 8. Raa · ~Raa Conj 7, 6

9. ∀x∀y[(Rxy ∨ Ryx) ⊃ Rxx] I.P. 2–8

2. *1.* <u>∀x∀y(Rxy ⊃ ~Ryx)</u>   /∀x~Rxx

> 2. ~∀x~Rxx I.P.A.
> 3. ∃x~~Rxx Q.N. 2
> 4. ~~Raa E.I. 3
> 5. Raa ⊃ ~Raa (2)U.I. 1
> 6. Raa D.N. 4
> 7. ~Raa M.P. 5, 6
> 8. Raa · ~Raa Conj. 6, 7

9. ∀x~Rxx I.P. 2–8

3. *1.* <u>∀x∀y∀z[(Rxy · ~Rxz) ⊃ Rxz]</u>   /∀x~Rxx

> 2. ~∀x~Rxx I.P.A.
> 3. ∃x~~Rxx Q.N. 2
> 4. ~~Raa E.I. 3
> 5. Raa D.N. 4
> 6. (Raa · Raa) ⊃ ~Raa (3)U.I. 1
> 7. Raa · Raa Du. 5
> 8. ~Raa M.P. 6, 7
> 9. Raa · ~Raa Conj. 5, 8

10. ∀x~Rxx I.P. 2–9

4. *1.* $\forall x {\sim} Rxx$ $\diagup \forall x \forall y (Rxy \supset {\sim} Ryx)$
    2. $\forall x \forall y \forall z [(Rxy \cdot Ryz) \supset Rxz]$

> *3.* ${\sim}\forall x \forall y (Rxy \supset {\sim} Ryx)$ *I.P.A.*
> *4.* $\exists x \exists y {\sim} (Rxy \supset {\sim} Ryx)$ *(2)Q.N. 3*
> *5.* ${\sim} (Rab \supset {\sim} Rba)$ *(2)E.I. 4*
> *6.* $Rab \cdot {\sim}{\sim} Rba$ *N.C. 5*
> *7.* $Rab \cdot Rba$ *D.N. 6*
> *8.* $(Rab \cdot Rba) \supset Raa$ *(3)U.I. 2*
> *9.* Raa *M.P. 8, 7*
> *10.* ${\sim} Raa$ *U.I. 1*
> *11.* $Raa \cdot {\sim} Raa$ *Conj. 9, 10*

12. $\forall x \forall y (Rxy \supset {\sim} Ryx)$ *I.P. 3–11*

5. *1.* $\forall x \forall y (Rxy \supset Ryx)$ $\diagup \forall x \forall y [(Rxy \lor Ryx) \supset Rxx]$
    2. $\forall x \forall y \forall z [(Rxy \cdot Ryz) \supset Rxz]$

> *3.* ${\sim}\forall x \forall y [(Rxy \lor Ryx) \supset Rxx]$ *I.P.A.*
> *4.* $\exists x \exists y {\sim} [(Rxy \lor Ryx) \supset Rxx]$ *(2)Q.N. 3*
> *5.* ${\sim} [(Rab \lor Rba) \supset Raa]$ *(2)E.I. 4*
> *6.* $(Rab \lor Rba) \cdot {\sim} Raa$ *N.C. 5*
> *7.* ${\sim} Raa$ *Simp. 6*
> *8.* $(Rab \cdot Rba) \supset Raa$ *(3)U.I. 2*
> *9.* $Rab \supset Rba$ *(2)U.I. 1*
> *10.* $Rab \lor Rba$ *Simp. 6*
> *11.* $Rba \lor Rab$ *Comm. 10*
> *12.* ${\sim}{\sim} Rba \lor Rab$ *D.N. 11*
> *13.* ${\sim} Rba \supset Rab$ *W.E. 12*
> *14.* ${\sim} Rab \lor Rba$ *W.E. 9*
> *15.* $Rba \lor {\sim} Rab$ *Comm. 14*
> *16.* ${\sim}{\sim} Rba \lor {\sim} Rab$ *D.N. 15*
> *17.* ${\sim} Rba \supset {\sim} Rab$ *W.E. 16*
>
>> *18.* ${\sim} Rba$ *I.P.A.*
>> *19.* ${\sim} Rab$ *M.P. 17, 18*
>> *20.* Rab *M.P. 13, 18*
>> *21.* $Rab \cdot {\sim} Rab$ *Conj. 20, 19*

> 22. *Rba I.P. 18–21*
> 23. *Rba ⊃ Rab U.I. 1*
> 24. *Rab M.P. 23, 22*
> 25. *Rab · Rba Conj. 24, 22*
> 26. *Raa M.P. 8, 25*
> 27. *Raa · ~Raa Conj. 26, 7*

28. *∀x∀y[(Rxy ∨ Ryx) ⊃ Rxx] I.P. 3–27*

CHAPTER 9

Page 364

1. We know, from metatheorem 3, that ND is deductively complete for arguments if and only if ND is deductively complete for statements. From metatheorem 6, we know that all truth-functional tautologies are theorems of ND; that is, we know that ND is deductively complete for statements. Hence, ND is deductively complete for arguments. Metatheorem 7 follows directly from metatheorems 3 and 6.

2. Yes. Any system that is capable of providing a "proof" for any argument *whatsoever* is complete and unsound. Providing formal proofs for all valid arguments dictates that such a system is complete. If it also is capable of "proving" invalid arguments, then is unsound.

3. Yes. A system that provides formal proof for only valid arguments, but not for all valid arguments, is sound and incomplete. We can create such a system by removing conditional proof from ND.

APPENDIX B

Page 371

1. It must be possible for $P_1, P_2, \ldots P_n$ and A, B, and C all to be true and for D to be false. The following argument is proved valid after making the conditional-proof assumptions:

P_1
P_2
.
.
.
P_n
A
B
C
——
∴ D

The above argument and the one given by the concept review question are both invalid if and only if $P_1, P_2, \ldots P_n$, and A, B, and C are true, and D is false. Hence, the above argument is valid if and only if the one given in the concept review question is valid.

2. No. Conditional proofs cannot partially overlap one another. Hence, since "partially contained" conditional proofs are not acceptable when constructing formal proofs, we do not need to justify them. Moreover, partially contained conditional proofs need not preserve truth. They *cannot* be justified.

Answers for All Selected Problems

CHAPTER 1

Exercises I, page 11

1. If you pass all the exams, then you will pass the course. It is false that you will pass the course. Hence, it is false that you will pass all the exams.

3. If the South won at Gettysburg, then the South won the Civil War. It is false that the South won the Civil War. Hence, it is false that the South won at Gettysburg.

Exercises II, page 12

1. Either Booker T. Washington created the NAACP or W. E. B. Du Bois created the NAACP. It is false that Booker T. Washington created the NAACP. Hence, W. E. B. Du Bois created the NAACP.

3. Either global temperatures will continue to rise or the theory of the greenhouse effect is false. It is false that global temperatures will continue to rise. Hence, the theory of the greenhouse effect is false.

Exercises III, page 17

1. Conclusion: Painting man is easy, but painting the workings of man's mind is difficult.
Premiss: Painting the working's of man's mind requires the artist not only to paint man, but to represent him so that gestures show the workings of his mind.

5. Conclusion: Where promiscuity prevails, women will always be more often the victims than the culprits.
Premiss: Women are more naturally monogamous than men; it is a biological necessity.

9. Conclusion: Be neither a borrower nor a lender.
Premiss: Loaning often results in loss of what has been loaned, and those involved often cease to be friends.

Exercises IV, page 24

1. Missing premiss: Promiscuity prevails.

5. Missing premiss: It is false that Mencken approves of violence.

9. The first premiss of structure II is unstated: If a girl must, in the course of her development, change the object of her love from a woman (her mother) to a man (her spouse), then a girl's development is more complex than that of a boy.

13. The second premiss of structure II is unstated: American professors write obscure articles and dissertations.

17. This argument has more than one reasonable completion. One possibility uses structure II:

    If the gods thought that there was no more dreadful punishment than futile and hopeless labor, then they condemned Sisyphus to ceaselessly rolling a rock to the top of a mountain.

    The gods thought that there was no more dreadful punishment than futile and hopeless labor.

    Hence, the gods condemned Sisyphus to ceaselessly rolling a rock to the top of a mountain.

CHAPTER 2

Exercises I, page 35

1. $G \supset E$

3. $E \supset A$

5. $H \supset F$

7. $L \supset H$

9. $I \supset R$

11. $C \supset T$

13. $S \supset A$

Exercises II, page 41

1. E. The English is giving the name of one expedition, and so a simple statement is being expressed. The sentence does *not* mean that the Lewis expedition and the Clark expedition explored the American Northwest.

3. $P \cdot I$. Neither the English nor the artificial indicates sequence.

5. G. The English does not intend a conjunction of two statements. "Rank and file" indicates a kind of membership, not two different memberships.

7. $S \cdot W$. The English probably indicated sequence, whereas the symbolization does not. We normally understand that a trial takes place prior to the reading of the verdict.

9. $L \cdot W$. Neither the English nor the artificial indicates sequence.

11. $A \cdot B$. The English probably indicates sequence, whereas the symbolization does not.

Exercises III, page 48

1. Provided we assume that Michigan and Florida exist, the statements are contradictories of one another: a. M; b. $\sim M$.

3. Contraries; both statements are false if Kanga neither buttoned nor unbuttoned her pouch: a. B; b. U.

5. Provided we assume that Australia and the United States exist, the statements are contradictories of one another: a. S; b. $\sim S$.

9. Contraries; both statements are false if the person is not looking for anyone: a. *H*; b. *D*.

Exercises IV, page 58

1. $D \supset B$

3. $D \lor {\sim}B$

5. $F \cdot S$

7. $A \lor {\sim}V$

9. ${\sim}(F \lor G)$

11. $D \supset B$

13. $E \supset (D \supset P)$

15. $(P \cdot S) \supset C$

Exercises V, page 59

1. $W \cdot E$

3. ${\sim}W \cdot {\sim}S$

5. $M \supset L$. The statement constants *M* and *L* must be used to abbreviate *statements*, not the words "marriage" and "love". "Marriage without love" indicates a kind of marriage, not the conjunction of two statements.

7. $F \cdot M$

9. $M \cdot P$

11. $S \lor B$

13. ${\sim}R \lor A$

15. $(A \lor H) \cdot {\sim}(A \cdot H)$

17. $D \supset E$

19. $L \lor R$

21. $(Q \lor C) \supset H$

23. $P \supset H$

25. $(T \cdot B) \supset C$

27. $S \supset (L \cdot D)$

29. $A \cdot B$

31. ${\sim}(I \lor B) \cdot R$

33. $({\sim}U \cdot {\sim}S) \supset {\sim}D$

35. $(R \supset A) \cdot (B \supset P)$

36. $(W \cdot E) \cdot [({\sim}T \lor {\sim}A) \supset ({\sim}R \lor {\sim}M)]$

W = Hitler no doubt wished to dominate the world.

T = The Treaty of Versailles treated Germany [so] badly.

E = The Treaty of Versailles ended World War I.

A = Chamberlain adopted a policy of appeasement.

R = Hitler was able to rise to power.

M = Hitler was able to begin his mission of world conquest.

The symbolization of this sentence is open to some debate. However, the sentence will normally be understood to assert both that Hitler wished to dominate the world and that the Treaty of Versailles ended World War II.

CHAPTER 3

Exercises I, page 72

1. T

3. T

5. F

7. F

9. T

11. F

13. T

15. T

17. F

21. T

25. T

29. F

Exercises II, page 75 (Final answers are in boldface type.)

1. $A \supset Y$

   T   F
   T **F** F

3. $\sim(A \cdot Y)$

   T   F
   T F F
   T T F F

5. $\sim A \supset \sim X$

   T   F
   FT   TF
   FT **T** TF

7. $A \supset (B \cdot Z)$

   T   T F
   T   T F F
   T **F** T F F

9. $(A \cdot X) \lor (B \cdot Y)$

   T   F   T   F
   T F F   T F F
   T F F **F** T F F

11. $\sim[(A \lor X) \cdot (B \lor Y)]$

   T   F   T   F
   T T F   T T F
   T T F **T** T T F
   F T T F **T** T T F

13. $(A \supset X) \lor (B \cdot C)$

   T   F   T   T
   T F F   T T T
   T F F **T** T T T

15. $A \supset (\sim X \supset Y)$

   T   F   F
   T   TF   F
   T   TF F F
   T **F** TF F F

17. $[(A \cdot B) \lor \sim C] \supset X$

   T T   T   F
   T T T   T   F
   T T T   FT   F
   T T T T FT   F
   T T T T FT **F** F

21. $\sim(A \supset X) \supset [B \cdot \sim(X \lor Z)]$

   T F   T   F   F
   T F F   T   F F F
   T T F F   T   T F F F
   T T F F   T T T F F F
   T T F F **T** T T T F F F

25. $\sim\{[(A \supset X) \lor (B \supset Y)] \supset Z\}$

   T   F   T   F   F
   T F F   T F F   F
   T F F **F** T F F   F
   T F F **F** T F F T F
   F T FF **F** T FF T F

Exercises III, page 80

1. <u>p ⊃ ~p</u>

    T F FT
    F T TF

3. <u>(p · q) · (p ⊃ ~q)</u>

    T T T   F   T   F FT
    T F F   F   T   T TF
    F F T   F   F   T FT
    F F F   F   F   T TF

5. <u>(p V q) ⊃ (p V r)</u>

    T T T   T   T T T
    T T T   T   T T F
    T T F   T   T T T
    T T F   T   T T F
    F T T   T   F T T
    F T T   F   F F F
    F F F   T   F T T
    F F F   T   F F F

7. <u>(p V q) ⊃ [(p V r) ⊃ q]</u>

    T T T   T   T T T   T T
    T T T   T   T T F   T T
    T T F   F   T T T   F F
    T T F   F   T T F   F F
    F T T   T   F T T   T T
    F T T   T   F F F   T T
    F F F   T   F T T   F F
    F F F   T   F F F   T F

Exercises IV, page 83

1. <u>p ⊃ p</u>

    T T T
    F T F
       └─── Tautologous

3. <u>(p · q) ⊃ p</u>

    T T T   T   T
    T F F   T   T
    F F T   T   F
    F F F   T   F
              └─── Tautologous

5. <u>(p ⊃ q) V (p ⊃ ~q)</u>

    T T T   T   T F FT
    T F F   T   T T TF
    F T T   T   F T FT
    F T F   T   F T TF
            └─── Tautologous

7. <u>[p V (q · r)] · ~[(p V q) · (p V r)]</u>

    T T   T T T   FF   T T T   T   T T T
    T T   T F F   FF   T T T   T   T T F
    T T   F F T   FF   T T F   T   T T T
    T T   F F F   FF   T T F   T   T T F

```
F T  T T T   F F   F T T  T  F T T
F F  T F F   F T   F T T  F  F F F
F F  F F T   F T   F F F  F  F T T
F F  F F F   F T   F F F  F  F F F
            └──── Self-contradictory
```

Exercises V, page 93

1. $p \lor q$

    p

    $\therefore \sim q$

$p \lor q$	p	$\sim q$	
T T T	T	F	Invalid
T T F	T	T	
F T T	F	F	
F F F	F	T	

(The row T T T / T / F is boxed)

3. $p \supset q$

    $\sim p$

    $\therefore q$

$p \supset q$	$\sim p$	q	
T T T	F	T	
T F F	F	F	
F T T	T	T	
F T F	T	F	Invalid

(The row F T F / T / F is boxed)

5. $\sim(p \cdot q)$

    p

    $\therefore \sim q$

Valid

$\sim(p \cdot q)$	p	$\sim q$
F T T T	T	F
T T F F	T	T
T F F T	F	F
T F F F	F	T

7. $\sim p \supset (p \lor q)$

    $\sim q \lor \sim p$

    $\therefore r \lor \sim p$

$\sim p \supset (p \lor q)$	$\sim q \lor \sim p$	$r \lor \sim p$	
F T T T T	F F F	T T F	
F T T T T	F F F	F F F	
F T T T F	T T F	T T F	
F T T T F	T T F	F F F	Invalid
T T F T T	F T T	T T T	
T T F T T	F T T	F T T	
T F F F F	T T T	T T T	
T F F F F	T T T	F T T	

(The row F T T T F / T T F / F F F is boxed)

9. $p \supset q$

    $r \supset q$

    q

    $\therefore p \lor r$

$p \supset q$	$r \supset q$	q	$p \lor r$	
T T T	T T T	T	T T T	
T T T	F T T	T	T T F	
T F F	T F F	F	T T T	
T F F	F T F	F	T T F	
F T T	T T T	T	F T T	
F T T	F T T	T	F F F	Invalid
F T F	T F F	F	F T T	
F T F	F T F	F	F F F	

(The row F T T / F T T / T / F F F is boxed)

Exercises VI, page 94

1. ~(S · T)   ~(p · q)

    T   q

    ∴ ~S   ∴ ~p

~(p · q)	q	~p	Valid
F T T T	T	F	
T T F F	F	F	
T F F T	T	T	
T F F F	F	T	

3. (E · S) ⊃ I   (p · q) ⊃ r

    E · ~S   p · ~q

    ∴ ~I   ∴ ~r

(p · q) ⊃ r	p · ~q	~r	
T T T T T	T F F	F	
T T T F F	T F F	T	
T F F T T	T T T	F	Invalid
T F F T F	T T T	T	
F F T T T	F F F	F	
F F T T F	F F F	T	
F F F T T	F F T	F	
F F F T F	F F T	T	

5. (T · L) ⊃ R   (p · q) ⊃ r

    ~R   ~r

    ∴ ~L ∨ ~T   ∴ ~q ∨ ~p

(p · q) ⊃ r	~r	~q ∨ ~p	Valid
T T T T T	F	F F F	
T T T F F	T	F F F	
T F F T T	F	T T F	
T F F T F	T	T T F	
F F T T T	F	F T T	
F F T T F	T	F T T	
F F F T T	F	T T T	
F F F T F	T	T T T	

7. H ∨ L   p ∨ q

    ~L · ~M   ~q · ~r

    ∴ H · ~M   ∴ p · ~r

$p \lor q$	$\sim q$	$\cdot$	$\sim r$	p	$\cdot$	$\sim r$	Valid
T T T	F	F	F	T F		F	
T T T	F	F	T	T T		T	
T T F	T	F	F	T F		F	
T T F	T	T	T	T T		T	
F T T	F	F	F	F F		F	
F T T	F	F	T	F F		T	
F F F	T	F	F	F F		F	
F F F	T	T	T	F F		T	

CHAPTER 4

Exercises I, page 103

1. $T \lor U$

3. $\sim T$

5. $(T \cdot U) \supset (T \lor \sim H)$

7. $T \supset U$
   T
   $\overline{\therefore U}$

9. T
   $\overline{\therefore T \lor U}$

11. $T \lor U$
    $\sim U$
    $\overline{\therefore T}$

13. $\dfrac{T \supset U}{\therefore (T \lor \sim H) \supset (U \lor \sim H)}$

Exercises II, page 104

1. All of a–k are instances; k is a parallel-instance.
3. e and h are instances; h is a parallel-instance.
5. None.
7. c and d are instances; c is a parallel-instance.

Exercises III, page 104

1. f is an instance. None are parallel-instances.
3. g is an instance. None are parallel-instances.
5. d is an instance. None are parallel-instances.

Exercises IV, page 123

1. 1. $(B \lor V) \supset C$ $\diagup C$
   2. B
   $\overline{3.\ B \lor V\ Add.\ 2}$
   4. $C\ M.P.\ 1, 3$

3. 1. $\sim V \cdot D$ $\diagup \sim V \lor D$
   2. $\sim V\ Simp.\ 1$
   3. $\sim V \lor D\ Add.\ 2$

5. 1. $A \supset B$ $\diagup D$
   2. $(B \lor C) \supset D$
   3. A
   $\overline{4.\ B\ M.P.\ 1, 3}$
   5. $B \lor C\ Add.\ 4$
   6. $D\ M.P.\ 2, 5$

7. 1. $B \supset V$ $\diagup T$
   2. $B \supset (D \cdot C)$
   3. $[V \cdot (D \cdot C)] \supset (R \cdot T)$
   4. B
   $\overline{5.\ V\ M.P.\ 1, 4}$
   6. $D \cdot C\ M.P.\ 2, 4$
   7. $V \cdot (D \cdot C)\ Conj.\ 5, 6$
   8. $R \cdot T\ M.P.\ 3, 7$
   9. $T\ Simp.\ 8$

Exercises V, page 124

1. 1. T $/A$
    2. $(T \lor W) \supset A$
    3. $T \lor W$ Add. 1
    4. A M.P. 2, 3

5. 1. $D \cdot P$ $/D \lor T$
    2. D Simp. 1
    3. $D \lor T$ Add. 2

9. 1. $A \cdot U$ $/A \cdot P$
    2. P
    3. A Simp. 1
    4. $A \cdot P$ Conj. 3, 2

13. 1. $B \supset E$ $/M$
    2. $[(B \supset E) \lor (P \cdot H)] \supset M$
    3. $(B \supset E) \lor (P \cdot H)$ Add. 1
    4. M M.P. 2, 3

3. 1. H $/(H \cdot S) \lor I$
    2. S
    3. $H \cdot S$ Conj. 1, 2
    4. $(H \cdot S) \lor I$ Add. 3

7. 1. $R \supset V$ $/V \lor L$
    2. R
    3. V M.P. 1, 2
    4. $V \lor L$ Add. 3

11. 1. $M \cdot T$ $/M \lor E$
    2. M Simp. 1
    3. $M \lor E$ Add. 2

15. 1. $F \lor T$ $/R \lor E$
    2. $(F \lor T) \supset [(L \supset I) \cdot (R \lor E)]$
    3. $(L \supset I) \cdot (R \lor E)$ M.P. 2, 1
    4. $R \lor E$ Simp. 3

Exercises VI, page 125

1. 1. $(S \cdot T) \supset C$ $/C$
    2. S
    3. T
    4. $S \cdot T$ Conj. 2, 3
    5. C M.P. 1, 4

5. 1. U $/T$
    2. $U \supset (A \cdot E)$
    3. $(A \cdot R) \supset T$
    4. R
    5. $A \cdot E$ M.P. 2, 1
    6. A Simp. 5
    7. $A \cdot R$ Conj. 6, 4
    8. T M.P. 3, 7

9. 1. $(A \lor F) \supset [(B \lor T) \supset R]$ $/R$
    2. A
    3. B
    4. $A \lor F$ Add. 2
    5. $(B \lor T) \supset R$ M.P. 1, 4
    6. $B \lor T$ Add. 3
    7. R M.P. 5, 6

13. 1. A $/C$
    2. $A \supset (V \supset R)$

3. $(R \lor T) \supset (C \cdot D)$

4. V _____

5. $V \supset R$ M.P. 2, 1

6. R M.P. 5, 4

7. $R \lor T$ Add. 6

8. $C \cdot D$ M.P. 3, 7

9. C Simp. 8

17. *1. $\sim(M \supset T)$*   /N

   2. $[\sim(M \supset T) \cdot (S \lor F)] \supset (E \supset N)$

   3. $U \supset (S \cdot E)$

   4. U _____

   5. $S \cdot E$ M.P. 3, 4

   6. S Simp. 5

   7. $S \lor F$ Add. 6

   8. $\sim(M \supset T) \cdot (S \lor F)$ Conj. 1, 7

   9. $E \supset N$ M.P. 2, 8

   10. E Simp. 5

   11. N M.P. 9, 10

Exercises VII, page 139

1. *1. $B \supset V$*   /$B \supset R$

   2. $V \supset R$

> *3. B C.P.A.*
> *4. V M.P. 1, 3*
> *5. R M.P. 2, 4*

   6. $B \supset R$ C.P. 3–5

5. *1. $(B \cdot D) \supset (C \cdot R)$*   /$B \supset R$

   2. D _____

> *3. B C.P.A.*
> *4. $B \cdot D$ Conj. 3, 2*
> *5. $C \cdot R$ M.P. 1, 4*
> *6. R Simp. 5*

   7. $B \supset R$ C.P. 3–6

9. *1. $(K \supset P) \supset T$*   /T

   2. $K \supset (P \cdot D)$

> *3. K C.P.A.*
> *4. $P \cdot D$ M.P. 2, 3*
> *5. P Simp. 4*

      6. *K ⊃ P C.P. 3–5*
      7. *T M.P. 1, 6*

13. *1. (B ∨ K) ⊃ [(V ∨ R)] ⊃ C]*   *∠B ⊃ (V ⊃ S)*
    2. (C ∨ A) ⊃ S

          3. B C.P.A.
          4. B ∨ K Add. 3
          5. (V ∨ R) ⊃ C M.P. 1, 4

              6. V C.P.A.
              7. V ∨ R Add. 6
              8. C M.P. 5, 7
              9. C ∨ A Add. 8
            10. S M.P. 2, 9

        11. V ⊃ S C.P. 6–10

    12. B ⊃ (V ⊃ S) C.P. 3–11

Exercises VIII, page 140

1. *1. C ⊃ (S · M)*   *∠M*
    2. C
    3. S · M M.P. 1, 2
    4. M Simp. 3

5. *1. (H · I) · (A · P)*   *∠(W · R) · (E · M)*
    2. (I ⊃ W) · (H ⊃ R)
    3. (A ⊃ E) · (P ⊃ M)
    4. I ⊃ W Simp. 2
    5. H · I Simp. 1
    6. I Simp. 5
    7. W M.P. 4, 6
    8. H ⊃ R Simp. 2
    9. H Simp. 5
    10. R M.P. 8, 9
    11. W · R Conj. 7, 10
    12. A ⊃ E Simp. 3
    13. A · P Simp. 1
    14. A Simp. 13
    15. E M.P. 12, 14
    16. P ⊃ M Simp. 3
    17. P Simp. 13
    18. M M.P. 16, 17
    19. E · M Conj. 15, 18
    20. (W · R) · (E · M) Conj. 11, 19

9.   *1. J · D   ⟋R ⊃ M*
     2. (D ∨ C) ⊃ T
     3. (R · T) ⊃ M

> *4. R C.P.A.*
> *5. D Simp. 1*
> *6. D ∨ C Add. 5*
> *7. T M.P. 2, 6*
> *8. R · T Conj. 4, 7*
> *9. M M.P. 3, 8*

     10. R ⊃ M C.P. 4–9

13.   *1. S ⊃ (R ⊃ V)   ⟋(S · R) ⊃ (T ∨ W)*
     2. V ⊃ (T · W)

> *3. S · R C.P.A.*
> *4. S Simp. 3*
> *5. R ⊃ V M.P. 1, 4*
> *6. R Simp. 3*
> *7. V M.P. 5, 6*
> *8. T · W M.P. 2, 7*
> *9. T Simp. 8*
> *10. T ∨ W Add. 9*

     11. (S · R) ⊃ (T ∨ W) C.P. 3–10

CHAPTER 5
Exercises I, page 144

1. $F \equiv T$ 5. $R \equiv C$
9. $S \equiv (T \cdot I)$

Exercises II, page 146

1. $X \equiv Y$

     F   F
     F T F

5. $(A \cdot X) \equiv (C \cdot Z)$

     T   F   T   F
     T F F   T F F
     T F F T T F F

Exercises III, page 148

1. $\sim (p \cdot q) \equiv (\sim p \cdot \sim q)$

F	T	T	T	T	F	F	F
T	T	F	F	F	F	F	T
T	F	F	T	F	T	F	F
T	F	F	F	T	T	T	T

Not tautologous, hence not logically equivalent.

5. $[p \lor (q \cdot r)] \equiv [(p \lor q) \cdot (p \lor r)]$

T	T	T	T	T	T	T	T	T	T	T	T	T
T	T	T	F	F	T	T	T	T	T	T	T	F
T	T	F	F	T	T	T	T	F	T	T	T	T
T	T	F	F	F	T	T	T	F	T	T	T	F
F	T	T	T	T	T	F	T	T	T	F	T	T
F	F	T	F	F	T	F	T	T	F	F	F	F
F	F	F	F	T	T	F	F	F	F	F	T	T
F	F	F	F	F	T	F	F	F	F	F	F	F

Tautologous, hence logically equivalent.

$p \lor (q \cdot r) \,::\, (p \lor q) \cdot (p \lor r)$

Exercises IV, page 166

1. 1. $(B \lor V) \supset C$ $/C$
   2. V
   ___
   3. $V \lor B$ Add. 2
   4. $B \lor V$ Comm. 3
   5. C M.P. 1, 4

5. 1. $(R \lor \sim P) \supset \sim S$ $/P$
   2. S
   ___
   3. $\sim (R \lor \sim P) \lor \sim S$ W.E. 1
   4. $\sim S \lor \sim (R \lor \sim P)$ Comm. 3
   5. $S \supset \sim (R \lor \sim P)$ W.E. 4
   6. $\sim (R \lor \sim P)$ M.P. 5, 2
   7. $\sim R \cdot \sim \sim P$ D.M. 6
   8. $\sim R \cdot P$ D.N. 7
   9. P Simp. 8

9. 1. $L \cdot B$ $/B \equiv L$
   2. L Simp. 1
   3. $L \lor \sim B$ Add. 2
   4. $\sim B \lor L$ Comm. 3
   5. $B \supset L$ W.E. 4
   6. B Simp. 1
   7. $B \lor \sim L$ Add. 6

3. 1. $\sim (O \cdot E)$ $/\sim E$
   2. O
   ___
   3. $\sim O \lor \sim E$ D.M. 1
   4. $O \supset \sim E$ W.E. 3
   5. $\sim E$ M.P. 4, 2

7. 1. $\sim (D \cdot \sim A) \supset Z$ $/Z$
   2. A
   ___
   3. $A \lor \sim D$ Add. 2
   4. $\sim D \lor A$ Comm. 3
   5. $\sim D \lor \sim \sim A$ D.N. 4
   6. $\sim (D \cdot \sim A)$ D.M. 5
   7. Z M.P. 1, 6

    8. ~L ∨ B *Comm. 7*
    9. L ⊃ B *W.E. 8*
    10. (B ⊃ L) · (L ⊃ B) *Conj. 5, 9*
    11. B ≡ L *M.E. 10*

Exercises V, page 167

1. (A ∨ B) · (A ∨ C)   3. ~A · (R ∨ Q)

5. [(~A · R) ∨ ~A] · [(~A · R) ∨ Q] (Note: left to right!)

7. (S · R) ∨ (U · C)

Exercises VI, page 167

1. *1. ~(W ∨ E)*   ∠~E
    2. ~W · ~E D.M. 1
    3. ~E Simp. 2

5. *1. ~E*   ∠~(E ∨ B)
    2. ~B
    3. ~E · ~B Conj. 1, 2
    4. ~(E ∨ B) D.M. 3

9. *1. (~F · ~F) ∨ T*   ∠F ⊃ T
    2. ~F ∨ T Du. 1
    3. F ⊃ T W.E. 2

13. *1. (J · U) · (N · V)*   ∠U · [J · (N · V)]
    2. (U · J) · (N · V) Comm. 1
    3. U · [J · (N · V)] Assoc. 2

Exercises VII, page 173

1. *1. A ⊃ U*   ∠~A
    2. ~(A · U)

>   *3. A I.P.A.*
>   *4. U M.P. 1, 3*
>   *5. A · U Conj. 3, 4*
>   *6. (A · U) · ~(A · U) Conj. 5, 2*

    7. ~A I.P. 3–6

3. *1. (~D ∨ S) ⊃ E*   ∠D
    2. ~D ⊃ ~E

>   *3. ~D I.P.A.*
>   *4. ~D ∨ S Add. 3*
>   *5. E M.P. 1, 4*
>   *6. ~E M.P. 2, 3*
>   *7. E · ~E Conj. 5, 6*

    8. D I.P. 3–7

5. *1.* $F \equiv G$ $\angle\sim F$
   2. $\sim G$

> *3.* F *I.P.A.*
> *4.* $(F \supset G) \cdot (G \supset F)$ *M.E. 1*
> *5.* $F \supset G$ *Simp. 4*
> *6.* G *M.P. 5, 3*
> *7.* $G \cdot \sim G$ *Conj. 6, 2*

   8. $\sim F$ *I.P. 3–7*

7. *1.* $\sim U \cdot \sim H$ $\angle\sim[U \lor (H \cdot B)]$

> *2.* $U \lor (H \cdot B)$ *I.P.A.*
> *3.* $\sim\sim U \lor (H \cdot B)$ *D.N. 2*
> *4.* $\sim U \supset (H \cdot B)$ *W.E. 3*
> *5.* $\sim U$ *Simp. 1*
> *6.* $H \cdot B$ *M.P. 4, 5*
> *7.* H *Simp. 6*
> *8.* $\sim H$ *Simp. 1*
> *9.* $H \cdot \sim H$ *Conj. 7, 8*

   10. $\sim[U \lor (H \cdot B)]$ *I.P. 2–9*

Exercises VIII, page 174

1. *1.* $P \supset \sim(N \cdot B)$ $\angle R$
   2. P
   3. $(\sim N \lor \sim B) \supset R$
   4. $\sim(N \cdot B)$ *M.P. 1, 2*
   5. $\sim N \lor \sim B$ *D.M. 4*
   6. R *M.P. 3, 5*

5. *1.* $B \supset R$ $\angle\sim B$
   2. $R \supset \sim B$

> *3.* B *I.P.A.*
> *4.* R *M.P. 1, 3*
> *5.* $\sim B$ *M.P. 2, 4*
> *6.* $B \cdot \sim B$ *Conj. 3, 5*

   7. $\sim B$ *I.P. 3–6*

9. *1.* $U \lor (U \lor N)$ $\angle\sim U \supset N$
   2. $(U \lor U) \lor N$ *Assoc. 1*
   3. $U \lor N$ *Du. 2*
   4. $\sim\sim U \lor N$ *D.N. 3*
   5. $\sim U \supset N$ *W.E. 4*

13. *1. M V ~A   ⊥M*
    2. A
    ─────────────────
    3. ~A V M Comm. 1
    4. A ⊃ M W.E. 3
    5. M M.P. 4, 2

17. *1. (R · W) V (R · F)   ⊥F*
    2. ~W
    ─────────────────────────
    3. ~~(R · W) V (R · F) D.N. 1
    4. ~(R · W) ⊃ (R · F) W.E. 3
    5. (~R V ~W) ⊃ (R · F) D.M. 4
    6. ~W V ~R Add. 2
    7. ~R V ~W Comm. 6
    8. R · F M.P. 5, 7
    9. F Simp. 8

21. *1. R ⊃ K   ⊥~R*
    2. R ⊃ ~K

    > *3. R I.P.A.*
    > *4. K M.P. 1, 3*
    > *5. ~K M.P. 2, 3*
    > *6. K · ~K Conj. 4, 5*

    7. ~R I.P. 3–6

25. *1. W ⊃ (U ≡ G)   ⊥W ⊃ ~U*
    2. ~G
    ───────────────────────

    > *3. W C.P.A.*
    > *4. U ≡ G M.P. 1, 3*
    > *5. (U ⊃ G) · (G ⊃ U) M.E. 4*
    > *6. U ⊃ G Simp. 5*
    >
    > > *7. U I.P.A.*
    > > *8. G M.P. 6, 7*
    > > *9. G · ~G Conj. 8, 2*
    >
    > *10. ~U I.P. 7–9*

    11. W ⊃ ~U C.P. 3–10

29. *1. T ⊃ U   ⊥R*
    2. ~(U · T)
    3. ~R ⊃ T

> 4. ~R I.P.A.
> 5. T M.P. 3, 4
> 6. U M.P. 1, 5
> 7. ~U ∨ ~T D.M. 2
> 8. U ⊃ ~T W.E. 7
> 9. ~T M.P. 8, 6
> 10. T · ~T Conj. 5, 9

  11. R I.P. 4–10

33. 1. (B · Q) ∨ T   /Q
  2. (T ⊃ C) · (C ⊃ Q)

> 3. ~Q I.P.A.
> 4. ~Q ∨ ~B Add. 3
> 5. ~B ∨ ~Q Comm. 4
> 6. ~(B · Q) D.M. 5
> 7. ~~(B · Q) ∨ T D.N. 1
> 8. ~(B · Q) ⊃ T W.E. 7
> 9. T M.P. 8, 6
> 10. T ⊃ C Simp. 2
> 11. C M.P. 10, 9
> 12. C ⊃ Q Simp. 2
> 13. Q M.P. 12, 11
> 14. Q · ~Q Conj. 13, 3

  15. Q I.P. 3–14

Exercises IX, page 183

1. 1. K ∨ U   /U
  2. ~K
  3. U D.S. 1, 2

5. 1. E ⊃ P   /(E ∨ R) ⊃ (P ∨ L)
  2. R ⊃ L

> 3. E ∨ R C.P.A.
> 4. (E ⊃ P) · (R ⊃ L) Conj. 1, 2
> 5. P ∨ L C.D. 4, 3

  6. (E ∨ R) ⊃ (P ∨ L) C.P. 3–5

9. 1. U ⊃ (M · T)   /S
  2. (T · M) ⊃ S
  3. B ⊃ S
  4. U ∨ B

3. 1. F ⊃ N   /F ⊃ P
  2. N ⊃ P
  3. F ⊃ P H.S. 1, 2

> 5. ~S I.P.A.
> 6. ~B M.T. 3, 5
> 7. U D.S. 4, 6
> 8. M · T M.P. 1, 7
> 9. T · M Comm. 8
> 10. S M.P. 2, 9
> 11. S · ~S Conj. 10, 5

12. S I.P. 5–11

13. 1. H ∨ C   ∠(P ∨ I) ⊃ (T ∨ R)
     2. I ⊃ U
     3. U ⊃ ~I
     4. P ⊃ (H ⊃ T)
     5. P ⊃ (C ⊃ R)
     6. I ⊃ ~I H.S. 2, 3
     7. ~I ∨ ~I W.E. 6
     8. ~I Du. 7

> 9. P ∨ I C.P.A.
> 10. P D.S. 9, 8
> 11. H ⊃ T M.P. 4, 10
> 12. C ⊃ R M.P. 5, 10
> 13. (H ⊃ T) · (C ⊃ R) Conj. 11, 12
> 14. T ∨ R C.D. 13, 1

15. (P ∨ I) ⊃ (T ∨ R) C.P. 9–14

Exercises X, page 184

1. 1. A ∨ C   ∠A ∨ (C · S)
    2. A ∨ S
    3. (A ∨ C) · (A ∨ S) Conj. 1, 2
    4. A ∨ (C · S) Dist. 3

5. 1. T ∨ ~D   ∠J ≡ D
    2. (T · D) ⊃ J
    3. J ⊃ D

> 4. D C.P.A.
> 5. ~~D D.N. 4
> 6. T D.S. 1, 5
> 7. T · D Conj. 6, 4
> 8. J M.P. 2, 7

9. D ⊃ J C.P. 4–8

10. $(J \supset D) \cdot (D \supset J)$ *Conj. 3, 9*
11. $J \equiv D$ *M.E. 10*

CHAPTER 6

Exercises I, page 196

1. True.

3. False.

5. Cannot be determined.

7. True.

9. True.

13. True.

Exercises II, page 196

1. p T
   q T
   r T

5. q T
   u F
   s F
   p T
   t T

Complete truth tables for some of the following problems have more than one line with all true premises and a false conclusion. Hence, there may be more correct solutions than those listed here.

9. u F
   t F
   p T
   q F
   s F
   r T

13. u F
    v F
    s F
    p T

Exercises III, page 197

1. $A \supset D$
   $D \supset R$
   $\underline{\sim R \lor \sim C}$
   $\therefore \sim A \supset C$
   Invalid

Form that has the argument as a parallel-instance:

$p \supset q$ p F
$q \supset r$ s F
$\underline{\sim r \lor \sim s}$ q F
$\therefore \sim p \supset s$ r T or F

5. 1. $A \equiv G$ ╱G
    2. $(G \equiv V) \cdot (A \equiv S)$
    3. $\underline{W \cdot (W \supset S)}$
    4. $W \supset S$ *Simp. 3*
    5. W *Simp. 3*
    6. S *M.P. 4, 5*
    7. $A \equiv S$ *Simp. 2*
    8. $(A \supset S) \cdot (S \supset A)$ *M.E. 7*
    9. $S \supset A$ *Simp. 8*
    10. A *M.P. 9, 6*
    11. $(A \supset G) \cdot (G \supset A)$ *M.E. 1*
    12. $A \supset G$ *Simp. 11*
    13. G *M.P. 12, 10*

9. $A \supset (C \cdot W)$
$(C \supset I) \lor \sim A$
$H \supset (P \lor A)$
$\underline{\sim I \cdot (W \cdot H)}$
$\therefore A$
Invalid

Form that has the argument as a parallel-instance:

$p \supset (q \cdot r)$ p F
$(q \supset s) \lor \sim p$ s F
$t \supset (u \lor p)$ r T
$\underline{\sim s \cdot (r \cdot t)}$ t T
$\therefore p$ u T
              q T or F

Exercises IV, page 216

1.

$p \cdot q$ ✓
$\sim q$
p
q
X   Inconsistent

3.

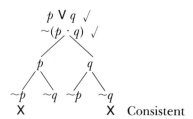

$p \lor q$ ✓
$\sim(p \cdot q)$ ✓

Consistent

5.

$p \supset q$ ✓
$p \cdot \sim q$ ✓
p

$\sim p$ q
X   **X**   Inconsistent

7.

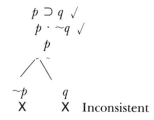

$\sim(p \lor q)$ ✓
$\sim p \supset \sim q$ ✓
$\sim p$
$\sim p$
$\sim q$

X Consistent

Exercises V, page 219

1. $\{p \supset q, q \supset \sim p, q\}$

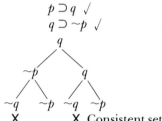

X   Consistent set, invalid argument

3. $\{p \equiv q, \sim p, \sim q\}$

$$p \equiv q \;\checkmark$$
$$\sim p$$
$$\sim q$$

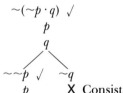

X   Consistent set, invalid argument

5. $\{\sim(\sim p \cdot q), p, q\}$

$$\sim(\sim p \cdot q) \;\checkmark$$
$$p$$
$$q$$

$\sim\sim p \;\checkmark \qquad \sim q$
$p \qquad\qquad$ X   Consistent set, invalid argument

7. $\{\sim p \supset \sim(p \lor q), \sim q \equiv \sim r, \sim(r \lor \sim p)\}$

$$\sim p \supset \sim(p \lor q) \;\checkmark$$
$$\sim q \equiv \sim r \;\checkmark$$
$$\sim(r \lor \sim p) \;\checkmark$$
$$\sim r$$
$$\sim\sim p \;\checkmark$$
$$p$$

$\sim q \qquad\qquad\qquad\qquad \sim\sim q \;\checkmark$
$\sim r \qquad\qquad\qquad\qquad \sim\sim r \;\checkmark$
$\qquad\qquad\qquad\qquad\qquad\qquad q$

$\sim\sim p \;\checkmark \qquad \sim(p \lor q) \;\checkmark \qquad r$
$p \qquad\qquad \sim p \qquad\qquad$ X
$\qquad\qquad\quad \sim q$

X   Consistent set, invalid argument

9. $\{p \equiv q, r \equiv q, q, \sim(p \cdot r)\}$

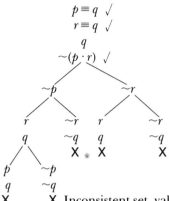

X   X Inconsistent set, valid argument

13. $\{p \equiv \sim q, r \lor (s \lor t), \sim p \supset \sim s, q, \sim(r \lor t)\}$

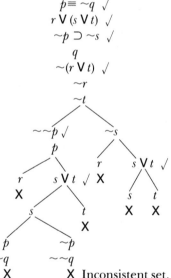

X   X Inconsistent set, valid argument

17. $\{p \supset (q \supset r), s \supset (t \supset u), (p \cdot q) \lor (s \cdot t), \sim(r \lor u)\}$

$$p \supset (q \supset r) \quad \checkmark$$
$$s \supset (t \supset u) \quad \checkmark$$
$$(p \cdot q) \lor (s \cdot t) \quad \checkmark$$
$$\sim(r \lor u) \quad \checkmark$$
$$\sim r$$
$$\sim u$$

p · q √   s · t √
  p   s

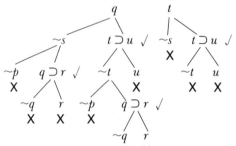

X X Inconsistent set, valid argument

Exercises VI, page 220

1. $(L \cdot P) \supset S$ $(p \cdot q) \supset r$
    P q
    ——————   ——————
    $\therefore L \supset S$ $\therefore p \supset r$

$(p \cdot q) \supset r \ \checkmark$
q
$\sim(p \supset r) \ \checkmark$
p
$\sim r$

$\sim(p \cdot q)\checkmark \qquad r$
$\qquad\qquad\quad$ X

$\sim p \qquad \sim q$
X $\qquad$ X Inconsistent set, valid argument

5. $(E \cdot R) \lor H$ $(p \cdot q) \lor r$
    $S \supset (E \cdot R)$ $s \supset (p \cdot q)$
    $S \supset \sim H$ $s \supset \sim r$
    ——————   ——————
    $\therefore \sim S$ $\therefore \sim s$

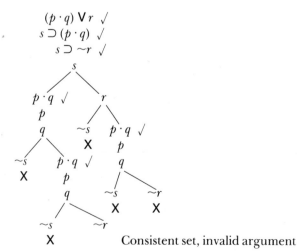

Consistent set, invalid argument

Exercises VII, page 223

1.

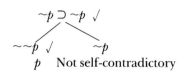

$\sim p \supset \sim p$ √

$\sim\sim p$ √ $\sim p$

p Not self-contradictory

$\sim(\sim p \supset \sim p)$ √
$\sim p$
$\sim\sim p$ √
p
X Tautologous

5.

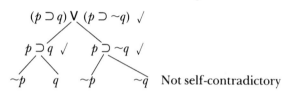

$(p \supset q) \lor (p \supset \sim q)$ √

$p \supset q$ √ $p \supset \sim q$ √

$\sim p$ q $\sim p$ $\sim q$ Not self-contradictory

$\sim\{(p \supset q) \lor (p \supset \sim q)\}$ √
$\sim(p \supset q)$ √
$\sim(p \supset \sim q)$ √
p
$\sim q$
p
$\sim\sim q$ √
q
X Tautologous

CHAPTER 7
Exercises I, page 231

1. Bw 5. $Gc \supset Wc$
9. $Gg \lor Gl$

Exercises II, page 239

1. $\forall x(Px \supset Rx)$ 3. $\forall x(Cx \supset Hx)$
5. $\forall x(Rx \supset \sim Bx)$ 7. $\forall x(Lx \supset Hx)$
9. $\forall x(Bx \supset \sim Px)$ 13. $\forall x(Px \supset Cx)$
17. $\forall x(Fx \supset Hx)$

Exercises III, page 243

1. $\forall x[Px \supset \sim(Mx \cdot Gx)]$ 5. $\forall x\{[(Cx \lor Hx) \lor Ix] \supset Ax\}$
9. $\forall x[(Ex \lor Bx) \supset \sim Fx]$
13. $\forall x\{(Bx \cdot Px) \supset [Dx \lor (Cx \lor Lx)]\}$
17. $\forall x\{Gx \equiv [Bx \cdot (Sx \cdot Dx)]\}$

Exercises IV, page 250

1. ∃xOx

9. ∃x(Px · Rx)

5. ∃x(Ax · Px)

13. ∃x(Sx · Bx)

Exercises V, page 252

1. ∃x[Nx · (Ex · Px)]

9. ∃x[Dx · ~(Wx · Mx)]

5. ∃x[(Cx · Wx) · ~Rx]

13. ∃x[Ux · (~Tx · Nx)]

Exercises VI, page 255

1. *Ep*

9. ∀x[(Px · Ex) ⊃ Dx]

17. ∀x(Ax ⊃ Cx)

25. ∃xSx

33. ∀x(Px ⊃ Ax)

5. *Ag · Sp*

13. ∀x(Fx ⊃ ~Sx)

21. *Pa · Ia*

29. ∃x[Ax · (Bx ∨ Ex)]

Exercises VII, page 266

1. *1. ∀x(Lx ⊃ Ex)*   /Ej
   2. Lj
   ――――――――――――
   3. Lj ⊃ Ej U.I. 1
   4. Ej M.P. 3, 2

5. *1. ∀x(Ex ⊃ Mx)*   /∃xMx
   2. Es
   ――――――――――――――――――

> *3. ~∃xMx I.P.A.*
> *4. ∀x~Mx Q.N. 3*
> *5. Es ⊃ Ms U.I. 1*
> *6. Ms M.P. 5, 2*
> *7. ~Ms U.I. 4*
> *8. Ms · ~Ms Conj. 6, 7*

   9. ∃xMx I.P. 3–8

9. *1. ∀x[(Yx ∨ Px) ⊃ (~Tx ⊃ Ox)]*   /∃xOx
   2. Yl · ~Tl
   ――――――――――――――――――――――――――――――――

> *3. ~∃xOx I.P.A.*
> *4. ∀x~Ox Q.N. 3*
> *5. (Yl ∨ Pl) ⊃ (~Tl ⊃ Ol) U.I. 1*
> *6. Yl Simp. 2*
> *7. Yl ∨ Pl Add. 6*
> *8. ~Tl ⊃ Ol M.P. 5, 7*
> *9. ~Tl Simp. 2*
> *10. Ol M.P. 8, 9*
> *11. ~Ol U.I. 4*
> *12. Ol · ~Ol Conj. 10, 11*

   13. ∃xOx I.P. 3–12

Exercises VIII, page 266

1. *1.* $\forall x(Ax \supset Ex)$ $/\therefore \sim Hf$
   2. $\forall x(Ex \supset \sim Hx)$
   3. Af
   _____
   4. Af $\supset$ *Ef U.I. 1*
   5. Ef $\supset$ $\sim Hf$ *U.I. 2*
   6. Ef M.P. 4, 3
   7. $\sim Hf$ *M.P. 5, 6*

Exercises IX, page 272

1. *1.* $\forall x(Rx \supset Tx)$ $/\therefore \exists x Tx$
   2. $\exists x Rx$
   _____

   > *3.* $\sim \exists x Tx$ *I.P.A.*
   > *4.* $\forall x \sim Tx$ *Q.N. 3*
   > *5. Ra E.I. 2*
   > *6. Ra* $\supset$ *Ta U.I. 1*
   > *7. Ta M.P. 6, 5*
   > *8.* $\sim Ta$ *U.I. 4*
   > *9. Ta* $\cdot$ $\sim Ta$ *Conj. 7, 8*

   10. $\exists x Tx$ *I.P. 3–9*

5. *1.* $\forall x(Ax \supset Ux)$ $/\therefore \exists x \sim Ax$
   2. $\sim Uj$
   _____

   > *3.* $\sim \exists x \sim Ax$ *I.P.A.*
   > *4.* $\forall x \sim \sim Ax$ *Q.N. 3*
   > *5. Aj* $\supset$ *Uj U.I. 1*
   > *6.* $\sim \sim Aj$ *U.I. 4*
   > *7. Aj D.N. 6*
   > *8. Uj M.P. 5, 7*
   > *9. Uj* $\cdot$ $\sim Uj$ *Conj. 8, 2*

   10. $\exists x \sim Ax$ *I.P. 3–9*

9. *1.* $\forall x[Ax \supset (Bx \cdot Cx)]$ $/\therefore \forall x(Ax \supset Bx)$

   > *2.* $\sim \forall x(Ax \supset Bx)$ *I.P.A.*
   > *3.* $\exists x \sim (Ax \supset Bx)$ *Q.N. 2*
   > *4.* $\sim (Aa \supset Ba)$ *E.I. 3*
   > *5. Aa* $\supset$ *(Ba* $\cdot$ *Ca) U.I. 1*
   > *6.* $\sim Aa$ $\vee$ *(Ba* $\cdot$ *Ca) W.E. 5*
   > *7.* $(\sim Aa \vee Ba) \cdot (\sim Aa \vee Ca)$ *Dist. 6*
   > *8.* $\sim Aa \vee Ba$ *Simp. 7*
   > *9. Aa* $\supset$ *Ba W.E. 8*
   > *10.* $(Aa \supset Ba) \cdot \sim (Aa \supset Ba)$ *Conj. 9, 4*

   11. $\forall x(Ax \supset Bx)$ *I.P. 2–10*

13. *1.* $\forall x[(Ax \lor Bx) \supset (Dx \cdot Cx)]$ $/\exists x(Dx \cdot Rx)$
    2. $\exists x(Bx \cdot Rx)$

> *3.* $\sim\exists x(Dx \cdot Rx)$ I.P.A.
> *4.* $\forall x\sim(Dx \cdot Rx)$ Q.N. *3*
> *5.* $Ba \cdot Ra$ E.I. *2*
> *6.* $(Aa \lor Ba) \supset (Da \cdot Ca)$ U.I. *1*
> *7.* Ba Simp. *5*
> *8.* $Ba \lor Aa$ Add. *7*
> *9.* $Aa \lor Ba$ Comm. *8*
> *10.* $Da \cdot Ca$ M.P. *6, 9*
> *11.* Da Simp. *10*
> *12.* Ra Simp. *5*
> *13.* $Da \cdot Ra$ Conj. *11, 12*
> *14.* $\sim(Da \cdot Ra)$ U.I. *4*
> *15.* $(Da \cdot Ra) \cdot \sim(Da \cdot Ra)$ Conj. *13, 14*

16. $\exists x(Dx \cdot Rx)$ I.P. *3–15*

Exercises X, page 272

1. *1.* $\forall x\sim(Ex \cdot Mx)$ $/\exists x\sim Mx$
   2. $\exists x(Tx \cdot Ex)$

> *3.* $\sim\exists x\sim Mx$ I.P.A.
> *4.* $\forall x\sim\sim Mx$ Q.N. *3*
> *5.* $Ta \cdot Ea$ E.I. *2*
> *6.* $\sim(Ea \cdot Ma)$ U.I. *1*
> *7.* $\sim Ea \lor \sim Ma$ D.M. *6*
> *8.* $Ea \supset \sim Ma$ W.E. *7*
> *9.* Ea Simp. *5*
> *10.* $\sim Ma$ M.P. *8, 9*
> *11.* $\sim\sim Ma$ U.I. *4*
> *12.* Ma D.N. *11*
> *13.* $Ma \cdot \sim Ma$ Conj. *12, 10*

14. $\exists x\sim Mx$ I.P. *3–13*

5.   *1.* ∀x[(Px · ~Ox) ⊃ ~Hx]   /∀x{[Px · (~Ox · ~Fx)] ⊃ (~Hx · Ax)}
     2. ∀x[(Px · ~Fx) ⊃ Ax]

> *3.* ~∀x{[Px · (~Ox · ~Fx)] ⊃ (~Hx · Ax)} *I.P.A.*
> *4.* ∃x~{[Px · (~Ox · ~Fx)] ⊃ (~Hx · Ax)} *Q.N.* 3
> *5.* ~{[Pa · (~Oa · ~Fa)] ⊃ (~Ha · Aa)} *E.I.* 4
> *6.* [Pa · (~Oa · ~Fa)] · ~(~Ha · Aa) *N.C.* 5
> *7.* Pa · (~Oa · ~Fa) *Simp.* 6
> *8.* ~(~Ha · Aa) *Simp.* 6
> *9.* (Pa · ~Oa) ⊃ ~Ha *U.I.* 1
> *10.* (Pa · ~Oa) · ~Fa *Assoc.* 7
> *11.* Pa · ~Oa *Simp.* 10
> *12.* ~Ha *M.P.* 9, 11
> *13.* (Pa · ~Fa) ⊃ Aa *U.I.* 2
> *14.* Pa *Simp.* 11
> *15.* ~Fa *Simp.* 10
> *16.* Pa · ~Fa *Conj.* 14, 15
> *17.* Aa *M.P.* 13, 16
> *18.* ~Ha · Aa *Conj.* 12, 17
> *19.* (~Ha · Aa) · ~(~Ha · Aa) *Conj.* 18, 8

   20. ∀x{[Px · (~Ox · ~Fx)] ⊃ (~Hx · Ax)} *I.P.* 3–19

7. *1. ∀x[Lx ⊃ (Wx · ~Tx)]*   ◺*∀x{[Px · (Lx ∨ Fx)] ⊃ ~(Tx · Wx)}*
    2. ∀x[Fx ⊃ (Tx · ~Wx)]

> *3. ~∀x{[Px · (Lx ∨ Fx)] ⊃ ~(Tx · Wx)} I.P.A.*
> *4. ∃x~{[Px · (Lx ∨ Fx)] ⊃ ~(Tx · Wx)} Q.N. 3*
> *5. ~{[Pa · (La ∨ Fa)] ⊃ ~(Ta · Wa)} E.I. 4*
> *6. [Pa · (La ∨ Fa)] · ~~(Ta · Wa) N.C. 5*
> *7. Pa · (La ∨ Fa) Simp. 6*
> *8. La ⊃ (Wa · ~Ta) U.I. 1*
> *9. ~La ∨ (Wa · ~Ta) W.E. 8*
> *10. (~La ∨ Wa) · (~La ∨ ~Ta) Dist. 9*
> *11. ~La ∨ ~Ta Simp. 10*
> *12. (~La ∨ ~Ta) ∨ ~Wa Add. 11*
> *13. ~La ∨ (~Ta ∨ ~Wa) Assoc. 12*
> *14. (~Ta ∨ ~Wa) ∨ ~La Comm. 13*
> *15. ~(Ta · Wa) ∨ ~La D.M. 14*
> *16. (Ta · Wa) ⊃ ~La W.E. 15*
> *17. ~~(Ta · Wa) Simp. 6*
> *18. Ta · Wa D.N. 17*
> *19. ~La M.P. 16, 18*
> *20. La ∨ Fa Simp. 7*
> *21. ~~La ∨ Fa D.N. 20*
> *22. ~La ⊃ Fa W.E. 21*
> *23. Fa M.P. 22, 19*
> *24. Fa ⊃ (Ta · ~Wa) U.I. 2*
> *25. Ta · ~Wa M.P. 24, 23*
> *26. ~Wa Simp. 25*
> *27. ~Wa ∨ ~Ta Add. 26*
> *28. ~(Wa · Ta) D.M. 27*
> *29. ~(Ta · Wa) Comm. 28*
> *30. (Ta · Wa) · ~(Ta · Wa) Conj. 18, 29*

31. ∀x{[Px · (Lx ∨ Fx)] ⊃ ~(Tx · Wx)} I.P. 3–30

Exercises XI, page 279

1. ∃xGx ⊃ ∀x~Ex
5. ∀x(Cx ≡ Bx)
9. ∀x(Sx ⊃ Ix) · ∀x(~Sx ⊃ Gx)
13. ∃x[(Ex · Vx) · ~Qx] ⊃ ∃x(Ex · ~Wx)
17. ∀x[Cx ⊃ (Px ∨ Fx)] ⊃ [∃x(Cx · Ox) · ∃x(Cx · ~Ox)]

Exercises XII, page 286

1.   *1. Mj* $\angle\exists xMx \cdot \exists x{\sim}Mx$
     2. ~Ms

> 3. ~∃xMx I.P.A.
> 4. ∀x~Mx Q.N. 3
> 5. ~Mj U.I. 4
> 6. Mj · ~Mj Conj. 1, 5

     7. ∃xMx I.P. 3–6

> 8. ~∃x~Mx I.P.A.
> 9. ∀x~~Mx Q.N. 8
> 10. ~~Ms U.I. 9
> 11. Ms D.N. 10
> 12. Ms · ~Ms Conj. 11, 2

     13. ∃x~Mx I.P. 8–12
     14. ∃xMx · ∃x~Mx Conj. 7, 13

5.   *1. ∀x(Qx ⊃ Tx)* $\angle\exists xQx \supset \exists x(Tx \cdot Vx)$
     2. ∀x(Qx ⊃ Vx)

> 3. ∃xQx C.P.A.
> 4. Qa E.I. 3

>> 5. ~∃x(Tx · Vx) I.P.A.
>> 6. ∀x~(Tx · Vx) Q.N. 5
>> 7. ~(Ta · Va) U.I. 6
>> 8. Qa ⊃ Ta U.I. 1
>> 9. Ta M.P. 8, 4
>> 10. Qa ⊃ Va U.I. 2
>> 11. Va M.P. 10, 4
>> 12. Ta · Va Conj. 9, 11
>> 13. (Ta · Va) · ~(Ta · Va) Conj. 12, 7

> 14. ∃x(Tx · Vx) I.P. 5–13

     15. ∃xQx ⊃ ∃x(Tx · Vx) C.P. 3–14

9. *1. ∀x(Ax ⊃ Bx) · ∀x(Bx ⊃ Ax)*   △∀x(Ax ≡ Bx)

> *2. ~∀x(Ax ≡ Bx) I.P.A.*
> *3. ∃x~(Ax ≡ Bx) Q.N. 2*
> *4. ~(Aa ≡ Ba) E.I. 3*
> *5. ∀x(Ax ⊃ Bx) Simp. 1*
> *6. ∀x(Bx ⊃ Ax) Simp. 1*
> *7. Aa ⊃ Ba U.I. 5*
> *8. Ba ⊃ Aa U.I. 6*
> *9. (Aa ⊃ Ba) · (Ba ⊃ Aa) Conj. 7, 8*
> *10. Aa ≡ Ba M.E. 9*
> *11. (Aa ≡ Ba) · ~(Aa ≡ Ba) Conj. 10, 4*

12. ∀x(Ax ≡ Bx) I.P. 2–11

Exercises XIII, page 287

1. *1. ∃x(Ox · Sx) ⊃ ∃x(Tx · ~Ex)*   △∀x(Ox ⊃ ~Sx)
   2. ∀x(Tx ⊃ Ex)
   3. ~∃x(Ox · Sx) ∨ ∃x(Tx · ~Ex) W.E. 1
   4. ∃x(Tx · ~Ex) ∨ ~∃x(Ox · Sx) Comm. 3
   5. ~~∃x(Tx · ~Ex) ∨ ~∃x(Ox · Sx) D.N. 4
   6. ~∃x(Tx · ~Ex) ⊃ ~∃x(Ox · Sx) W.E. 5
   7. ∀x~(Tx · ~Ex) ⊃ ~∃x(Ox · Sx) Q.N. 6
   8. ∀x(~Tx ∨ ~~Ex) ⊃ ~∃x(Ox · Sx) D.M. 7
   9. ∀x(Tx ⊃ ~~Ex) ⊃ ~∃x(Ox · Sx) W.E. 8
   10. ∀x(Tx ⊃ Ex) ⊃ ~∃x(Ox · Sx) D.N. 9
   11. ~∃x(Ox · Sx) M.P. 10, 2
   12. ∀x~(Ox · Sx) Q.N. 11
   13. ∀x(~Ox ∨ ~Sx) D.M. 12
   14. ∀x(Ox ⊃ ~Sx) W.E. 13

3. *1. ∀x(Jx ≡ Px)*   △∃xJx · ∃x~Jx
   2. ∃xPx · ∃x~Px

> *3. ~∃xJx I.P.A.*
> *4. ∀x~Jx Q.N. 3*
> *5. ∃xPx Simp. 2*
> *6. Pa E.I. 5*
> *7. Ja ≡ Pa U.I. 1*
> *8. (Ja ⊃ Pa) · (Pa ⊃ Ja) M.E. 7*
> *9. Pa ⊃ Ja Simp. 8*
> *10. Ja M.P. 9, 6*
> *11. ~Ja U.I. 4*
> *12. Ja · ~Ja Conj. 10, 11*

13. ∃xJx I.P. 3–12

---

14. ~∃x~Jx I.P.A.
15. ∀x~~Jx Q.N. 14
16. ∃x~Px Simp. 2
17. ~Pb E.I. 16
18. Jb ≡ Pb U.I. 1
19. (Jb ⊃ Pb) · (Pb ⊃ Jb) M.E. 18
20. Jb ⊃ Pb Simp. 19
21. ~~Jb U.I. 15
22. Jb D.N. 21
23. Pb M.P. 20, 22
24. Pb · ~Pb Conj. 23, 17

---

25. ∃x~Jx I.P. 14–24
26. ∃xJx · ∃x~Jx Conj. 13, 25

Exercises XIV, page 294

Some arguments can be shown to be invalid with different values from those listed below.

1. Invalid as shown by a one-member model:

$$\frac{Fa}{\therefore\ Ga \supset\ \sim Fa}$$

Fa T; *Ga* T

5. Invalid as shown by a two-member model:

$$\frac{(Aa \cdot \sim Ba)\ \vee\ (Ab \cdot \sim Bb)}{(Ra \cdot \sim Ba)\ \vee\ (Rb \cdot \sim Bb)}$$
$$\therefore\ (Aa \cdot Ra)\ \vee\ (Ab \cdot Rb)$$

Ab T; *Bb* F; *Ba* F; *Aa* F; *Ra* T; *Ab* T; *Rb* F; and others.

9. Invalid as shown by a three-member model:

$$(Aa \cdot \sim Ba)\ \vee\ (Ab \cdot \sim Bb)\ \vee\ (Ac \cdot \sim Bc)$$
$$(Ca \cdot Ba)\ \vee\ (Cb \cdot Bb)\ \vee\ (Cc \cdot Bc)$$
$$\frac{(\sim Ca \cdot Da)\ \vee\ (\sim Cb \cdot Db)\ \vee\ (\sim Cc \cdot Dc)}{\therefore\ (Aa \cdot Da)\ \vee\ (Ab \cdot Db)\ \vee\ (Ac \cdot Dc)}$$

Aa F; *Db* F; *Dc* F; *Cb* T; *Bb* T; *Bc* F; *Ac* T; *Ca* F; *Da* T

Exercises XV, page 296

3. Invalid as shown by a one-member model:

$$(Ca \cdot Ra)\ \supset\ (Ca \supset Ra)$$
$$\frac{Ha \cdot \sim Ca}{\therefore\ Ha \cdot \sim Ra}$$

Ra T; *Ca* F; *Ha* T

Exercises XVI, page 301

If an invalid argument has more than one open path, there will be more values that determine invalidity than those listed below.

1.

$$\forall x[(Ax \cdot Bx) \supset Cx] \ *$$
$$\exists x(Ax \cdot Bx) \ \checkmark$$
$$\sim\exists xCx \ \checkmark$$
$$\forall x\sim Cx \ *$$
$$Aa \cdot Ba \ \checkmark$$
$$Aa$$
$$Ba$$
$$\sim Ca$$
$$(Aa \cdot Ba) \supset Ca \ \checkmark$$

```
           /        \
  ~(Aa · Ba) √      Ca
    /    \           X
 ~Aa    ~Ba
   X      X      Valid
```

5.

$$\forall x[Ax \supset (Bx \lor Cx)] \ *$$
$$\forall x(Bx \supset Rx) \ *$$
$$\sim\forall x(Ax \supset Rx) \ \checkmark$$
$$\exists x\sim(Ax \supset Rx) \ \checkmark$$
$$\sim(Aa \supset Ra) \ \checkmark$$
$$Aa$$
$$\sim Ra$$
$$Ba \supset Ra \ \checkmark$$

```
              /      \
           ~Ba       Ra
  Aa ⊃ (Ba V Ca) √    X
        /      \
     ~Aa      Ba V Ca √
      X        /    \
            Ba      Ca
             X
```

Invalid; all of the following are true: $Ca, \sim Ba, \sim Ra, Aa$.

Exercises XVII A, page 302

Some arguments can be shown to be invalid with different values from those listed below.

1. 1. $\forall x(Tx \supset Cx)$ $/\sim Tc$
   2. $\sim Cc$
   _____
   3. $Tc \supset Cc$ U.I. 1
   4. $\sim Tc \lor Cc$ W.E. 3
   5. $Cc \lor \sim Tc$ Comm. 4
   6. $\sim\sim Cc \lor \sim Tc$ D.N. 5
   7. $\sim Cc \supset \sim Tc$ W.E. 6
   8. $\sim Tc$ M.P. 7, 2

5. Invalid as shown by a two-member model:

$$(Ca \cdot Aa) \lor (Cb \cdot Ab)$$
$$\underline{(Ca \cdot Na) \lor (Cb \cdot Nb)}$$
$$\therefore [Ca \cdot (Aa \cdot Na)] \lor [Cb \cdot (Ab \cdot Nb)]$$

Na F; *Ab* F; *Ca* T; *Aa* T; *Cb* T; *Nb* T

9.   *1.* $\forall x(Sx \equiv Lx)$ $\diagup\forall x(Dx \supset \sim Rx)$
     2. $\forall x(Rx \equiv Sx)$
     3. $\forall x(Dx \supset \sim Lx)$

> *4.* $\sim\forall x(Dx \supset \sim Rx)$ I.P.A.
> *5.* $\exists x \sim (Dx \supset \sim Rx)$ Q.N. 4
> *6.* $\sim(Da \supset \sim Ra)$ E.I. 5
>
> > *7.* Da C.P.A.
> > *8.* $Da \supset \sim La$ U.I. 3
> > *9.* $\sim La$ M.P. 8, 7
> > *10.* $Sa \equiv La$ U.I. 1
> > *11.* $(Sa \supset La) \cdot (La \supset Sa)$ M.E. 10
> > *12.* $Sa \supset La$ Simp. 11
> > *13.* $\sim Sa \lor La$ W.E. 12
> > *14.* $La \lor \sim Sa$ Comm. 13
> > *15.* $\sim\sim La \lor \sim Sa$ D.N. 14
> > *16.* $\sim La \supset \sim Sa$ W.E. 15
> > *17.* $\sim Sa$ M.P. 16, 9
> > *18.* $Ra \equiv Sa$ U.I. 2
> > *19.* $(Ra \supset Sa) \cdot (Sa \supset Ra)$ M.E. 18
> > *20.* $Ra \supset Sa$ Simp. 19
> > *21.* $\sim Ra \lor Sa$ W.E. 20
> > *22.* $Sa \lor \sim Ra$ Comm. 21
> > *23.* $\sim\sim Sa \lor \sim Ra$ D.N. 22
> > *24.* $\sim Sa \supset \sim Ra$ W.E. 23
> > *25.* $\sim Ra$ M.P. 24, 17
>
> *26.* $Da \supset \sim Ra$ C.P. 7–25
> *27.* $(Da \supset \sim Ra) \cdot \sim(Da \supset \sim Ra)$ Conj. 26, 6

   28. $\forall x(Dx \supset \sim Rx)$ I.P. 4–27

13. Invalid as shown by a two-member model:

$$(Ra \supset Ca) \cdot (Rb \supset Cb)$$
$$(Ha \cdot \sim Wa) \lor (Hb \cdot \sim Wb)$$
$$\underline{(Ha \cdot \sim Ca) \lor (Hb \cdot \sim Cb)}$$
$$\therefore [\sim Ca \cdot (\sim Wa \cdot \sim Ra)] \lor [\sim Cb \cdot (\sim Wb \cdot \sim Rb)]$$

Wa T; *Hb* T; *Wb* F; *Cb* T; *Ha* T; *Ca* F; *Ra* F; *Rb* F

17. Invalid as shown by a two-member model:

$$[Na \cdot (Va \cdot Oa)] \lor [Nb \cdot (Vb \cdot Ob)]$$
$$(Na \cdot \sim Va) \lor (Nb \cdot \sim Vb)$$
$$(Na \supset Ra) \cdot (Nb \supset Rb)$$
$$\underline{(Aa \supset Va) \cdot (Ab \supset Vb)}$$
$$\therefore (Aa \cdot \sim Ra) \lor (Ab \cdot \sim Rb)$$

Na T; *Va* F; *Nb* T; *Vb* T; *Ob* T; *Ra* T; *Rb* T; *Aa* F; *Ab* F

Exercises XVII B, page 302

If an invalid argument has more than one open path, there will be more values that determine invalidity than those listed.

1.

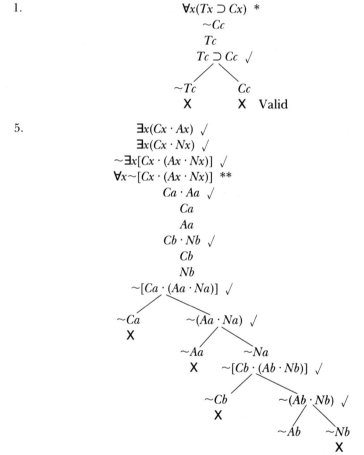

5.

Invalid; all of the following are true: ~*Ab*, ~*Na*, *Nb*, *Cb*, *Aa*, *Ca*.

9.
$$\forall x(Sx \equiv Lx) \ *$$
$$\forall x(Rx \equiv Sx) \ *$$
$$\forall x(Dx \supset \sim Lx) \ *$$
$$\sim\forall x(Dx \supset \sim Rx) \ \checkmark$$
$$\exists x\sim(Dx \supset \sim Rx) \ \checkmark$$
$$\sim(Da \supset \sim Ra) \ \checkmark$$
$$Da$$
$$\sim\sim Ra \ \checkmark$$
$$Ra$$
$$Da \supset \sim La \ \checkmark$$

$\sim Da$	$\sim La$
X	$Ra \equiv Sa \ \checkmark$

Ra	$\sim Ra$
Sa	$\sim Sa$
$Sx \equiv Lx \ \checkmark$	**X**

Sa	$\sim Sa$
La	$\sim La$
X	**X** Valid

13.

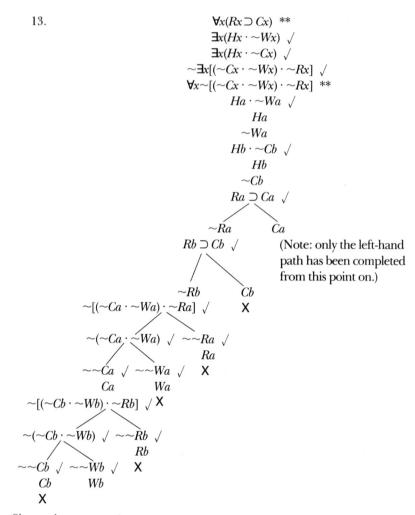

Since at least one path remains open, this argument is invalid. All of the following are true: Wb, Ca, $\sim Rb$, $\sim Ra$, $\sim Cb$, Hb, $\sim Wa$, Ha.

17.

$$\exists x[Nx \cdot (Vx \cdot Ox)] \;\checkmark$$
$$\exists x(Nx \cdot \sim Vx) \;\checkmark$$
$$\forall x(Nx \supset Rx) \;**$$
$$\forall x(Ax \supset Vx) \;**$$
$$\sim \exists x(Ax \cdot \sim Rx) \;\checkmark$$
$$\forall x \sim (Ax \cdot \sim Rx) \;**$$
$$Na \cdot \sim Va \;\checkmark$$
$$Na$$
$$\sim Va$$
$$Nb \cdot (Vb \cdot Ob) \;\checkmark$$
$$Nb$$
$$(Vb \cdot Ob) \;\checkmark$$
$$Vb$$
$$Ob$$
$$Na \supset Ra \;\checkmark$$

```
                    ~Na         Ra
                     X·      Nb ⊃ Rb  √

                             ~Nb        Rb
                              X      Aa ⊃ Va  √

                                    ~Aa        Va
                                  Ab ⊃ Vb  √   X

                                ~Ab      Vb
                     ~(Aa · ~Ra)  √   ~(Aa · ~Ra)  √

                        ~Aa    ~~Ra  √/~Aa      ~~Ra  √
             ~(Ab · ~Rb)  √      Ra ~(Ab · ~Rb)  √  Ra

          ~Ab      ~~Rb  √      ~Ab      ~~Rb  √
                     Rb                    Rb
```

Invalid; all of the following are true: *Rb, ~Aa, ~Ab, Rb, Ra, Ob, Vb, Nb, ~Va, Na.*

1.

$$\exists x(Fx \cdot Sx) \ \checkmark$$
$$\sim[\exists xFx \cdot \exists xSx] \ \checkmark$$
$$Fa \cdot Sa \ \checkmark$$
$$Fa$$
$$Sa$$

$$\sim\exists xFx \ \checkmark \qquad \sim\exists xSx \ \checkmark$$
$$\forall x\sim Fx \ * \qquad \forall x\sim Sx \ *$$
$$\sim Fa \qquad \sim Sa$$
$$\mathsf{X} \qquad\qquad \mathsf{X} \quad \text{Valid}$$

5.

$$\forall x(Tx \supset Hx) \ *$$
$$\forall x(Lx \supset Nx) \ *$$
$$\sim[\forall x(Nx \supset Tx) \supset \forall x(Lx \supset Hx)] \ \checkmark$$
$$\forall x(Nx \supset Tx) \ *$$
$$\sim\forall x(Lx \supset Hx) \ \checkmark$$
$$\exists x\sim(Lx \supset Hx) \ \checkmark$$
$$\sim(La \supset Ha) \ \checkmark$$
$$La$$
$$\sim Ha$$
$$Ta \supset Ha \ \checkmark$$

$$\sim Ta \qquad\qquad Ha$$
$$La \supset Na \ \checkmark \qquad \mathsf{X}$$

$$\sim La \qquad Na$$
$$\mathsf{X} \qquad Na \supset Ta \ \checkmark$$

$$\sim Na \qquad Ta$$
$$\mathsf{X} \qquad\quad \mathsf{X} \quad \text{Valid}$$

1.   *1. ∃xAx ⊃ ∀x(~Px V Cx)*   ⟋∀x(~Px V Cx)
    2. ∃x(Mx · Dx)
    3. ∀x(Dx ⊃ Ax)
    _____

        4. ~∃xAx I.P.A.
        5. ∀x~Ax Q.N. 4
        6. Ma · Da E.I. 2
        7. Da ⊃ Aa U.I. 3
        8. Da Simp. 6
        9. Aa M.P. 7, 8
       10. ~Aa U.I. 5
       11. Aa · ~Aa Conj. 9, 10

12. ∃xAx I.P. 4–11
13. ∀x(~Px V Cx) M.P. 1, 12

5. Invalid as shown by a one-member model:

$(Ga \supset Ca) \supset (Ea \supset Ca)$
$La \supset Ea$
———————————
$\therefore La \supset Ca$

La T; *Ca* F; *Ea* T; *Ga* T

Exercises XIX B, page 307

1.

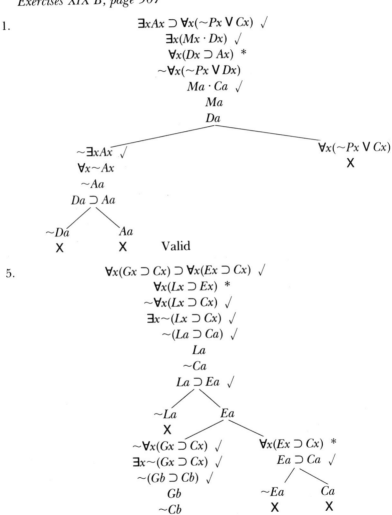

Invalid; all of the following are true: $\sim Cb$, Gb, Ea, $\sim Ca$, La.

CHAPTER 8

Exercises I, page 317

1. *Lpl*   5. *Dve*

9. a. $\forall x \forall y[(Px \cdot Wxy) \supset Gxy]$ or $\forall x[Px \supset \forall y(Wxy \supset Gxy)]$
    b. $\forall x \forall y[(Px \cdot Wxy) \supset \sim Gxy]$ or $\forall x[Px \supset \forall y(Wxy \supset \sim Gxy)]$
    c. $\exists x[Px \cdot \exists y(Wxy \cdot Gxy)]$
    d. $\exists x[Px \cdot \exists y(Wxy \cdot \sim Gxy)]$
    e. $\exists x[Px \cdot \forall y(Wxy \supset \sim Gxy)]$
13. $\forall x \forall y[Gx \supset (Nyx \supset Wyx)]$ or $\forall x[Gx \supset \forall y(Nyx \supset Wyx)]$
17. $\forall x\{(Px \cdot Sx) \supset \forall y[(Py \cdot \sim Sy) \supset \sim Hyx]\}$

Exercises II, page 328

1. 1. Hab $\diagup \exists x \exists y Hxy$

> 2. $\sim \exists x \exists y Hxy$ I.P.A.
> 3. $\forall x \forall y \sim Hxy$ (2)Q.N. 2
> 4. $\sim Hab$ (2)U.I. 3
> 5. $Hab \cdot \sim Hab$ Conj. 1, 4

6. $\exists x \exists y Hxy$ I.P. 2–5

5. 1. $\exists x \forall y Axy$ $\diagup \forall x \exists y Ayx$

> 2. $\sim \forall x \exists y Ayx$ I.P.A.
> 3. $\exists x \forall y \sim Ayx$ (2)Q.N. 2
> 4. $\forall y \sim Aya$ E.I. 3
> 5. $\forall y Aby$ E.I. 1
> 6. $\sim Aba$ U.I. 4
> 7. Aba U.I. 5
> 8. $Aba \cdot \sim Aba$ Conj. 7, 6

9. $\forall x \exists y Ayx$ I.P. 2–8

9. 1. $\forall x \forall y[(Ax \cdot Byx) \supset Cy]$ $\diagup \forall x(Bxa \supset Cx)$
    2. Aa

> 3. $\sim \forall x(Bxa \supset Cx)$ I.P.A.
> 4. $\exists x \sim (Bxa \supset Cx)$ Q.N. 3
> 5. $\sim (Bba \supset Cb)$ E.I. 4
> 6. $(Aa \cdot Bba) \supset Cb$ (2)U.I. 1
>
> > 7. Bba C.P.A.
> > 8. $Aa \cdot Bba$ Conj. 7, 2
> > 9. Cb M.P. 6, 8
>
> 10. $Bba \supset Cb$ C.P. 7–9
> 11. $(Bba \supset Cb) \cdot \sim (Bba \supset Cb)$ Conj. 10, 5

12. $\forall x(Bxa \supset Cx)$ I.P. 3–11

Exercises III, page 329

1.   *1.* $\forall x \forall y (Bxy \supset Hxy)$ $\underline{\diagup \exists x Hnx}$
   2. $\exists x Bnx$

> *3.* $\sim \exists x Hnx$ I.P.A.
> *4.* $\forall x \sim Hnx$ Q.N. 3
> *5.* Bna E.I. 2
> *6.* $Bna \supset Hna$ (2) U.I. 1
> *7.* Hna M.P. 6, 5
> *8.* $\sim Hna$ U.I. 4
> *9.* $Hna \cdot \sim Hna$ Conj. 7, 8

   10. $\exists x Hnx$ I.P. 3–9

5.   *1.* $\forall x \forall y [(Px \cdot Fxy) \supset Lxy]$ $\underline{\diagup \forall x[(Px \cdot Fxe) \supset Lxe]}$

> *2.* $\sim \forall x[(Px \cdot Fxe) \supset Lxe]$ I.P.A.
> *3.* $\exists x \sim [(Px \cdot Fxe) \supset Lxe]$ Q.N. 2
> *4.* $\sim [(Pa \cdot Fae) \supset Lae]$ E.I. 3
> *5.* $(Pa \cdot Fae) \supset Lae$ (2)U.I. 1
> *6.* $[(Pa \cdot Fae) \supset Lae] \cdot \sim [(Pa \cdot Fae) \supset Lae]$ Conj. 5, 4

   7. $\forall x[(Px \cdot Fxe) \supset Lxe]$ I.P. 2–6

9.   *1.* $\forall x \forall y [(Mx \cdot My) \supset (Uxy \supset Axy)]$
         $\underline{\diagup \forall x \forall y \forall z \{[(Mx \cdot My) \cdot Wz] \supset (Uxy \supset Fzxy)\}}$
   2. $\forall x \forall y \{(Mx \cdot My) \supset [Axy \supset \forall z(Wz \supset Sxzy)]\}$
   3. $\forall x \forall y \forall z \{[(Mx \cdot My) \cdot Wz] \supset (Sxzy \supset Fzxy)\}$

> *4.* $\sim \forall x \forall y \forall z \{[(Mx \cdot My) \cdot Wz] \supset (Uxy \supset Fzxy)\}$ I.P.A.
> *5.* $\exists x \exists y \exists z \sim \{[(Mx \cdot My) \cdot Wz] \supset (Uxy \supset Fzxy)\}$
>   (3)Q.N. 4
> *6.* $\sim \{[(Ma \cdot Mb) \cdot Wc] \supset (Uab \supset Fcab)\}$ (3)E.I. 5
> *7.* $(Ma \cdot Mb) \supset [Aab \supset \forall z(Wz \supset Sazb)]$ (2)U.I. 2
> *8.* $\sim \{\sim [(Ma \cdot Mb) \cdot Wc] \vee (Uab \supset Fcab)\}$ W.E. 6
> *9.* $\sim \sim [(Ma \cdot Mb) \cdot Wc] \cdot \sim (Uab \supset Fcab)$ D.M. 8
> *10.* $\sim \sim [(Ma \cdot Mb) \cdot Wc]$ Simp. 9
> *11.* $(Ma \cdot Mb) \cdot Wc$ D.N. 10
> *12.* $Ma \cdot Mb$ Simp. 11
> *13.* $Aab \supset \forall z(Wz \supset Sazb)$ M.P. 7, 12
> *14.* $\sim (Uab \supset Fcab)$ Simp. 9
> *15.* $\sim (\sim Uab \vee Fcab)$ W.E. 14
> *16.* $\sim \sim Uab \cdot \sim Fcab$ D.M. 15
> *17.* $\sim \sim Uab$ Simp. 16
> *18.* Uab D.N. 17

> 19. $(Ma \cdot Mb) \supset (Uab \supset Aab)$ (2)U.I. 1
> 20. $Uab \supset Aab$ M.P. 19, 12
> 21. Aab M.P. 20, 18
> 22. $\forall z(Wz \supset Sazb)$ M.P. 13, 21
> 23. $Wc \supset Sacb$ U.I. 22
> 24. Wc Simp. 11
> 25. $Sacb$ M.P. 23, 24
> 26. $[(Ma \cdot Mb) \cdot Wc] \supset (Sacb \supset Fcab)$ (3)U.I. 3
> 27. $Sacb \supset Fcab$ M.P. 26, 11
> 28. $Fcab$ M.P. 27, 25
> 29. $\sim Fcab$ Simp. 16
> 30. $Fcab \cdot \sim Fcab$ Conj. 28, 29

31. $\forall x \forall y \forall z \{[(Mx \cdot My) \cdot Wz] \supset (Uxy \supset Fzxy)\}$ I.P. 4–30

Exercises IV, page 331

1.   1. $\forall x \forall y[(Hx \cdot Fy) \supset Lxy]$ $\angle \forall x \forall y[(Hx \cdot Fy) \supset \sim Lyx]$
     2. $\underline{\forall x \forall y(Lxy \supset \sim Lyx)}$

> 3. $\sim \forall x \forall y[(Hx \cdot Fy) \supset \sim Lyx]$ I.P.A.
> 4. $\exists x \exists y \sim [(Hx \cdot Fy) \supset \sim Lyx]$ (2)Q.N. 3
> 5. $\sim [(Ha \cdot Fb) \supset \sim Lba]$ (2)E.I. 4
> 6. $(Ha \cdot Fb) \supset Lab$ (2)U.I. 1
> 7. $Lab \supset \sim Lba$ (2)U.I. 2
>
> > 8. $Ha \cdot Fb$ C.P.A.
> > 9. Lab M.P. 6, 8
> > 10. $\sim Lba$ M.P. 7, 9
>
> 11. $(Ha \cdot Fb) \supset \sim Lba$ C.P. 8–10
> 12. $[(Ha \cdot Fb) \supset \sim Lba] \cdot \sim [(Ha \cdot Fb) \supset \sim Lba]$ Conj. 11, 5

13. $\forall x \forall y[(Hx \cdot Fy) \supset \sim Lyx]$ I.P. 3–12

Exercises V, page 336

1. Invalid as shown by the two-member model, $\{a, h\}$.

$$\frac{Dah}{\therefore Daa \cdot Dah}$$

Daa F; Dah T

3. Invalid as shown by the two-member model, $\{a, b\}$.

$$\frac{(Daa \lor Dba) \cdot (Dab \lor Dbb)}{\therefore (Daa \cdot Dab) \lor (Dba \cdot Dbb)}$$

Daa F; Dbb F; Dba T; Dab T

5. Invalid as shown by the two-member model, $\{a, b\}$

$$\frac{[Qa \supset (Aaa \lor Aab)] \cdot [Qb \supset (Aba \lor Abb)]}{\therefore [(Qa \supset Aaa) \cdot (Qa \supset Aab)] \lor [(Qb \supset Aba) \cdot (Qb \supset Abb)]}$$

Qa T; *Qb* T; *Aaa* F; *Abb* F; *Aab* T; *Aba* T

9. Invalid as shown by the three-member model, $\{a, b, c\}$.

$$\frac{\begin{array}{l}(Caaa \cdot Cbaa) \lor (Caab \cdot Cbab) \lor (Caac \cdot Cbac) \lor (Caba \cdot Cbba) \lor \\ (Cabb \cdot Cbbb) \lor (Cabc \cdot Cbbc) \lor (Caca \cdot Cbca) \lor (Cacb \cdot Cbcb) \lor \\ (Cacc \cdot Cbcc) \\ (Caca \lor Cbca) \lor (Cacb \lor Cbcb) \lor (Cacc \lor Cbcc)\end{array}}{\therefore (Caca \cdot Cbca) \lor (Cacb \cdot Cbcb) \lor (Cacc \cdot Cbcc)}$$

Caca F; *Cacb* F; *Cacc* F; *Caab* T; *Cbab* T; *Cbca* T (and alternative sets of values)

Exercises VI A, page 339

1. Invalid as shown by the two-member model, $\{f, a\}$.

$$\frac{Pf \cdot [(Cf \supset \sim Rff) \cdot (Ca \supset \sim Raf)]}{\therefore \begin{array}{l}[(Pf \cdot Cf) \supset \sim Rff] \cdot [(Pf \cdot Ca) \supset \sim Raf] \cdot \\ [(Pa \cdot Cf) \supset \sim Rfa] \cdot [(Pa \cdot Ca) \supset \sim Raa]\end{array}}$$

Pf T; *Rff* F; *Ca* F; *Pa* T; *Cf* T; *Rfa* T

5. Invalid as shown by the one-member model, $\{a\}$.

$$\frac{(Ea \cdot La) \supset Saa}{\therefore Ea \equiv La}$$

Ea T; *La* F

9. 1. $\forall x[Px \supset \exists y(Fy \cdot Hxy)]$ $\diagup \forall x \forall y[(Px \cdot Wy) \supset Sxy]$
    2. $\forall x[Wx \supset \forall y(Fy \supset \sim Hxy)]$
    3. $\forall x \forall y \forall z\{Fx \supset [(Hyx \cdot \sim Hzx) \supset Syz]\}$

> 4. $\sim \forall x \forall y[(Px \cdot Wy) \supset Sxy]$ *I.P.A.*
> 5. $\exists x \exists y \sim [(Px \cdot Wy) \supset Sxy]$ (2) *Q.N. 4*
> 6. $\sim [(Pa \cdot Wb) \supset Sab]$ (2) *E.I. 5*
> 7. $(Pa \cdot Wb) \cdot \sim Sab$ *N.C. 6*
> 8. $Pa \supset \exists y(Fy \cdot Hay)$ *U.I. 1*
> 9. $Pa \cdot (Wb \cdot \sim Sab)$ *Assoc. 7*
> 10. Pa *Simp. 9*
> 11. $\exists y(Fy \cdot Hay)$ *M.P. 8, 10*
> 12. $Fc \cdot Hac$ *E.I. 11*
> 13. $Wb \supset \forall y(Fy \supset \sim Hby)$ *U.I. 2*
> 14. $Pa \cdot Wb$ *Simp. 7*
> 15. Wb *Simp. 14*
> 16. $\forall y(Fy \supset \sim Hby)$ *M.P. 13, 15*
> 17. $Fc \supset \sim Hbc$ *U.I. 16*

18. *Fc Simp. 12*
19. *~Hbc M.P. 17, 18*
20. *Fc ⊃ [(Hac · ~Hbc) ⊃ Sab] (3) U.I. 3*
21. *(Hac · ~Hbc) ⊃ Sab M.P. 20, 18*
22. *Hac Simp. 12*
23. *Hac · ~Hbc Conj. 22, 19*
24. *Sab M.P. 21, 23*
25. *~Sab Simp. 7*
26. *Sab · ~Sab Conj. 24, 25*

27. *∀x∀y[(Px · Wy) ⊃ Sxy] I.P. 4–26*

Exercises VI B, page 339

1. $\dfrac{Pf \cdot \forall x(Cx \supset \sim Rxf)}{\therefore \forall x \forall y[(Px \cdot Cy) \supset \sim Ryx]}$

$$Pf \cdot \forall x(Cx \supset \sim Rxf) \ \checkmark$$
$$\sim\forall x\forall y[(Px \cdot Cy) \supset \sim Ryx] \ \checkmark$$
$$\exists x\exists y\sim[(Px \cdot Cy) \supset \sim Ryx] \ \checkmark$$
$$\sim[(Pa \cdot Cb) \supset \sim Rba] \ \checkmark$$
$$Pa \cdot Cb \ \checkmark$$
$$\sim\sim Rba \ \checkmark$$
$$Rba$$
$$Pa$$
$$Cb$$
$$Pf$$
$$\forall x(Cx \supset \sim Rxf) \ *$$
$$Cb \supset \sim Rbf \ \checkmark$$

```
        ∕‾‾‾‾‾‾‾‾‾
    ~Cb         ~Rbf
     X      Invalid
```

~Rbf T; *Pf* T; *Rba* T; *Cb* T; *Pa* T; *Rba* T

5. $\dfrac{\forall x\forall y[(Ex \cdot Ly) \supset Sxy]}{\therefore (\forall x)(Ex \equiv Lx)}$

$$\forall x\forall y[(Ex \cdot Ly) \supset Sxy] \ *$$
$$\sim\forall x(Ex \equiv Lx) \ \checkmark$$
$$\exists x\sim(Ex \equiv Lx) \ \checkmark$$
$$\sim(Ea \equiv La) \ \checkmark$$

```
            ∕‾‾‾‾‾‾‾‾‾‾‾
        Ea              ~Ea
       ~La               La
 (Ea · La) ⊃ Saa √   (Ea · La) ⊃ Saa √

 ∕‾‾‾‾‾‾‾‾‾        ∕‾‾‾‾‾‾‾‾‾
~(Ea·La) √ Saa   ~(Ea·La) √  Saa

 ∕‾‾‾‾           ∕‾‾‾‾
~Ea  ~La        ~Ea  ~La
 X               X
```

Invalid: ~*La* T; *Ea* T; *Saa* T. Or ~*Ea* T; *Saa* T; *La* T.

9. $\forall x[Px \supset \exists y(Fy \cdot Hxy)]$
   $\forall x[Wx \supset \forall y(Fy \supset \sim Hxy)]$
   $\forall x \forall y \forall z\{Fx \supset [(Hyx \cdot \sim Hzx) \supset Syz]\}$
   $\therefore \forall x \forall y[(Px \cdot Wy) \supset Sxy]$

$$\forall x[Px \supset \exists y(Fy \cdot Hxy)] \ *$$
$$\forall x[Wx \supset \forall y(Fy \supset \sim Hxy)] \ *$$
$$\forall x \forall y \forall z\{Fx \supset [(Hyx \cdot \sim Hzx) \supset Syz]\} \ *$$
$$\sim \forall x \forall y[(Px \cdot Wy) \supset Sxy] \ \sqrt{}$$
$$\exists x \exists y \sim [(Px \cdot Wy) \supset Sxy] \ \sqrt{}$$
$$\sim [(Pa \cdot Wb) \supset Sab] \ \sqrt{}$$
$$Pa \cdot Wb \ \sqrt{}$$
$$\sim Sab$$
$$Pa$$
$$Wb$$
$$Pa \supset \exists y(Fy \cdot Hay) \ \sqrt{}$$

$$\sim Pa \qquad \exists y(Fy \cdot Hay) \ \sqrt{}$$
$$\textbf{X} \qquad Fc \cdot Hac \ \sqrt{}$$
$$Fc$$
$$Hac$$
$$Wb \supset \forall y(Fy \supset \sim Hby) \ \sqrt{}$$

$$\sim Wb \qquad \forall y(Fy \supset \sim Hby) \ *$$
$$\textbf{X} \qquad Fc \supset \sim Hbc \ \sqrt{}$$

$$\sim Fc \qquad \sim Hbc$$
$$\textbf{X} \quad Fc \supset [(Hac \cdot \sim Hbc) \supset Sab] \ \sqrt{}$$

$$\sim Fc \qquad (Hac \cdot \sim Hbc) \supset Sab \ \sqrt{}$$
$$\textbf{X}$$

$$\sim (Hac \cdot \sim Hbc) \ \sqrt{} \qquad Sab$$
$$\textbf{X}$$

$$\sim Hac \qquad \sim\sim Hbc \ \sqrt{}$$
$$\textbf{X} \qquad Hbc$$
$$\textbf{X}$$

All paths close. Hence, the argument is valid.

CHAPTER 9
Exercises I, page 345

1. $[(p \lor q) \cdot p] \supset \sim q$ 5. $[\sim(p \cdot q) \cdot p] \supset \sim q$
9. $\{[(p \supset q) \cdot (r \supset q)] \cdot q\} \supset (p \lor r)$

Exercises II, page 346

1. $[(p \lor q) \cdot p] \cdot q$ 5. $[\sim(p \cdot q) \cdot p] \cdot q$
9. $\{[(p \supset q) \cdot (r \supset q)] \cdot q\} \cdot \sim(p \lor r)$

Exercises III, page 350

1. $A \supset A$

> 1. A C.P.A.

2. $A \supset A$ C.P. 1
5. $A \supset (B \supset A)$

> 1. A C.P.A.
>
> > 2. B C.P.A.
> > 3. $A \cdot B$ Conj. 1, 2
> > 4. A Simp. 3
>
> 5. $B \supset A$ C.P. 2–4

6. $A \supset (B \supset A)$ C.P. 1–5

Some systems have a rule called "reiteration," which allows an available statement to be reiterated into a proof. Since ND lacks this inference, the conjunction step is required on line 3 so that A can be validly brought back into the proof.

9. $[(A \supset B) \cdot (B \supset C)] \supset (A \supset C)$

> 1. $(A \supset B) \cdot (B \supset C)$ C.P.A.
>
> > 2. A C.P.A.
> > 3. $A \supset B$ Simp. 1
> > 4. B M.P. 3, 2
> > 5. $B \supset C$ Simp. 1
> > 6. C M.P. 5, 4
>
> 7. $A \supset C$ C.P. 2–6

8. $[(A \supset B) \cdot (B \supset C)] \supset (A \supset C)$ C.P. 1–7

13. $[(A \lor B) \lor C] \lor (C \supset \sim C)$

> 1. $\sim\{[(A \lor B) \lor C] \lor (C \supset \sim C)\}$ *I.P.A.*
> 2. $\sim[(A \lor B) \lor C] \cdot \sim(C \supset \sim C)$ *D.M. 1*
> 3. $\sim[(A \lor B) \lor C]$ *Simp. 2*
> 4. $\sim(A \lor B) \cdot \sim C$ *D.M. 3*
> 5. $\sim C$ *Simp. 4*
> 6. $\sim(C \supset \sim C)$ *Simp. 2*
> 7. $\sim(\sim C \lor \sim C)$ *W.E. 6*
> 8. $\sim\sim C$ *Du. 7*
> 9. C *D.N. 8*
> 10. $C \cdot \sim C$ *Conj. 9, 5*

11. $[(A \lor B) \lor C] \lor (C \supset \sim C)$ *I.P. 1–10*

Exercises IV, page 350

1. $(A \lor B) \cdot (\sim A \cdot \sim B)$ is self-contradictory. Hence, $\sim[(A \lor B) \cdot (\sim A \cdot \sim B)]$ must be a theorem.

> 1. $(A \lor B) \cdot (\sim A \cdot \sim B)$ *I.P.A.*
> 2. $(A \lor B) \cdot \sim(A \lor B)$ *D.M. 1*

3. $\sim[(A \lor B) \cdot (\sim A \cdot \sim B)]$ *I.P. 1–2*

5. $[A \supset (B \lor C)] \cdot \sim[B \supset (A \supset C)]$ is self-contradictory. Hence, $\sim\{[A \supset (B \supset C)] \cdot \sim[B \supset (A \supset C)]\}$ must be a theorem.

> 1. $[A \supset (B \supset C)] \cdot \sim[B \supset (A \supset C)]$ *I.P.A.*
> 2. $[A \supset (B \supset C)] \cdot \sim[\sim B \lor (A \supset C)]$ *W.E. 1*
> 3. $[A \supset (B \supset C)] \cdot \sim[\sim B \lor (\sim A \lor C)]$ *W.E. 2*
> 4. $[A \supset (B \supset C)] \cdot \sim[(\sim B \lor \sim A) \lor C]$ *Assoc. 3*
> 5. $[A \supset (B \supset C)] \cdot \sim[(\sim A \lor \sim B) \lor C]$ *Comm. 4*
> 6. $[A \supset (B \supset C)] \cdot \sim[\sim A \lor (\sim B \lor C)]$ *Assoc. 5*
> 7. $[A \supset (B \supset C)] \cdot \sim[\sim A \lor (B \supset C)$ *W.E. 6*
> 8. $[A \supset (B \supset C)] \cdot \sim[A \supset (B \supset C)$ *W.E. 7*

9. $\sim\{[A \supset (B \supset C)] \cdot \sim[B \supset(A \supset C)]\}$ *I.P. 1–8*

Exercises V, page 357

1. A tautology.

3. Not a tautology.

5. A tautology.

Exercises VI, page 363

1. 1. $A \supset (B \supset A)$ *Assumption*
   2. $\sim A \lor (\sim B \lor A)$ *W.E. applied twice on line 1*

   1. $A \lor \sim A$ *Theorem of ND*
   2. $(A \lor \sim A) \lor \sim B$ *Add. 1*
   3. $(\sim A \lor A) \lor \sim B$ *Comm. 2*
   4. $\sim A \lor (A \lor \sim B)$ *Assoc. 3*
   5. $\sim A \lor (\sim B \lor A)$ *Comm. 4*

5. 1. $(A \cdot B) \supset [(A \equiv B) \lor C]$ *Assumption*
   2. $\sim(A \cdot B) \lor \{[(\sim A \lor B) \cdot (\sim B \lor A)] \lor C\}$ *M.E. and W.E. on 1*
   3. $(\sim A \lor \sim B) \lor \{[(\sim A \lor B) \cdot (\sim B \lor A)] \lor C\}$ *D.M. 2*
   4. $(\sim A \lor \sim B) \lor \{C \lor [(\sim A \lor B) \cdot (\sim B \lor A)]\}$ *Comm. 3*
   5. $(\sim A \lor \sim B) \lor \{[C \lor (\sim A \lor B)] \cdot [C \lor (\sim B \lor A)]\}$ *Dist. 4*
   6. $\{(\sim A \lor \sim B) \lor [C \lor (\sim A \lor B)]\} \cdot \{(\sim A \lor \sim B) \lor [C \lor (\sim B \lor A)]\}$ *Dist. 5*

   1. $B \lor \sim B$ *Theorem of ND*
   2. $A \lor \sim A$ *Theorem of ND*
   3. $(B \lor \sim B) \lor [(\sim A \lor C) \lor \sim A]$ *Add. 1*
   4. $(\sim B \lor B) \lor [(\sim A \lor C) \lor \sim A]$ *Comm. 3*
   5. $\sim B \lor \{B \lor [(\sim A \lor C) \lor \sim A]\}$ *Assoc. 4*
   6. $\sim B \lor \{[B \lor (\sim A \lor C)] \lor \sim A\}$ *Assoc. 5*
   7. $\sim B \lor \{[(B \lor \sim A) \lor C] \lor \sim A\}$ *Assoc. 6*
   8. $\sim B \lor \{[(\sim A \lor B) \lor C] \lor \sim A\}$ *Comm. 7*
   9. $\sim B \lor \{[C \lor (\sim A \lor B)] \lor \sim A\}$ *Comm. 8*
   10. $\sim B \lor \{\sim A \lor [C \lor (\sim A \lor B)]\}$ *Comm. 9*
   11. $(\sim B \lor \sim A) \lor [C \lor (\sim A \lor B)]$ *Assoc. 10*
   12. $(\sim A \lor \sim B) \lor [C \lor (\sim A \lor B)]$ *Comm. 11*
   13. $(A \lor \sim A) \lor [\sim B \lor (C \lor \sim B)]$ *Add. 2*
   14. $[\sim B \lor (C \lor \sim B)] \lor (A \lor \sim A)$ *Comm. 13*
   15. $\{[\sim B \lor (C \lor \sim B)] \lor A\} \lor \sim A$ *Assoc. 14*
   16. $\{\sim B \lor [(C \lor \sim B) \lor A]\} \lor \sim A$ *Assoc. 15*
   17. $\{\sim B \lor [C \lor (\sim B \lor A)]\} \lor \sim A$ *Assoc. 16*
   18. $\{[C \lor (\sim B \lor A)] \lor \sim B\} \lor \sim A$ *Comm. 17*
   19. $[C \lor (\sim B \lor A)] \lor (\sim B \lor \sim A)$ *Assoc. 18*
   20. $[C \lor (\sim B \lor A)] \lor (\sim A \lor \sim B)$ *Comm. 19*
   21. $(\sim A \lor \sim B) \lor [C \lor (\sim B \lor A)]$ *Comm. 20*
   22. $\{(\sim A \lor \sim B) \lor [C \lor (\sim A \lor B)]\} \cdot$
       $\{(\sim A \lor \sim B) \lor [C \lor (\sim B \lor A)]\}$ *Conj. 12, 21*

Index